IMMUNOLOGICAL TOLERANCE

A Reassessment of Mechanisms of the Immune Response

Perspectives in Immunology

A Series of Publications Based on Symposia

Maurice Landy and Werner Braun (eds.)
IMMUNOLOGICAL TOLERANCE
A Reassessment of Mechanisms of the Immune Response
1969

In preparation:

H. Sherwood Lawrence and Maurice Landy (eds.)
MEDIATORS OF CELLULAR IMMUNITY
1969

Lionel A. Manson and Maurice Landy (eds.)
MEMBRANE-ASSOCIATED ANTIGENS OF
MAMMALIAN CELLS
1970

Brook Lodge — the conference site

Immunological Tolerance

A Reassessment of Mechanisms of the Immune Response

Edited by
Maurice Landy

and
Werner Braun

National Institute of
Allergy and
Infectious Diseases

Institute of Microbiology
Rutgers
The State University

Proceedings of an International Conference
Held at Brook Lodge
Augusta, Michigan
September 18-20, 1968

Academic Press
New York • London—1969

ACADEMIC PRESS, INC.
111 Fifth Avenue, New York, New York 10003

United Kingdom Edition published by
ACADEMIC PRESS, INC. (LONDON) LTD.
Berkeley Square House, London W.1

LIBRARY OF CONGRESS CATALOG CARD NUMBER 68-59165

PRINTED IN THE UNITED STATES OF AMERICA

LIST OF CONFEREES

Bertie F. Argyris, Syracuse University, Syracuse, New York

Robert Auerbach, University of Wisconsin, Madison, Wisconsin

Baruj Benacerraf, National Institute of Allergy and Infectious Diseases, Bethesda, Maryland

Werner Braun, Rutgers, The State University, New Brunswick, New Jersey

Sven Britton, Karolinska Institutet, Stockholm, Sweden

Alain E. Bussard, Institut Pasteur, Paris, France

Ruggero Ceppellini, Institute of Medical Genetics, University of Turin, Turin, Italy

B. Cinader, University of Toronto, Toronto, Canada

Melvin Cohn, Salk Institute for Biological Science, La Jolla, California

D. A. L. Davies, G. D. Searle and Company, Ltd., Bucks, England

Gerald M. Edelman, The Rockefeller University, New York, New York

Herman Friedman, Albert Einstein Medical Center, Philadelphia, Pennsylvania

P. G. H. Gell, The University of Birmingham, Birmingham, England

Edward Golub, Purdue University, Lafayette, Indiana

Robert A. Good, University of Minnesota, Minneapolis, Minnesota

A. Arthur Gottlieb, Harvard Medical School, Boston, Massachusetts

J. L. Gowans, University of Oxford, Oxford, England

Milan Hasek, Institute of Experimental Biology and Genetics, Prague, Czechoslovakia.

James Howard, University of Edinburgh, Edinburgh, Scotland

J. H. Humphrey, National Institute for Medical Research, London, England

Maurice Landy, National Institute of Allergy and Infectious Diseases, Bethesda, Maryland

Sidney Leskowitz, Harvard Medical School, Boston, Massachusetts

J. F. A. P. Miller, The Walter and Eliza Hall Institute of Medical Research, Melbourne, Australia

N. A. Mitchison, National Institute for Medical Research, London, England

Erna Möller, Karolinska Institutet, Stockholm, Swenden

Goran Möller, Karolinska Institutet, Stockholm, Sweden

Alan Munro, University of Cambridge, Cambridge, England

G. J. V. Nossal, The Walter and Eliza Hall Institute of Medical Research, Melbourne, Australia

Otto J. Plescia, Rutgers, The State University, New Brunswick, New Jersey

K. Rajewsky, University of Cologne, Cologne, Germany

Robert S. Schwartz, Tufts University School of Medicine, Boston, Massachusetts

Michael Sela, The Weizmann Institute of Sciences, Rehovoth, Israel

Eli Sercarz, University of California, Los Angeles, California

Arthur M. Silverstein, The Johns Hopkins University School of Medicine, Baltimore, Maryland

Morten Simonsen, University of Copenhagen, Copenhagen, Denmark

Gregory W. Siskind, New York University School of Medicine, New York, New York

Richard T. Smith, University of Florida College of Medicine, Gainesville, Florida

J. Sterzl, Institute of Microbiology, Prague, Czechoslovakia

G. Jeanette Thorbecke, New York University School of Medicine, New York, New York

Jonathan W. Uhr, New York University School of Medicine, New York, New York

Byron H. Waksman, Yale University School of Medicine, New Haven, Connecticut

William O. Weigle, Scripps Clinic and Research Foundation, La Jolla, California

PREFACE

Immunological tolerance is a phenomenon that has long been equally fascinating to the investigator of basic biological phenomena and to the clinician. There was a time when it was regarded as a separate, distinct phenomenon to be constrasted with immunological responsiveness. Recent years have seen changes in ideas and the development of techniques which led to the recognition that tolerance is a good deal more than a lack of response. It is now apparent that tolerance is not only an important part of immune responsiveness but also an exceedingly versatile tool for the analysis of the immune response itself. Immunological non-responsiveness has thus become an issue of great fascination for the immunologist and the various other scientific disciplines that in recent years profited so greatly by adopting immunology as a critical field for the analysis of molecular aspects of mammalian cell genetics, differentiation, biosynthesis, and interactions among cell types.

As a consequence of these recent swift-paced changes, a conference on immunological tolerance was able to attract leading immunologists and allied scientists for an uninhibited discussion of the topic within the framework of a reassessment of diverse aspects of immunology. At the same time it was the hope of the sponsoring agency, the National Institute of Allergy and Infectious Diseases, that a conference on this subject would place the phenomenon of tolerance in its proper perspective within a rapidly developing general field. This hope seems to have been realized, as a perusal of the pages that follow will demonstrate. At the same time discussions produced an awareness of factors and experiments that will prove important for the ultimate application of the basic principles of non-responsiveness to clinical practice, especially in the field of organ transplantation.

In planning the conference, a format was chosen that would assure informality, depart from the conventional presentation of formal papers, but yet would lend itself to a later transmission of the essential points of all discussions to a diverse outside audience. Thus, in the beautiful setting of Brook Lodge at Augusta, Michigan, an international group of 42 scientists participated in three days of discussions on a large variety of topics, all of which were relevant to the problem of immunological non-responsiveness. The meeting was divided into six sessions which were equivalent to the six chapters of this compilation of the discussions. Each session was opened by a presentation of central issues and personal results by a previously scheduled spokesman whose major task it was to delineate the area and to raise issues for discussion. These presentations, as well as the far-ranging discussions that followed, were recorded by stenotype, and it is this complete record that furnished the material contained in this volume. The discussion introducers as well as all discussants had an opportunity to edit their remarks before leaving Brook Lodge. We took this edited transcript and, having warned the participants appropriately in advance, edited it further by eliminating some material, rearranging some of the sequences of discussion, and simplifying the dialogue throughout in an effort to reach a higher degree of readability. We sincerely hope that in the process of making such changes, we neither detracted too much from individual styles nor introduced interpretations other than those intended by the authors.

The chairmen of the six sessions, designated in advance, had the task of conducting each session in such a way that each subject could be examined maximally without too much diversion into extraneous issues and into topics to be covered by other sessions. It was, nevertheless, unavoidable that some issues arose repeatedly in different sessions. We have made no attempt to consolidate such material; all rearrangements made in the present record were kept within individual sessions. We hope that the reappearance of certain issues in different parts of this book will not detract from the readability and from the opportunity to locate, within the pages to follow, many of the crucial issues of current experimentation and thinking in immunology.

There are several people who deserve a special expression of gratitude for having made this volume possible: Mr. Eli Wallach, whose expert stenotypy effectively captured the very lively discussions; Mrs. Evelyn Rosenstein, whose secretarial expertise provided an infinite array of essential services throughout; and the staff of Academic Press who eased the transition from typescript to book. We must, however, make special acknowledgment of the wise and efficient assistance of our colleague, Dr. N. A. Mitchison. He scrutinized the entire volume prior to its publication and gave us the invaluable benefit of his counsel and knowledge.

Maurice Landy
Werner Braun

New Brunswick, New Jersey
January, 1969

INTRODUCTORY NOTE

The National Institute of Allergy and Infectious Diseases, through its Extramural Programs, has for many years provided what has become traditional support for research in basic immunology. This is an outgrowth of the historic fact that present-day immunology had its origins in medical microbiology, and in attempts at immunological control of infectious disease, the area that has been this Institute's primary responsibility during its entire history. Immunology has now spread far beyond its identification with infectious diseases alone. However, the association of NIAID with immunology has been maintained throughout and has been projected into the contemporary, greatly enlarged scope of this discipline.

It became evident some time ago that there were still other ways in which this Institute could foster a more productive development of this discipline, notably in the area of communication. In the 1960's we have been accumulating immunological information in such volume and at so rapid a pace as to exceed our capacity to organize, assess, integrate, and fully utilize it. It is increasingly apparent that the traditional meetings do little more than present us with an overabundance of additional data. No small part of this problem is the stereotyped format of large symposia, crowded with formal papers summarizing published data and largely devoid of incisive discussion, criticism, or any serious attempt at evaluation.

Accordingly, I envisioned our developing a series of conferences in selected areas of immunology now ripe for review or newly emerging with special implications; the intent being to emphasize assessment of progress, to develop ideas and concepts, and, wherever possible, to project needs and to identify opportunities. The number of participants would be limited in order to assure close and maximally productive interchange. In planning the first of these international conferences I am greatly indebted to Drs. Hasek, Mitchison, Nossal, and Smith, who served with me as an organizing committee and give generously of their time and imagination in arriving at the present treatment of the extensive terrain encompassed in a comprehensive consideration of immunological tolerance.

INTRODUCTORY NOTE

The beauty, seclusion, and tranquility of Brook Lodge contributed im-
measurably to the success of the conference, providing many distinctive
features which favored unusually effective interaction among the conferees.
It is a pleasure to acknowledge the generosity of the Upjohn Research Or-
ganization, their warm concurrence in our plans, and the fine cooperation
of Dr. Norman Marshall, in putting their magnificent conference site at our
disposal.

The Extramural Programs of this Institute provided the necessary finan-
cial support for the conference, including travel for overseas participants,
expert stenotypy, and the various elements connected with the preparation of the transcript for publication. For the record, it should be noted that
these funds derive from a category used at NIAID discretion primarily for
facilitating communication; as such, they do not in any way compete with
funds for support of research.

Maurice Landy
Chief, Allergy and Immunology Branch
Extramural Programs, National Institute of
Allergy and Infectious Diseases

Bethesda, Maryland
January, 1969

CONTENTS

I

PROPERTIES OF ANTIGENS IN RELATION TO RESPONSIVENESS AND NON-RESPONSIVENESS

Particulate vs. soluble antigens – Activation, antibody synthesis and proliferation of antibody-forming cells as separate events – Antibodies of differing affinity as a factor in non-responsiveness – Thermodynamic considerations – Role of the carrier – Genetic aspects of non-responsiveness – Dosage effects – Termination of tolerance – "Silence" vs. elimination of immuno-competent cells in non-responsiveness – Relationship between the "tolerant" and the "productive" state of lymphocytes – Exhaustive differentiation as a factor in non-responsiveness – Fate of antigen *in vivo* – Recruitment vs. proliferation of antibody-forming cells – Purging of cell-receptors.

1

I. PROPERTIES OF ANTIGENS

DR. BENACERRAF: I will describe first some generally accepted facts concerning the relationship between antigen structure and its ability to induce tolerance, then propose a hypothesis to account for these facts, and lastly, point out some questions that I feel need to be asked and discussed.

I feel that among the most important of these facts is the observation that in an adult, an antigen whose physicochemical properties allow its free diffusion in body fluids is more tolerogenic than immunogenic. In contrast, antigens whose physicochemical properties (or the presence of antibodies) cause their concentration in the cells of the reticuloendothelial system or on the surface of macrophages, are recognized as being more immunogenic. I shall not take the time to describe the numerous experiments carried out by many of us to substantiate this point, as they are known to most of you.

Two types of explanations have been proposed to account for these observations relating localizing properties and fate of antigens, with tolerance or immunity. One of the explanations is that in adult animals tolerance is achieved by freely diffusible antigens because of the direct contact of such antigens with specific cells of thymic origin--before they encounter antigen in or on macrophages. Thus, contact with antigen before it goes to the macrophages would lead to tolerance. When it is tolerant, such a cell is inhibited to differentiate or proliferate. On the other hand, if a specific cell reacts with antigen after it is "processed" by macrophages, or after it has been localized on the surface of macrophages, then the environment in the lymphoid tissue where this occurs, or the contact with macrophage-bound antigen, causes it to differentiate and proliferate.

But there is another explanation that has been proposed by Dr. Claman to account for the immunogenic difference between particulate and soluble antigens; that is that particulate antigens act on macrophages as adjuvants, and as a consequence of their uptake by these cells, macrophages produce

3

some non-specific material which induces the sensitive cell, which has reacted with antigen in its environment to differentiate and to proliferate. Evidence from experiments on the production of tolerance in vitro by direct contact of lymphocytes with antigen should settle this problem.

The general statement can be made that tolerance results from the contact of a sensitive cell with antigen when, either in the absence of proper localization or processing of the antigen or because of the introduction of immunosuppressive agents (agents that tend to stop proliferation), the clonal proliferation of the sensitized cell is abolished. This, it seems to me, is the basis for all the mechanisms of tolerance induction.

After these considerations concerning the relationship between the diffusible or particulate nature of antigens and tolerance and immunity, we might try to see whether on a similar basis we can explain the fascinating phenomenon of low-dose tolerance to protein antigens described by Dr. Mitchison; this phenomenon is observed most particularly with soluble antigens. Indeed, one can easily understand that low-dose tolerance may be the result of the fact that when too little of a soluble and diffusible antigen is injected, it contains an insufficient amount of the aggregated fraction capable of being localized by the macrophages. Then the soluble unaggregated fraction acts as a tolerizing antigen. Thus the prediction can be made that with a preparation of a soluble antigen that has been freed of particulates, the phenomenon of low-dose tolerance should not be observed since all doses should then induce tolerance; this, I believe, is the case. The phenomenon of low-dose tolerance should depend upon the competition between the most immunogenic and most tolerogenic fractions of soluble antigens. Within a certain dose range enough of the immunogenic fraction is administered to stimulate immunity.

The next question we can ask is: how is tolerance induced, and how do the general properties of antigen affect tolerance or affect immunity? By this I don't mean to refer to the fate of the antigen but rather to the chemical properties of the antigen itself. Three hypotheses can be proposed in this respect. First, tolerance can result from the destruction of a specific cell by antigen as originally suggested by Dr. Burnet. Second, it can result from the inhibition of the differentiation of the cell by antigen, the cell remaining dormant for its normal lifetime, with the possibility that it may eventually revert to a non-tolerant state. According to the third mechanism, tolerance may result when an antigen causes the differentiation of the cell to an antibody-producing cell without proliferation or with minimal proliferation. This last possibility was originally suggested by Dr. Sterzl who provided some data in favor of such an interpretation. Of the three hypotheses, I think that, at the present time, evidence exists only for the last two.

There are indeed antigens to which tolerance is produced by virtue of the fact that antigen can stimulate antibody synthesis but not clonal proliferation. This particular mechanism has been observed with the pneumococcus polysaccharide by Dr. Howard in mice and by Drs. Paul and Siskind of our laboratory in rabbits. I would like now to illustrate this point. We have confirmed the original observation of Dr. McLeod that the pneumococcus polysaccharide is capable of stimulating a secondary response in rabbits that have been immunized previously with the whole organism. Table 1 shows the nature of the secondary response in rabbits immunized with pneumococcus type III when boosted with a half milligram of SSS III. A booster response is obtained with the polysaccharide only after 6 months have elapsed. A considerable secondary response is observed with pneumococcus polysaccharide late in immunization because such a response presumably requires that enough memory cells accumulate from the primary immunization to respond to the polysaccharide. Figure 1 shows the nature of the response curve; it is very sharp, it peaks at 8 days and the level of antibody is down at 16 days. The response is not sustained, suggesting that specific cells have not been stimulated to proliferate by the polysaccharide. This interpretation is supported further by the observation that the spleen cells of such animals, maintained in vitro, are not stimulated to synthesize DNA by a wide range of polysaccharide concentrations whereas under the same circumstances protein antigens would produce such stimulation. These results suggest that the specific cells that have been stimulated to produce antibody do not proliferate and therefore tolerance to the polysaccharide results. This is also shown in Fig. 2 which presents results of repeated challenges with the same 0.5 mg dose of polysaccharide. A typical response is seen only after the first challenge; repeated challenges demonstrate that tolerance has been established by the first challenge. This

TABLE 1

The secondary response of rabbits immunized with pneumococcus Type III
and boosted with SSS III

Rabbits	Time of Boost after Primary[a]	Pre-Boost Level			Post-Boost Level			
		Time after Primary						
		Day 7	Day 14	Day of Boost	Day 4	Day 7	Day 10	Day 17
	months	*mg/ml*			*mg/ml*			
112	1	0.90	0.62	0.20	0.08	0.09		
116	1	1.17	0.71	0.37	0.17	0.12		
125	1	1.92	1.15	0.40	0.25	0.31		
128	1	3.89	2.13	0.60	0.44	0.38		
131	1	1.33	0.59	0.26	0.14	0.07		
110	1½	2.45	1.37	0.26	0.16	0.16	0.15	0.13
133	1½		0.61	0.12	0.07	0.14	0.13	0.09
137	1½		0.13	0.03	0.02	0.03	0.03	0.03
139	1½		1.45	0.19	0.09	0.14	0.12	0.07
120	6	0.74	0.38	0.03	0.08	0.25		0.05
121	6		0.31	0.00	0.14	0.33		0.07
134	6		0.64	0.05	0.02	0.06		0.02
135	6		0.70	0.02	0.07	0.15		0.00
114	9	3.46	1.79	0.00	0.04	0.32	0.15	0.08
118	9	1.06	0.59	0.01	0.08	0.28	0.16	0.02
119	9		1.41	0.06	0.15	1.37	1.35	0.76
126	9	1.37	0.74	0.04	0.05	0.18	0.13	0.07

[a] Animals boosted at 1 month received 0.4 mg S III intraperitoneally and 0.1 mg intravenously. All others received 0.5 mg S III intravenously. Anti-S III antibody concentration was measured by quantitative precipitin analysis.

(Data reproduced with permission of Journal of Immunology)

again indicates that the memory cells that have been produced by primary immunization are capable of being boosted by the polysaccharides alone, but are not stimulated to proliferation. This state of affairs results in exhaustion of the specific cell population as far as this system is concerned; this then is in keeping with the data to be presented later by Dr. Howard.

The question must be asked: what are the properties of antigens which, aside from stimulating specific antibody synthesis by specific cells, can also evoke their proliferative response? The carrier molecule in the pneumococcus polysaccharide system has these properties; in other systems they are probably also associated with the carrier.

The other question one may ask is: are there other systems aside from those involving non-metabolizable antigens of the pneumococcus polysaccharide type, in which the

I. PROPERTIES OF ANTIGENS

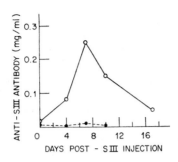

Fig. 1 Anti-S III secondary response to 0.5 mg of S III in
rabbits immunized with type III pneumococci 6 to 9
months earlier. Open circles indicate average values for the serum anti-S III concentrations of 6
rabbits boosted with type III pneumococci;closed
circles represent average values for the serum
anti-S III concentrations of four normal rabbits
who received an intravenous injection of 0.5 mg
S III.

(Data reproduced with permission of Journal of
Immunology)

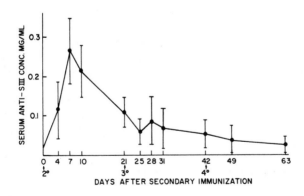

Fig. 2 The secondary tertiary and quaternary responses to
0.5 mg of SSS III in rabbits immunized with type
III pneumococci 9 months earlier

7

ratio of cells that go to proliferation to cells that go to
differentiation (and antibody synthesis) may be influenced
by the properties of the antigen? The answer to this question is yes. This type of effect has been observed with
protein antigens as a function of the dose. If large amounts
of antigen are injected, more cells tend to go to antibody
synthesis and differentiation than when small amounts of
antigen are employed. In contrast, when low doses of antigens are used, less cells mature to antibody synthesis and
more cells are stimulated to proliferate in preparation for
the secondary response. I think there are ample data from
many laboratories, including our own, demonstrating this
phenomenon.

The last point I want to address myself to, deals with
the fact that antibody-producing cells are a heterogeneous
population of cells synthesizing antibodies of different
affinity. Since the audience is composed almost exclusively
of immunobiologists with very few immunochemists, and since
those immunochemists that are here are distinguished by their
understanding of biology, I think it is not necessary to deal
with the problem of whether these cells are precommitted to
the synthesis of a specific antibody before antigens are injected. However, it is a generally accepted fact that immunocompetent cells are committed to the synthesis of a
specific immunoglobulin before the antigen is introduced.
Indeed, if this were not the case, it would be very difficult
to explain tolerance as was recognized by Dr. Burnet very
early in the game. This being the case, the same conclusions that apply to antibody-producing cells must also apply
to cells that can be rendered tolerant by antigen. Since
for a given antigen the antibody-producing cells are a heterogeneous population of cells, each producing an antibody with
different affinity for the antigen, the same thing can be
said about the cells that are rendered tolerant. Therefore,
one would expect that the same thermodynamic considerations
that apply to the binding of antigens by specific antibody
and to the stimulation of cells for the immune response,
should also apply for tolerance induction. By this it is
meant that if tolerance is achieved, with low doses of antigen, we should expect that the tolerance has a narrow specificity since tolerance would have been achieved by affecting
only those cells that are most specific for the antigen.
Under such a regimen cross-reacting cells should not be rendered tolerant.

I. PROPERTIES OF ANTIGENS

On the contrary, if a large amount of antigen is used to achieve high-dose tolerance, or if the low tolerance regimen is increased progressively so that the animals are eventually exposed to a large concentration of antigen, a much larger width of tolerance specificity should be observed since many more low-affinity cells are rendered tolerant. Tables 2 and 3 illustrate this point.

TABLE 2

Antibody produced by BSA-tolerant rabbits
immunized with DNP_{10} BSA

	Antibody (mg/ml) precipitated by:			
	BSA	DNP_{10}-BSA	DNP-BF	DNP_{10}-BSA-BSA
Control (5 animals)	1.08 ± .77	2.52 ± 1.38	0.35 ± .14	1.44 ± .72
	0.17	2.10	0.52	1.93
	0.27	1.01	0.45	0.74
	0.13	0.61	0.03	0.48
Rabbits rendered	0.01	0.13	0.02	0.12
tolerant by	0.01	0.09	0.02	0.08
1 mg regime	1.24	2.53	0.14	1.29
	2.70	2.55	0.04	--
	0.67	1.30	0.14	0.63
	0.59	2.62	0.65	2.03

I hasten to add that the data are similar to data from Dr. Cinader's laboratory, both groups having reached the same conclusions. Table 2 shows an experiment that was carried out by Drs. Paul, Siskind and Thorbecke. Rabbits were rendered tolerant by a low-dose regimen in which the highest dose injected was one mg of BSA. Rabbits rendered tolerant were identified by the fact that they did not respond to alum-precipitated BSA. They were injected with DNP_{10} BSA to "break tolerance" by a method originally introduced by Dr. Weigle. The antibodies specific for BSA, DNP-BSA and DNP-fibrinogen were measured. It is evident that when one mg constitutes the largest dose (a total of nine mg were given to a 2-3 kg rabbit) most animals make a considerable amount of anti-BSA when challenged with DNP_{10} BSA; the resulting antibodies, however, have a lower affinity for BSA than the antibody produced by a normal animal. These animals also make a fair amount of anti-DNP. Rabbits also can be brought from a state of low-dose tolerance to a state of high-dose tolerance by weekly injections of 100 mg of BSA. The results obtained after challenge with DNP-BSA are shown in Table 3. Almost no anti-BSA was produced; at a time when there is no BSA in the circulation, there is also almost no anti-DNP produced because the degree of tolerance is now so profound that cells only partially specific for BSA and also specific for DNP-BSA have been affected.

TABLE 3

Antibody produced by BSA-tolerant rabbits
immunized with DNP_{10} BSA

	Antibody (mg/ml) precipitated by:			
	BSA	DNP_{10}-BSA	DNP-BF	DNP_{10}-BSA-BSA
Control (5 animals)	1.08 ± .77	2.52 ± 1.38	0.35 ± .14	1.44 ± .72
	< 0.01	0.14	0.00	0.14
	< 0.01	0.11	0.01	0.11
	< 0.01	0.12	0.02	0.12
Rabbits rendered	0.01	0.38	0.09	0.37
tolerant by	0.01	0.24	0.10	0.23
100 mg regime	0.10	0.46	0.22	0.36

It would seem that in discussing tolerance one has to take into consideration thermodynamic considerations affecting the reaction of antigen with cells producing antibodies of different affinity. I hope that Dr. Siskind will present some data showing that when tolerance is induced in a system in which antibody affinity can be measured, and in which tolerance is either only partial or is disappearing, the

I.   PROPERTIES OF ANTIGENS

antibody produced is of very low affinity since only high-
affinity cells are rendered tolerant.

It is therefore very important, that one recognizes that
a cell has basically a receptor ("antibody") and that tolerance involves a reaction of antigen with this cell-associated
receptor, the reaction being governed by considerations of
affinity and concentration. There are, however, some tolerance experiments which cannot be explained simply by such
thermodynamic considerations. More specifically, some
studies carried out in our laboratory indicate that tolerance may sometimes involve two cells and not one cell, in
a manner that is still not understood.

Thus, you are all familiar with the fact that there are
guinea pigs which do not respond to DNP-polylysine (DNP-PLL).
Nevertheless, these guinea pigs can be induced to form large
amounts of anti-DNP-PLL if they are immunized with this antigen bound to a foreign carrier which is by itself immunogenic, such as ovalbumin or BSA. However, when these guinea
pigs are made tolerant to the carrier albumin, these animals
are no longer capable of making anti DNP-PLL when immunized
with complexes of DNP-PLL and the tolerated carrier protein.
This result was obtained despite the fact that we could not
detect any degree of specificity for the carrier BSA in the
anti-DNP-PLL produced by the control guinea pigs that had
not been rendered tolerant. Thus, in this system we find
that tolerance to an antigen suppressed its ability to act
as a carrier for a hapten.

These are the issues that I want to raise with respect
to the nature and the state of antigen and tolerance. I do
not leave you with a single theory but rather with many
questions to discuss and to resolve.

DR. SISKIND: I would like to say something about the effect
of partial immunological tolerance on antibody-binding affinity. Dr. Thies and I made rabbits partially tolerant to
DNP-horse serum albumin. This was done either in newborn
animals by giving large doses of antigen or in adult animals by a low-dose method. In both cases immunization with
DNP-HSA in complete Freund's adjuvants elicited formation
of a small amount of anti-DNP that had extremely low affinity. The binding energy for DNP-PLL was reduced by approximately 2 kilocalories as compared with the binding energy
of the antibody produced in normal animals. It thus appears

11

that cells that make antibody of the highest binding affinity for the antigenic determinant are the cells that are most readily rendered tolerant by an appropriate tolerance-inducing procedure.

This point can be carried one step further. Drs. Werblin, Benacerraf and I made animals tolerant to DNP-rabbit serum albumin and then challenged them with DNP-BGG in incomplete Freund's adjuvants. Under these circumstances, the amount of anti-DNP made by the tolerant animals was approximately equal to that produced by the normal rabbit. However, the affinity of this antibody for DNP-PLL was slightly reduced (approximately one kilocalorie) as compared with that made by normal animals. Thus again cells of highest avidity for the antigenic determinant were rendered tolerant. This emphasizes the role of antigen interacting with "cell-associated antibody" in the process of tolerance induction.

DR. SCHWARTZ: Did you, in addition to measuring the affinity, identify the molecular class of the antibody being produced?

DR. SISKIND: All of this work was carried out in rabbits and the antibody involved was presumably IgG.

DR. LESKOWITZ: I would like to raise the point of whether we are really dealing with a problem of differences in affinity of antibodies to a single determinant, or perhaps with different categories of antibodies directed to different antigenic determinants. I imagine that all affinity measurements were made with DNP-epsilon-N-lysine or something of this sort. When you immunize with DNP-protein, it is possible to get DNP, let us say on tyrosine, to function as a determinant, and it is conceivable that some antibody might be made to this. Presumably this kind of antibody would have a lower affinity to DNP-epsilon-N-lysine. I wonder if there were any efforts made to find out whether the antibody of low affinity to DNP-lysine might have had a higher affinity for another potential determinant on the immunizing antigen, such as O-DNP-tyrosine?

DR. SISKIND: I think that there is no reason at all to doubt that some antibody molecules might be stimulated by the DNP-lysine determinant and bind to some other related compound with higher affinity than they bind to DNP-lysine.

This, however, would not necessitate assuming that they were
stimulated by DNP on tyrosine. They might very well have
arisen in response to DNP on lysine which they also bind
strongly. I don't think that this can be clearly differentiated.

DR. LESKOWITZ: What I am suggesting is that the tolerance
you achieve might not result in a decrease in inherent affinity of antibody so much as a change in the specificity
of the antibody which is then regarded as an apparent change
in affinity.

DR. SISKIND: The concepts of specificity and affinity are
inter-related. I don't think that they can be separated
reasonably in the sense that when one says that an antibody
has a high affinity, it is meant that this is a molecule
that has a high degree of specificity. I would say that
affinity is a quantitative measure of specificity. I don't,
therefore, differentiate the two terms in this sense. Since
one cannot carry out binding measurements with the intact
antigen, one must realize that to some extent what is seen
depends on what is selected as the determinant. In the experiments we are describing, we have used DNP-lysine which
is certainly, from the energetic point of view, the major
portion of the determinant. One is really attempting to
assay something that is as close as possible to the average
properties of the heterogeneous pool of antibody molecules.
It should be noted that we are dealing with an average
property of the entire population and not with the characteristics of any single molecule in the heterogeneous population.

DR. SELA: First of all, we must define the determinant. I
would not define haptens, such as DNP, as determinants, but
rather as an immunodominant tip of a determinant. Thus, in
the case of polypeptides the determinant has the size of
around 4 amino acids, and with polysaccharides around 6
sugar units. So, when you discuss antibodies to a hapten,
you inevitably discuss antibodies of somewhat different
specificities.

The second point I would like to make concerns the carrier. If one takes a protein to which one attaches a type
of hapten that, as I have just stated, is not a determinant
but rather an immunodominant portion of a determinant, and
one calls the protein a "carrier" then obviously the

13

decision is reached that the "carrier" participates in the specificity. Indeed, chemically it is the "carrier," but immunologically it contributes to the determinant. I would define a "carrier" as that part of an antigenic molecule that does not contribute to the specificity or affinity of the antibodies formed. The "carrier" would, by definition, be completely inert in reactions with the combining site of an antibody, even though it may play an important role in controlling the structure and biosynthesis of the antibody molecule. I mention this in order not to confuse the immuno- logical role of the "carrier."

The next point I want to mention is that we are discuss- ing specificity and affinity, but this would imply that the specificity of cross-tolerance is the same as the specifi- city of antigen-antibody reactions. Both from the work of Dr. Austin and from work of our own laboratory, it is clear that there is no correlation between the two specificities (Nossal, Austral. J. Ex. Biol. Med. Sci., 44:341, 1960; Sela, Nobel Symposium 3:466, 1967; Bauminger and Sela, Israel J. Med. Sci., in press). There are systems in which antibodies to a certain antigen cross-react well with another related antigen, but when tolerance is induced to the first one, tolerance to the second one is not obtained and vice-versa. There are systems which do not cross-react at all in terms of antigen-antibody interactions, and nevertheless the in- duction of tolerance to one antigen may yield total toler- ance to the second one. Thus, e.g. an antiserum to (Tyr, Glu)-multichain polyalanine cross-reacts well with a linear copolymer of tyrosine and glutamic acid, and hardly at all with (Lys, Glu)-multichain polyalanine. On the other hand, rabbits tolerant to the first antigen have proved to be only partially tolerant to the linear copolymer and essentially unresponsive to the (Lys, Glu) polyalanine.

The last point I would like to raise concerns affinity. I think Dr. Siskind mentioned a difference of one kilocal- orie; this is, however, just the order of magnitude of R + ln K, and consequently of border-line significance.

DR. SISKIND: When you look at the straightforward tolerance experiment (the first experiment that I described) the de- crease in affinity was 2 kilocalories or more. This is, of course, highly significant.

In the second experiment that we described, animals toler- ant to DNP-RSA were immunized with DNP-BGG. Based on carrier

specificity one would not have anticipated the marked depression in affinity that was actually observed. This decrease was approximately 1 kilocalorie. Although this is
not a large change it is certainly within the limits of what
can be measured. Statistically the results were significant
at the 5% level of confidence.

I would like to say one more thing with regard to the
question of carrier specificity. Paul, Benacerraf and I
have made some attempt to estimate, in the DNP system, the
magnitude of the carrier-specific effects. This was done by
comparing the binding affinity of anti-DNP-PLL for DNP-lysine and for a lowly derivatized DNP polylysine. The low
degree of derivatization was to avoid aggregation. We also
compared the binding affinities of antibodies to several
DNP-proteins. From the resulting measurements, the total
magnitude of the carrier-specific effects can be estimated
to be about 30% of the total binding energy. The magnitude
of this carrier effect is thus quite significant, but,
nevertheless, most of the binding energy is contributed by
interaction with the haptenic portion of the total determinant.

DR. UHR: In regard to reduced binding affinity in tolerant
animals, can Dr. Siskind exclude a role for persisting antigen in the host as a means of removing antibody of high-
binding affinity preferentially? I have in mind not only
antigen in the circulation but also extra-circulatory antigen.

DR. SISKIND: I can't prove that there is no removal of high-
affinity antibody by excess antigen which may bring about the
decrease in binding affinity that we observe in partially
tolerant rabbits. This is the same problem that came up
when, with Dr. Eisen, I studied the effect of antigen dose
on antibody affinity. If one immunizes with a large dose of
antigen, one obtains lower affinity antibody than when one
immunizes with a lower dose of antigen. In dealing with
such data one could ask: is the decrease in affinity obtained with above optimal doses of antigen the result of
binding of high-affinity antibody by excess antigen? To
take this one step further: is the low affinity of antibody
early in the immune response, such as seen by Dr. Eisen and
myself, due to binding of the higher affinity antibody by
antigen still present from the original immunizing dose?

Drs. Steiner and Eisen pursued this question in in vitro experiments in which they took cells from animals at various times during the course of the immune response (resulting from different doses of antigen) and cultured them for several hours in the absence of antigen; they then measured the affinity of the antibody produced in culture during this short period of time. These experiments clearly showed that there was a change in the affinity of the antibody being synthesized and this change was associated with the difference in antigen dose and the time elapsed after immunization. These observations were clearly not the result of binding of high affinity antibody by antigen.

CHAIRMAN SMITH: But this did not apply to the tolerance situation?

DR. SISKIND: The amounts of antigen injected in the immunization studies were not that different from the amounts given in the tolerance experiments. Consequently, the magnitude of the problem of antibody binding would be more or less the same. One other line of evidence can be based on observations that Dr. Thies and I made recently. The evidence is again indirect because we have not actually removed cells from tolerant animals and measured the affinity of the antibody produced in the absence of antigen. If one immunizes an animal with an optimal dose of antigen, say 0.5 mg of DNP-BGG, there will be a rapid increase in antibody-binding affinity with time after immunization. If the entire system was based merely on binding of high-affinity antibody by antigen, one should be able to terminate this increase in affinity by a second injection of a large amount of antigen. However, if a second injection of antigen is given approximately ten days after the first injection, the result will not be affected by it. The animal will continue to make higher and higher affinity antibody maturing at a normal or even accelerated rate. Thus, the mere injection of additional antigen does not seem to be sufficient to terminate this type of "maturation" and does not seem to be able to result in a sufficient binding of high affinity antibody to produce the effects seen in tolerant animals.

I would also like to mention that the affinities seen in the partially tolerant animals are among the lowest affinities we have ever measured in this system. Thus, I feel fairly confident that this is a real effect. When these

16

tolerant animals are observed for a period of time, they show a gradual increase in the affinity of the antibody they produce. While this is a very slow process, it eventually leads to affinities somewhere near normal.

DR. BENACERRAF: Dr. Sela was quite correct in emphasizing that one can not explain everything on the basis of thermodynamic considerations. Nevertheless, we should not forget that some of the known phenomena can be explained on that basis. Other experiments cannot. All this points to the probability that there are two ways, involving two stages, in which tolerance can be induced; one involves the specificity of the determinant and one involves specificity of the inducer system.

CHAIRMAN SMITH: By this do you mean "carrier?"

DR. BENACERRAF: Carrier, if you want.

DR. MITCHISON: I agree with Dr. Benacerraf's reservations regarding the simple thermodynamic theory. I think there are few here who would question the notion that there are receptors. The question is whether these really matter in the control of the immune response or whether local concentrating mechanisms, as I would call them, or induction mechanisms, as you would call them, serve to dominate the picture in such a way as to make the considerations of affinity fairly, but not entirely, trivial.

I should like to throw in two more observations. We have looked at the affinity of antibodies made to BSA in mice treated with low doses of this antigen, and have not been able to find a shift in affinity of the kind that one would expect from Dr. Siskind's observations. I think the phenomenon he describes does occur but may represent a small effect, or may simply not operate in certain circumstances because local concentrating mechanisms predominate. The elementary affinity hypothesis predicts that if you introduce antigen in concentrations in the region of 10^{-8} to 10^{-9} molar you should not touch antibody with an affinity of 10^{-6} or 10^{-7} molar; this you in fact do, so that local concentrating mechanisms do appear to operate.

Another consideration we ought not to forget is the paradox of haptens not inducing unresponsiveness. This is not simply a matter of the energy of binding. We have, for

17

example, kept mice infused with hapten at 2×10^{-6} molar for as long as three days. This is the equivalent of something like 200 micrograms of protein. Had it been protein, it would certainly have been sufficient to induce a measure of nonresponsiveness, yet the haptens induced no detectable tolerance.

DR. COHN: I would like to ask Dr. Benacerraf if there is any evidence suggesting that the failure of guinea pigs to respond to polylysine may not be merely a case of tolerance in the non-responders. All one would have to assume would be a simple genetic mechanism which causes the non-responders to produce something like polylysine and thus to be tolerant. In order to achieve this, I would assume that the regulatory gene may be involved in the underlying mutation and not the gene as you are assuming.

DR. BENACERRAF: No, but I think it's worth discussing the point.

DR. COHN: A mating of responder by non-responder yields a responding phenotype. The assumption of my argument is that the responder does not produce polylysine, the non-responder does produce it, and therefore it is tolerant. I am assuming that the non-responder carries a mutant regulatory gene which fails to regulate the synthesis of polylysine. As a result of failure, polylysine is produced throughout the life of the animal. Therefore, if you cross the two types of animals your phenotype will be one in which you do not have the synthesis of polylysine; you have turned it off and therefore the hybrid will be a responder. Thus, my assumptions predict that the mutation distinguishing responder from non-responder does not involve a structural gene but a regulatory gene.

DR. BENACERRAF: We have attempted to induce tolerance to polylysine in the responders and found that this does not work very well.

DR. COHN: This is critical to the argument.

DR. HUMPHREY: This argument presupposes an inability of finding any response whatsoever to DNP-polylysine in non-responders. By a variety of criteria they do not respond, but are you really sure that there is no response at all?

The reason I ask this is that Drs. Liacopoulos and Ben-Ephraim did find an antibody response in the non-responding guinea pigs.

DR. BENACERRAF: I would be both imprudent and foolish to state that non-responder animals don't produce any antibody to the DNP determinant on the polylysine molecule, especially when one considers the fact that after immunization with DNP-polylysine coupled to guinea pig albumin (which occurs normally in vivo) some animals make low but measurable amounts of anti-DNP. However, if one studies an analagous antigen which is governed by the same genetic control, that is the glutamyl-lysine polymer and conjugates it with DNP (this is not a charged molecule and does not bind to albumin) different results are obtained. We made a study of how little antibody could be detected in non-responders immunized with DNP-GL. After repeated immunizations with adjuvant, we came to the conclusion that the responder animals made amounts of antibody ranging from a few hundred µg to over one mg of anti-DNP per ml. In non-responder animals no anti-DNP was found. The amount of antibody that could have been detected by the method used, had it been present, would be less than 0.25 µg of anti-DNP per/ml. If one looks at the cellular responses by in vitro measurements of the incorporation of H_3 thymidine in response to the antigen, the responder animal will give a very clear response, the non-responder animal gives no response whatsoever.

The other question is one that you raised with respect to the dose levels. In this particular system we attempted to find out whether there was a dose range for the response to DNP-PLL by responder guinea pigs starting with 1 µg up to 1 mg, and we did not find that dosage made any difference in this range.

For whatever it may be worth, I may add some further evidence to help analyze whether in this system we are dealing with genetic dominance or not. Drs. Foster and Lamelin in our laboratory were successful in transferring responder status or responder capacity to irradiated non-responder animals with bone-marrow cells from responders. This experiment was similar, in a sense, to what has been achieved by Dr. McDevitt and associates in an analogous system.

19

DR. CINADER: I would like to consider briefly the possible
role of tolerance in the genetic aspects of responsiveness,
mentioned by Dr. Benacerraf. The inheritance of immunological responsiveness to foreign macromolecules is subject to
multiple genetic control, which may be partly direct (geno-
typic) and partly indirect (phenotypic). One aspect of indirect control might be tolerance-dependent restriction of
immunogenicity ("steering mechanism"). This hypothesis
was tested by examining in mice the inheritance of the
capacity to make antibody to MuB1 (a complement component).
If this capacity depended on tolerance to MuB1 we could de-
duce the mode of the inheritance of immune responsiveness
from the mode of inheritance of the capacity to synthesize
MuB1. Since MuB1 is inherited under the control of a single
gene and in a dominant manner, one would expect that immune
responsiveness to MuB1 would be inherited in a recessive
manner and under the indirect control of a single gene. Experiments showed that tolerance to MuB1 can be induced by
physiological quantities of this complement component and
that genetic analysis of immune responsiveness is compatible
with tolerance-mediation. This type of inheritance is recessive. It would therefore seem probable that the dominant
inheritance described by Dr. Benacerraf is not explained by
this type of tolerance mediation. However, control by another type of tolerance mediation may nevertheless, be involved. This second type of tolerance mediator control may
depend on the dose levels which separate the genotype in
which tolerance is induced from the genotype in which an
antibody response is induced. In other words, Dr. Benacerraf might be observing a genetic control of the dose levels
at which tolerance is induced. Non-responders may, in fact,
be animals in which tolerance is induced with relatively
low doses of antigen.

DR. WEIGLE: Dr. Cinader's suggestion is well taken. I am
not suggesting, however, that it applies to Dr. Benacerraf's
experiments. We have carried out some experiments in which
guinea pigs were immunized with BSA in adjuvant (guinea pigs
don't make an immune response to an aqueous preparation of
BSA). When guinea pigs were injected with 5 mg of BSA in
adjuvant no antibody response occurred. In other experiments we have found that approximately 30% of serum proteins
escaped from adjuvant during the first 24 to 48 hours following injection. It thus appeared that the albumin was

escaping from the adjuvant and inducing an unresponsive state
before the animals could make an antibody response. When we
lowered the dose of BSA in the adjuvant to extremely small
amounts, the guinea pigs did make an antibody response.
When small amounts of the aqueous preparation of BSA were
injected at the same time as the BSA in adjuvant, the antibody response was inhibited and the guinea pigs became tolerant. These data demonstrate that you can indeed get an unresponsive state with what is considered to be an immunizing
dose of antigen.

DR. UHR: I want to comment on the use of thermodynamic
terms in regard to stimulation of immune responses and induction of tolerance. I do not think that sufficient emphasis has been put on the differences between the measurements that have been performed in test tubes and the _in vivo_
reactions in which we are really interested.

The measurements in test tubes concern interactions of
freely diffusible molecules, antibody and antigen, usually
hapten, in an equilibrium situation. In regard to _in vivo_
reactions, from the purely thermodynamic point of view, the
situation is tremendously complicated. For example, one or
both of the molecular participants may be on larger and
possibly fixed objects--for instance, antigen on dendritic
processes or on the surface of a macrophage, and antibody
may be bound to the surface of a motile lymphocyte.

CHAIRMAN SMITH: I think that this is a very important
point, because once a cell containing one of the partners of
the reaction encounters a freely diffusible component, the
cell is not indifferent to it; it initiates a series of reactions that may change the entire arrangement of the two
molecules. For example, it almost always initiates pinocytosis which brings the reactants inside the cell; environmental conditions are then no longer identical with those
that existed previously.

DR. NOSSAL: In a later session of this conference Dr.
Miller is going to present data that will shed new light on
the question of the role of the carrier. Therefore, it
would seem to be salutary to reopen this discussion when we
have a bit more information on the notion that two cell
types, rather than one cell type, are involved in the recognition process. In other words, I fear that much of what we

are saying is premature, because germane data are going to be discussed later during this conference.

DR. EDELMAN: I hope it may clarify some aspects if I mention some of the questions that a chemist would ask if you are going to talk in thermodynamic terms. First, the systems we are dealing with are obviously heterogeneous in the sense of chemical terminology. That is to say, reactions do not occur in free solution. This does not mean that one has to abandon thermodynamics, but operationally it means that one has to show that one has a truly reversible adsorption isotherm. If one has a heterogeneous system like the one containing a number of receptors, then one has to determine the number of cells and the number of receptors on each cell, because otherwise one cannot measure K, the association constant. The second question that one has to ask is whether the operation is a reversible one. Otherwise it is pretty foolish to talk about thermodynamics. Of course there are probably many things that could make for irreversibility, but I have not enough information to say what they may be. The third thing that strikes me is the assumption that the specificity is proportional to the binding constant. It is a curious fact that the range of binding constants of antibodies is much larger than the range of binding constants of enzymes where we do have some picture of the fit. In the case of some enzymes we have a crystallographic picture and one obtains a pretty good fit. So one has to ask the question: is the higher binding efficiency of some antibodies related to steric parameters of above a certain value, is it related to the number of possible contact points, which would add to the energy? Finally, I think there is an implicit assumption in all of this, and that is the existence of some kind of threshold which is either proportional to the number of receptors or possibly to the tightness of the fit, depending on your model. I bring up these questions only because to discuss thermodynamics in the absence of an operational equivalent could be hazardous, although it might ultimately turn out to be correct.

DR. SISKIND: Drs. Mitchison, Uhr, and Edelman have brought up points with which I completely agree. Although I have been arguing in favor of the importance of energetic considerations in the induction of tolerance and immunity, I

don't for a minute mean to imply that this is either a hard
chemical argument or the end-all from the biological point
of view. To talk in thermodynamic terms one has to be not
only concerned about surface interactions and phase changes,
but one also must assume that the animal functions at equilibrium. None of us would be so naive as to assume that an
animal with discretely located reactive elements (cells)
functions under thermodynamic equilibrium conditions in the
sense that one can achieve a chemical equilibrium in a test
tube. I want to emphasize that we have not neglected these
complications and that we do not deny the fact that the
energetic argument which we have been pushing in the course
of this discussion is merely one way of looking at a limited
aspect of the problem.

The fact that so many data have been accumulated that fit
the predictions of a simple energetic theory implies that one
of the steps in the process between the injection of antigen
and the ultimate formation of antibody involves the interaction of preformed antibody molecules with antigen in a
"relatively" simple manner. Obviously, when I said that
affinity represented a quantitative representation of specificity I did not mean specificity in terms of a lock and key
type of model. Nor did I mean to imply that by specificity
I meant a geometric fit. I meant the potential for chemical
interaction. From this point of view I think it is perfectly reasonable to describe specificity in energetic terms,
antibody having the highest binding affinity for a particular determinant being the most specific.

DR. SELA: I think that what Dr. Edelman said concerning
reversible thermodynamics is perfectly correct. When one
comes to a system as complicated as the one mentioned by Dr.
Uhr, it will be very difficult if not impossible to use
thermodynamics. Nevertheless, the problems may be tackled
on a quantitative level, by using the kinetic approach, and
from kinetics much can be learned. The only data reported
until now are concerned with the reaction of an antibody
with a hapten, a reaction which is diffusion-controlled and
extremely quick. When one proceeds from such a system to
measure the kinetics of the reaction of a macromolecular
antigen with an antibody, the reaction is orders of magnitude slower.

DR. BENACERRAF: I think that from the foregoing discussion

emerges general agreement on some of the factors that play a role in the induction of tolerance. We have all agreed that given the problem involved in the encounter of an antigen with the specific cell and given the concentrating mechanism in the animal, specificity, and therefore affinity, must play a role. We also agree that there is a problem of induction where recognition of antigenicity plays a role in a manner that we do not yet fully understand. We have, however, been promised by Dr. Nossal that this phenomenon will be clarified later on by work from his Institute.

I wonder if we now could discuss some of the earlier points which I made with respect to the mechanisms by which cells are rendered tolerant. Are cells made tolerant because they are killed? Are cells made tolerant because they are made to differentiate without proliferation, as has been shown by Drs. Sterzl and Howard in some of their experiments, or are they made tolerant because they are just "paralyzed" until they lose their antigen in some diffusible manner?

DR. WEIGLE: I would like to direct attention to Dr. Benacerraf's finding that in rabbits made tolerant to low doses of BSA, the BSA-tolerant state could be terminated by injecting DNP-BSA. However, when tolerance had been induced with a high dose, it could not be terminated by injecting DNP-BSA. I consider this a very important point carrying a great deal of biological significance.

In our own work, rabbits were injected with 500 mg of BSA during the first 4 or 5 days of life. I don't know whether you would call this high or low-dose tolerance. We tested these rabbits 3 or 4 months after the last injection of antigen. The animals were then injected with arsanil-sulfanil-BSA or with a cross-reacting antigen which readily resulted in a termination of the tolerant state. However, if at this time we injected even very small amounts of native BSA (as arsanil-sulfanil-BSA), the termination of the tolerance did not occur. In a similar experiment, when we injected rabbits with an aqueous preparation of arsanil-sulfanil-rabbit thyroglobulin, the natural tolerance to rabbit thyroglobulin was terminated with the production of both thyroiditis and antibody to thyroglobulin. Just as in the case of BSA, the injection of natural thyroglobulin together with a small amount of arsanil-sulfanil-thyroglobulin prevented both thyroiditis and the production of antibody. I, therefore, think that this may represent a general mechanism preventing a massive threat of production of autoimmune diseases.

As a result of virus transformation, trauma, or various other injuries, we obviously come in contact with antigens that cross-react with normal body constituents. The presence of small amounts of self components in the circulation may well inhibit autoimmunity or the termination of natural responses. The ease with which experimental autoimmune diseases such as aspermatogenesis, thyroiditis, uveitis, encephalomyelitis, etc. are produced may be the consequence of insufficient quantities of circulating antigen which would be required to prevent a termination of tolerance. Thyroglobulin, for example, is present in the circulation of normal human beings in a concentration of 10^{-11} molar. This concentration is apparently sufficient to inhibit a termination of tolerance to thyroglobulin in the absence of a strong antigenic stimulus; a strong antigenic stimulation, however, can terminate the natural tolerance to thyroglobulin.

DR. BENACERRAF: The data I presented in no way contradict the findings of Dr. Weigle. We did not say that there is no tolerance in the absence of anti-BSA following a 0.5 mg tolerance dose in adult rabbits; there is some, but certainly less than one would get with 1 mg. On the whole, I think our data are clearly compatible with yours, and I fully agree with everything you have said.

CHAIRMAN SMITH: Now I would like to shift gears just a bit. One central question is this: is there indeed a tolerant cell? Does the tolerant state represent the absence of responding cells or is there some middle ground between two possibilities, namely, a capacity of a cell to recognize antigen but a suppression of replication by some unidentified mechanism; as a variable to the last possibility one might suggest that only antibody production itself is arrested.

I would like to call on Dr. Sterzl to state his point of view regarding this problem.

DR. STERZL: Figure 3 summarizes the differentiation of immunocompetent cells. This well-known scheme (Sterzl J., Silverstein A., Advances in Immunol. 6, 337, 1967) was named the "unitarian concept" because we assume that for the different phases of the immune response (e.g. primary and secondary responses, tolerance) there exists a common precursor cell (immunocompetent or X cell) for individual antigenic determinants.

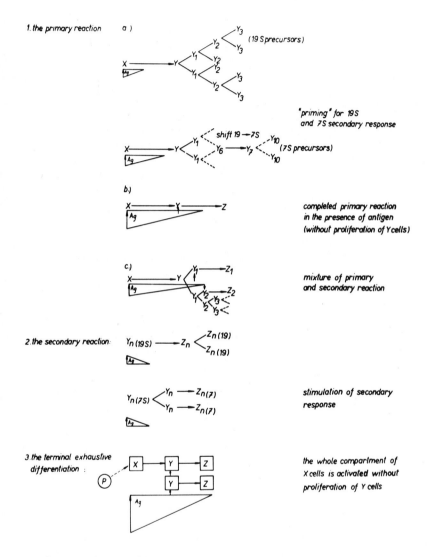

Fig. 3   A scheme illustrating possible pathways in the
differentiation of immuno-competent cells

(Data reproduced with permission of Cold Spring
Harbor Symposia)

I. PROPERTIES OF ANTIGENS

Depending on the quantity and quality of the antigen injected, the immunocompetent cells (X) are activated along
different pathways into proliferating cells (Y). Proliferation or its restriction are of central importance; they can
result either in secondary responses or in immunological
inhibition.

The first situation outlined in Fig. 3 illustrates the
effect of injecting antigen in amounts so small that it is
not available during the entire process of differentiation.
Under these circumstances the immunocompetent cells are
activated into the proliferative state only, and are "primed"
for the secondary response without completing the primary
response (for experimental data see Cold Spring Harbor Symp.
Quant. Biol. 32, 493, 1967). Cells activated by antigen and
prepared for the secondary response (Y cells) have increased
binding capacity for the antigen (Sterzl J., Jilek M.,
Nature 216, 1233, 1967).

According to our results, limited proliferation of activated cells (Y), caused either by small doses of antigen or
by the injection of antiserum against the antigen, or by
drugs inhibiting proliferation, is involved in the formation
of cells producing 19S antibody (situation 1a). If the proliferation of activated cells continues beyond 5 to 7 gener-
ations, a "genetic shift" (i.e. the activation of a gene
region controlling gamma chain synthesis) is assumed to
occur in the antibody-precursor cells (Y). This "genetic
shift," leading to the synthesis of the new gamma chain,
could be analogous to the genetic shift in the precursor
line of hemoblasts in which the shift from fetal to adult
hemoglobin occurs.

The next situation (1b) illustrates the differentiation
of immunocompetent cells under conditions in which all
stages occur in the presence of antigen resulting in restriction of proliferation. After the primary stimulus
with large doses of antigen, all susceptible immunocompetent
cells are activated (1 per 10^6 lymphoid cells) and differentiate without proliferation into antibody-forming cells
(about 1-10 per 10^6 lymphoid cells). Antibody-producing
cells have a half-life of 2-3 days. Because the quantity
of activated Y cells did not, in this instance, increase by
proliferation, subsequent doses of antigen will react only
with a small number of immunocompetent cells, resulting in
a state of apparent immunological inhibition, i.e. tolerance.

This situation, i.e. the production of tolerance follow-ing an initial immunological response was demonstrated in our laboratory for different antigens: bacterial antigen (Sterzl J., Trnka Z. Nature 179, 918, 1957), and sheep ery-throcytes (Sterzl J., Nature 209, 416, 1966). Similar re-sults have been reported by Siskind et al. (J. Exper. Med. 127, 55, 1967) who observed that the injection of 50 mg of DNP into rabbits led to a rapid antibody response, which in turn led to a depression of the immune response. However, when the animals were immunized with 0.5 mg of DNP antigen, a slight primary antibody response occurred and was followed by a vigorous secondary response after boosting at 50 days.

In the most recent experiments from our laboratory, Dr. Medlin demonstrated a similar mechanism for the establish-ment of immunological paralysis to pneumococcal polysacchar-ide Type III. Following the injection of this polysacchar-ide into mice in quantities of 10-100 µg, i.e. doses that are paralyzing, specific antibody-forming cells were de-tected by a plaque technique using mouse erythrocytes with adsorbed polysaccharide. On the sixth day after immuniza-tion, 500-1000 antibody-producing cells were found but these disappeared subsequently as the state of paralysis was established. These results support our hypothesis that tolerance is the result of a restricted proliferation and an ensuing exhaustive differentiation of cells that are sensitive to the given antigenic determinant.

DR. HOWARD: Part of the experimental evidence I should like to present on the cellular response to Type III pneumococcal polysaccharide is in agreement with the results of Dr. Sterzl. Our experiments also have been with mice but em-ployed the Biozzi rosette (immunocyto-adherence) technique rather than the plaque assay. CBA red cells were sensitized with Type III polysaccharide and were incubated with syn-geneic spleen cells from immunized and from paralyzed mice.

The passive hemagglutinin response to immunizing doses of 0.5 and 5 µg and to a paralyzing dose of 500 µg are shown in Fig. 4. Note particularly the extremely early rise (12 hours) in the 0.5 µg group and note that the animals that had received 500 µg are almost completely paralyzed. Out of a total of 89 animals examined in the latter group, 76 had titers of less than 1:2.

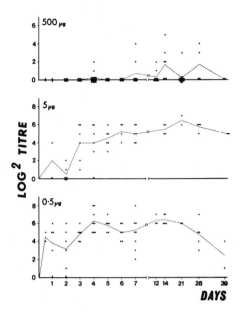

Fig. 4   Humoral antibody response of CBA mice to different
doses of pneumococcal polysaccharide type III. The
response was measured by passive hemagglutination
using sensitized CBA erythrocytes.

(Data reproduced with permission of Clinical and
Experimental Immunology)

Figure 5. summarizes the results obtained on the number
of rosette-forming cells (RFC) in the spleens of these paralyzed animals taken at various intervals after antigen
injection. As early as 24 hours after antigen, the number
of RFC per spleen is already close to maximal. Cellular
proliferation therefore appears to play a minimal role in
this response, as proposed by Dr. Benacerraf. The surprising feature, however, is that the immune cells persisted for very much longer than in the work mentioned by
Dr. Sterzl. This may be partly attributable to the use of
the rosette rather than the plaque technique, the former
being capable of detecting both IgM and IgG-forming cells.
Also, the absolute number of antibody-forming cells detected by the rosette method is as a rule very much higher
than in the plaque technique.

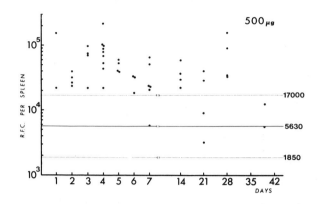

Fig. 5 Rosette-forming cells (immunocyto-adherence) in the
spleens of CBA mice receiving a "paralysing" dose
of 500 µg of type III pneumococcal polysaccharide.
Each point represents one animal and the horizontal
lines the mean ±2 SD of 30 non-immunized controls.

(Data reproduced with permission of Clinical and
Experimental Immunology)

The background control cited in these tables represents
the geometric mean value of 30 non-immunized control animals plus or minus 2 standard deviations calculated on log
transformed data. All tests of specificity regarding the
RFC in these cell suspensions were satisfactory; the addition of 100 µg of polysaccharide/ml to the incubation mixture, or the substitution of sham-sensitized cells, inhibited rosette formation to the original low background.
Figure 6 represents the RFC response in the spleens of
mice given the 5 µg immunizing dose. The cellular response
was no greater than in the paralyzed group and appears to
be less well maintained.

With regard to the interpretation of these results, I
should like to refer to some earlier experiments which Dr.
Siskind and I did, which indicated 3 peculiarities of
pneumococcus polysaccharide as an antigen. First of all,
part of the polysaccharide injected remains circulating for
long periods in paralyzed animals and is fully immunogenic
on transfer to normal mice. Secondly, the extent of uptake
of the antigen in macrophages appears to have little or no
influence on the subsequent dose-response curve. It is just

30

as easy to paralyze a normal animal and an animal in which
the macrophage uptake of polysaccharide has been greatly
increased.   Thus, i.v. injection of SSS III, complexed with
methylated BSA (insoluble) into a splenectomized animal, will
paralyze just as effectively as the same quantity injected
i.p. in soluble form into mice with a functioning spleen.

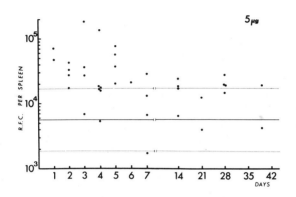

Fig. 6   Rosette-forming cells, as in Fig. 5, but following
an immunizing dose of 5 µg

(Data reproduced with permission of Clinical and
Experimental Immunology)

Our interpretation of such data is that phagocytosed polysaccharide is subsequently released by a process of exocytosis, which once again brings up the old idea of a "treadmill" mechanism for paralysis by this antigen, at least in
the early stages of the development of paralysis.   We were
completely unable to find evidence for a low-dose zone
tolerance with these polysaccharides.

CHAIRMAN SMITH: Then in respect to pneumococcal polysaccharides, you are saying the tolerant cell is an immune cell.

DR. HOWARD: Under the conditions studied, an immune response was marked by antigen persistence.   We could not detect tolerance at the cellular level.

DR. FRIEDMAN: I would like to present some results concerning immune tolerance to sRBC in adult and in neonatal

mice. These results are essentially similar to some of the observations of Dr. Sterzl with piglets and rabbits. Our interpretation, however, is different. We have induced a tolerant state to sRBC in neonatal mice by multiple injections of sRBC. Relatively similar results may be obtained in adult mice treated simultaneously with cyclophosphamide (cytoxan) and sRBC. The data in Fig. 7 are concerned only with the effect of multiple injections of sRBC into normal

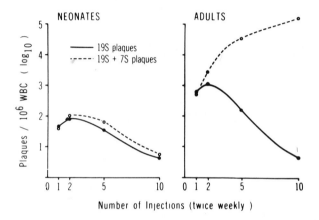

Fig. 7 The number of PFC in spleens of adult and neonatal mice given either single or multiple injections of sRBC. Solid line indicates 19S PFC per 10^6 spleen cells; dashed line the number of 19S and 7S PFC. On the right is the PFC response of adult mice, 8 weeks or older, tested for the number of PFC 4 days after the last injection; on the left is the number of PFC in neonatal mice 4 days after the last injection. A dose of 4 x 10^8 sRBC was given i.p. at 3 to 4 day intervals.

neonatal and adult mice. In adult mice, we obtain essentially the same results as those reported by Drs. Fitch and Rowley, except that as anticipated, multiple injections of sRBC results in a depression of the number of 19S(IgM) plaque-forming cells (PFC) and the concomitant appearance

of 7S(IgG) PFC detected by the indirect enhancement procedure.
Some degree of "tolerance" may be occurring since the number
of PFC level off after having attained a maximum number of
about 10^6 per spleen. Twice weekly injections of sRBC for
5 to 6 weeks resulted in the appearance of about 10^5 to 10^6
7S PFC, but only 10^2 or 10^3 19S PFC. Entirely different results were obtained with neonatal mice. Multiple injections
of sRBC into newborn mice resulted in a marked inhibition of
both 19S and 7S PFC. This inhibition was most marked when
mice received 2 or 3 weekly injections of 10^8 sRBC for a
period of 6 weeks or longer. Challenge of these mice at a
subsequent time failed to elicit a normal immune response.
The question has been asked as to the immune status, on the
recall level, of these mice during the period of time when
tolerance was being induced. In the prior experiments mice
were treated with sRBC for several weeks, then rested for
several weeks, and challenged. As can be seen in Fig. 8
there were essentially no 7S or 19S PFC in mice given 16
injections of sRBC over a period of 5 to 6 weeks. There was
also no response (= no PFC) in one week-old mice following
1 or 2 injections of sRBC. At 2 weeks of age, after 5 to 6
injections of sRBC, many mice showed a low response. At 3
to 4 weeks of age, after 8 injections of antigen, there was
a maximum response of almost 30 19S PFC per 10^6 spleen cells
tested. The number of 7S PFC was even less. However, this
small number of PFC seems to represent, during the induction
period of tolerance, a proliferation of specific 19S and 7S-
forming cells. The serum titers were usually negative, probably due to the "masking" of antibody by excess antigen.

It should be pointed out that the number of 30 PFC per
10^6 spleen cells is markedly lower than in an adult mouse
(10^5 PFC). Nevertheless, the number of PFC in the neonatally
treated mice represents an increase of about 30 to 40 fold.

We do not interpret these results as exhaustive differentiation, or an exhaustion of immunocompetent cells as proposed by Drs. Sterzl and Sercarz, respectively. We take into
account the complex mosaic of antigens on sRBC. If, for
example, this involved only 4 major antigenic groupings A,
B, C, and D, tolerance could be induced to the major antigen
A, even after injection of only a relatively small amount.
It may take 3 or 4 injections or more before tolerance is induced to antigen B. Meanwhile, antibody-forming cells specific for B may appear even though the mice are already tolerant to antigen A. Additional injection of sRBC, increasing

33

the concentration of antigen B, may result in tolerance. In this manner the mice would have first formed antibody to the "minor" antigens on the red blood cell surface before sufficient antigen was administered to induce tolerance to all of the postulated antigens. Consequently, the proliferation of antibody-forming cells may be spurious in terms of the entire sRBC.

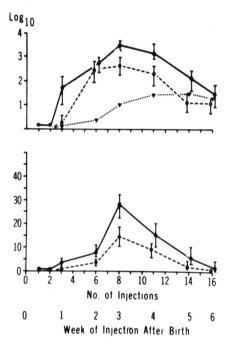

Fig. 8 The number of PFC per spleen and per 10^6 splenocytes in mice that received sRBC as neonates. The solid line shows the number of 19S PFC detected by the direct procedure and the dashed line the number of 7S PFC detected by the indirect procedure. The "background" PFC count in non-immunized neonates is shown by the dotted line. Each point represents the average of 4 to 6 animals injected with 4×10^8 sRBC at birth and twice weekly thereafter.

We have extended such studies to tests, with lipopolysaccharides (LPS) of E. coli as antigen using the (a) bacteriolytic plaque assay (Schwartz and Braun, Science, 1965) and (b) the indirect hemolytic plaque assay with LPS-sensitized erythrocytes. E. coli PFC would be expected to be found in neonatal mice receiving a tolerance-inducing dose of 10 to 100 μg of LPS at birth. However, an increase in PFC specific for E. coli was detected only with the bacteriolytic plaque assay, using viable E. coli as the indicator. With the indirect hemolytic plaque assay only an occasional PFC was observed. We interpret these results as showing a complex immune response in mice to a probable multiplicity of antigens in the LPS. Minor antigens in the LPS may be present on the surface of the intact bacteria and in the small amount of the extracted LPS used to sensitize the RBC.

Thus, tolerance to sRBC and bacterial antigens is a complex phenomenon even when studied at the cellular level. Experiments concerning presence or absence of antibody formation during the inductive period of tolerance must be examined critically in view of the complexity of the antigens used.

DR. WAKSMAN: It seems to me that all data, including those of Dr. Howard, are consistent with two distinct possibilities. One is that some members of the total pool of cells which could respond to a given antigen become tolerant and others immune; depending on the dose used, one may have a preponderance of one or the other. The experiments that have been reviewed may have involved a choice of dose that gives mainly tolerance, thus leading to tolerance in the majority of the cells and an immune response in a very small number of the cell population. An alternative interpretation is Dr. Sterzl's suggestion that antibody-forming cells are being made tolerant by exhaustive differentiation. It seems to me that the real difference between the two alternatives may be only a quantitative one. If the antibody-forming cells identified by Dr. Howard were the total pool of cells capable of responding, then there ought to be as many of these as in a maximal immune response, except that they are not dividing. Actually, however, the number of cells was rather small, a one log increase from background. This would suggest that these cells represent simply a tiny part of the total available pool, which happened to be pushed into a response rather than into tolerance.

DR. BENACERRAF: I think at this time we should discuss the data that I described earlier concerning the secondary

35

response to polysaccharides in rabbits. In my opinion, that also constituted evidence of exhaustive differentiation with an incomplete antigen of a similar type. You will remember that we have observed a significant secondary response to a first challenge with polysaccharides, but on repeated challenge, once the secondary cell population had been exhausted, the animals no longer responded, suggesting an exhaustive differentiation in the absence of proliferation.

DR. MITCHISON: I would like to point out 2 things about what Dr. Howard had to say. First of all, if his mechanism is a general one and applies to tolerance of red cells, we can all go home since there is no such thing as tolerance. He is, however, talking about something entirely different. This is not tolerance at the cellular level, but what Dr. Sercarz calls antibody production on a treadmill; the mechanism for producing antibody is working perfectly well but the products are absorbed, so we simply confuse the issue by bringing red cells in here. I would, therefore, like to ask Dr. Howard to what extent he is prepared to generalize. In particular, I would like to ask what he thinks about the tolerance to dextran. Let me remind you of the important work of Drs. Coulson and Stevens who showed that prior injection of free dextran into guinea pigs prevents a subsequent response of the animals to dextran administered in the form of washed bacteria. The apparent paralysis lasts for a period of at least 6 weeks, if I remember correctly. We also know that dextran is eliminated from the circulation very efficiently. Tests with anthrone have shown that the level of dextran in the circulation falls fairly rapidly to a minute fraction of the initial level. Recent work with mice, carried out with Dr. Himmelspach, has shown that dextran is cleared to a level below one-ten thousandth of the initial dose, although some tolerance remains. I would like to ask Dr. Howard how he reconciles these data with his concept of exocytosis.

DR. HOWARD: I would like to respond first to Dr. Waksman and then to Dr. Mitchison. The actual increase in the number of RFC over the background level was the same in both the immunized and the paralyzed groups of animals, about 10-fold. Also in some other tests which I did not show, a similar result was obtained with mice after immunization with only 0.5 µg. The 10-fold increase in cells is entirely

36

compatible with measurements that have been made on the quantity of circulating antibody in the mouse. The amounts involved are extremely small, being of the order of 5 or 10 µg per ml.

As far as any generalized extrapolation of these results is concerned, I should make it clear that quite obviously our interpretation is not that all immunological paralysis is interpretable in this way, or even that all polysaccharide paralysis is, but merely that at least part of the phenomenon of paralysis by pneumococcal polysaccharide detected in the intact animal is explicable on a treadmill basis.

In the early weeks examined in these experiments, any antibody formed in these animals would be neutralized by the quantity of antigen circulating in the serum, an amount which is perfectly adequate to do this. I think that as far as the dextran experiments are concerned it is fairly obvious that a mechanism of central inhibition has been produced. It is open to reinvestigation, however, to what extent this inhibition is produced during paralysis with pneumococcal polysaccharide.

DR. MÖLLER: I would like to make a general comment regarding exhaustive proliferation. A burst of antibody production preceding tolerance induction need not be considered an argument for exhaustive proliferation of antigen-sensitive cells. We have found that tolerance can be induced during the exponential phase of antibody synthesis. Expression of tolerance requires 60-70 hours. Prior to that period antibody synthesis proceeds normally and the number of producing cells increases exponentially. We have interpreted this in terms of an instantaneous induction of tolerance in antigen-sensitive cells, whereas cells that have already been triggered go on and divide. The latter cells are antigen-independent; they cannot be made tolerant; and they cannot be made to divide faster by antigen. According to this concept tolerance induction is a suppression of antigen-sensitive cells, without necessarily assuming that they are exhausted by proliferation.

CHAIRMAN SMITH: If I understand correctly, this is essentially what Dr. Waksman has suggested earlier, namely that it depends on when in their differentiation the cells are hit by antigen.

DR. UHR: It seems to me that the critical evidence that would differentiate Dr. Möller's interpretation from Dr. Sterzl's is the proliferative history of the antibody-forming cell. There are several published studies that indicate that all antibody-forming cells in a secondary response have arisen through proliferation. If Dr. Sterzl can document, in a definitive manner, that there are antibody-forming cells in the partially tolerant animal that have not arisen through cell division, he would then have strong support for his interpretation.

DR. STERZL: Of course if one observes an immune response preceeding the onset of tolerance one should think about 2 possible pathways: one portion of the immunocompetent cell population is diverted directly to the state of tolerance (being killed by antigen or repressed on receptor sites) and the other portion differentiates towards an immune response.

Because we are not able to follow experimentally the process by which cells are converted directly to the tolerant state, let us examine that small portion of the cell population that is differentiating towards the immune response. Is it not the usual case to expect an anamnestic response from these cells? Nevertheless, in our experiments the second injection of antigen is followed instead by tolerance or paralysis. These results would indicate that the portion of cells that did differentiate into the immune response followed a different pathway from the typical immune response. Therefore, we have proposed that the cells activated by antigen can differentiate without proliferation into antibody-forming cells, this event taking place without the establishment of memory cells. After the death of the antibody-forming cells, there is a temporary exhaustion of cells sensitive to the antigen, this being a state of tolerance.

DR. MÖLLER: They are exhausted because they only have a very limited life span. The antigen-sensitive cells divide in response to antigenic stimulation but they cannot be detected since they do not produce antibodies. Antibody-producing cells are recruited from antigen-sensitive cells, and producing cells proliferate for 70 hours after which time they seem to disappear. There is evidence to suggest that during the immune response there is a constant recruitment of new antigen-sensitive cells which have expanded exponentially to antibody-producing cells. The tolerogenic dose of antigen

may prevent this recruitment, but has no effect on the antibody producing cells that have already been triggered.

DR. STERZL: I think we are still running around the central
question, that is, must the cell activated by antigen undergo
proliferation before it becomes an antibody-forming cell?
There is indirect information from tests with immunosuppressive drugs (Sterzl, in Immunity, Cancer and Chemotherapy,
Acad. Press 1967, p.71), and from multiplication curves
(Simonsen, M., J. Exp. Med., 1967), that under certain conditions the differentiation of immunocompetent cells may proceed without mitosis.   I would like to document this point
further by data obtained in the true primary response in
germ-free newborn piglets which have no background of plaque-
forming cells.   Piglets were immunized i.v. with 10 ml of a
20% suspension of sRBC and C_{14} thymidine was injected in a
dose of 0.2 μC/gm body weight every 5 hours until the first
appearance of PFC, which was about 72 hours after immunization.   Radioautography of the PFC was performed as described
earlier (Sterzl et al.:   Molecular and Cellular Basis of
Antibody Formation, Acad. Press, 1965).   In the earliest detectable group of antibody-forming cells (about $500/10^8$
lymphoid cells), 75% incorporated C_{14} thymidine and 25%
were without label.   When the antibody-forming cells were
tested later on (96 hours after immunization and later) the
increase in the number of antibody-forming cells was due
mostly to mitotic division and nearly 100% of the antibody-
forming cells were labeled.

DR. HUMPHREY: To follow up Dr. Howard's point, I would like
to talk very briefly about some experiments that we did with
Dr. Janeway using synthetic polypeptides provided by Dr.
Sela.   As shown by Drs. Sela and Janeway, the D-polypeptides,
(Tyr-Ala-Glu) and (Tyr-Glu-Lys) are immunogenic in mice in
small doses, whereas in higher doses they are not immunogenic but apparently tolerogenic.   In contrast, corresponding L-polypeptides are immunogenic over a much wider dose
range.   We have looked at what happened to these D-polypeptides labelled with I_{125} when they are injected into mice.
They very rapidly disappear from the circulation and are
taken up by macrophages in which they appear to persist.
They are broken down and excreted extremely slowly (only
12-18% in 21 days).   The interesting thing is that although
the great majority of the material remains within macrophages,

there is in the plasma a constant very low level of circulating material which behaves like the original polypeptides.
This resembles the situation described for SSS III by Dr.
Howard. So far we have not been able to test for the presence of RFC or PFC. However, there is a strong indication
that the mice are not making antibodies under these circumstances. When we looked for localization of the labelled
D-polypeptides on the dendritic cells of the germinal center
(which is an extremely sensitive method for detecting traces
of antibody that have localized there and then pick up antigen) we found none. With immunogenic L-polypeptides at a
corresponding dose, localization occurred as expected. This
suggests that perhaps the paralyzed mice are not making antibody under these circumstances. One finding in these studies surprised me. When we used as control I_{125}-labelled
L-(Tyr, Glu) gelatin, given us by Dr. Sela, this also disappeared rapidly from the circulation but in contrast it was
rapidly broken down, about 99% of the radioactivity being
eliminated from the body within 5 days. When we examined
the plasma of these mice at 17 days, we found a very low
level of macromolecular labelled material which appeared to
be the original (Tyr, Glu) gelatin. Thus, while the great
majority of these digestable polypeptides had disappeared,
a minute fraction of the retained material was apparently
still circulating in the blood. This may mean that the
phenomenon is not confined to what we consider to be indi-
gestible materials.

DR. BENACERRAF: One point is quite clear to me. You are
having tolerance because the specific cells, the clones, are
not stimulated to proliferate by the incomplete antigen.
Why in this case you don't stimulate proliferating clones
must depend on the lack of a property of the antigen, because when you inject the whole pneumococcus organism you
inject, in effect, an equal amount of polysaccharide and
yet you stimulate high levels of antibodies. Thus, the important question with which we are concerned is why you do
or do not get proliferating clones in response to an antigen; this is the central issue in tolerance problems. Now,
why do specific cells proliferate in some cases and not in
others? Is it the dosage effect in some cases? Is it the
nature of the antigen in other cases?

DR. SERCARZ: In our laboratory, Dr. Byers has demonstrated
that in the same cell population of rabbit lymph nodes,

primed to BSA, you can demonstrate either exhaustion or paralysis. If you take a primed lymph node from control animals, place it in tissue culture and stimulate it with optimum amount of antigen, you will get a normal antibody response in vitro. However, if you take the animal and inject it with a large amount of BSA several days before you remove the lymph node, you can demonstrate a very definite response, yet subsequently, in vitro, the rabbit lymph node is unable to respond to antigenic stimulation. Therefore, you have exhausted the potential of that lymphoid population to respond to BSA.

On the other hand, you can put the primed lymph node fragment in culture and add sufficient antigen to prevent the occurrence of this response. It is interesting that in such a situation the antigen must be in contact with the lymph node from the beginning, because if you first add a small amount of antigen and then follow this, even within several hours, with a large dose of antigen, you can no longer prevent the response. Thus, you can turn off the antibody response provided sufficient antigen is given soon enough, and you see subsequently no signs of an antibody response; this would be characteristic of exhaustion. Consequently, exhaustive proliferation and paralysis can occur in the same population.

I would also like to make a comment relating to the question whether these are, in fact, tolerant cells. Several cases have been reported in which by giving a large dose of antigen the antibody response can be delayed for several days. First is the case of Dr. Ivanyi involving a high-dose paralysis system using human albumin in chickens. Secondly, it was shown by Dr. Byers in our in vitro system that when a high dose of BSA is left in contact with primed rabbit lymph node fragments the appearance of the response can be delayed by several days. Likewise, Drs. Britton and Möller have shown that a later peak in antibody response to LPS is obtained if a large dose of antigen is administered. We can also show a delay in the antibody response to beta galactosidase with a very sensitive cellular assay system, in which the peak of the response to 1 mg of antigen is later than that to 10 µg. In conclusion, one can view large doses of antigen, delaying an immune response, as causing temporary reversible paralysis, which is then followed by immunity.

DR. SCHWARTZ: I would like to comment on the assumption that

we know what the kinetics of antibody-forming cells are.
In fact, we do not. It has been tacitly assumed in these
discussions that antibody-forming cells divide exponentially.
There is, however, no evidence to support this contention.
It is just as reasonable to assume that the kinetics of
these cells follow a steady state rather than being exponential. It is known that most normal mammalian cells are in a
steady state of proliferation and do not divide exponentially.
Exponential growth is seen only occasionally, for example,
in neoplastic cells. This may mean that Dr. Sterzl's scheme
indicating the exponential proliferation of Y and Z cells is
incorrect. In a steady state, the X cell would form two
daughter cells, one of which reverts back to an X cell, the
other becoming a Y cell. I think this is a very important
point in understanding where the cellular locus of action of
antigen may be. For example, one might imagine that the
cell that is reverting back to the stem cell state is the
tolerant sensitive unit, and not the cell that is going on
to the Y state.

DR. NOSSAL: I want to ask Dr. Schwartz how he explains a
dividing antibody-forming cell. It would seem to me that
if one can demonstrate a cell in the actual act of mitosis,
turning out large amounts of antibody and making a plaque,
it is almost self-evident that both of the progeny of that
cell must be antibody-forming cells.

DR. SCHWARTZ: I have also seen dividing plaque-forming
cells. However, these are very rare, and one has to look
at innumerable antibody-forming cells before you see a dividing antibody-forming cell. By contrast, they are all incorporating H_3 thymidine, which means that they are all proliferating. But the actual number of mitoses that you do
see in a spleen cell population is extremely small.

DR. NOSSAL: Just as a brief technical comment, I agree that
if you look at a thousand cells at an early stage of the
response, the actual number of mitotic figures is small.
If you treat now with colchicin and two hours later look
again,you will find a number of mitoses that is of the
order that you would have predicted. I think the answer to
the apparent dilemma may be a technical one. I think we
are dealing with a class of cells here in which the metaphase is either not very typical or is passed through very

quickly. I personally don't think that the number of mitotic events in these cells is very different from what you would expect from other cells.

DR. BUSSARD: I think it is clear that in our system with peritoneal cells, cells can produce antibody without dividing. For example, we can have production of plaques in the presence of colchicine and FUDR which blocks cell division. Second, we can have, in certain cases, very fast plaque formation, i.e. within a few hours after placing the cells in tissue culture. Thirdly, you can have cells that attach to glass, are unable to divide, but produce plaques.

   I don't see why we can't have both mechanisms operate at the same time. Cells may divide and produce an exponential rise in plaque-forming activity, which is, for example, shown by the in vitro data of Drs. Mishell and Dutton, but this does not exclude the possibility that cells can also react directly without dividing.

   Dr. Nossal said that it has been shown that a dividing cell can be found in the center of a plaque. This, however, does not mean that both progeny of the dividing cell are producing antibody. It would be interesting to follow the fate of the two cells to see whether one of the cells becomes a memory cell and not a "producer," and the second one a producing cell. After all, it does not follow a priori that both daughter cells would have to be producers.

DR. SCHWARTZ: Right.

DR. LESKOWITZ: I suggest that we may have a situation where all parties are correct. If I remember Dr. Tannenberg's work correctly, it concerned 19S PFC only and the situation Dr. Schwartz described may well obtain for those particular cells. The other work on dividing plasma cells may concern mature 7S antibody-producing cells in division. I am not sure whether this observation has been extended to 19S producing cells.

DR. SCHWARTZ: It is entirely possible that a cell can be turned on to differentiate into an antibody-forming cell and then revert back into a stem cell. There is no evidence for or against this point. In fact, it is possible that some very large blast cells that have not yet developed an ergastoplasmic lamella can transform back into a lymphocyte and enter the pool of antigen-sensitive cells.

To answer Dr. Leskowitz, I don't think you can identify any type of dividing cell by morphology alone during mitosis.

DR. RAJEWSKY: I think there was one point missing in Dr. Schwartz' argument. There can be an expotential increase of PFC and for this one cannot account by asymmetrical division.

DR. SCHWARTZ: The well-known kinetics of cells rising exponentially only shows that the rate of appearance of antibody-forming cells is exponential. It does not tell anything about the generation time of these cells. When the generation time is measured by independent methods, it turns out to be much slower than the rate of appearance of these cells. The number of PFC doubles, but the actual generation time appears to be somewhere between 13 and 14 hours. So we must conclude that differentiation plays an important role in this system. The induction of differentiation in these cells is, of course, highly complicated, because there are many things that happen to the antigen before it gets to the lymphocyte.

DR. RAJEWSKY: An appropriate model has been proposed by Drs. Dutton and Mishell. A large population of cells is stimulated by antigen to grow exponentially with a normal division time. From this a single population of plaque-forming cells is derived by differentiation which proceeds more and more rapidly with time. The doubling time of the plaque-forming cells will thus be shorter than the generation time of the actually dividing cells.

DR. UHR: I think I have to disagree. The one hard fact we have in terms of dynamics is that some cells go through replication before they differentiate into antibody-forming plasma cells. This is consistent with other models of differentiation in other cellular systems. Unless I am mistaken, there is no precedent as yet for a heterogeneity of other cell types in terms of differentiation pattern, namely, for a cell to become a differentiated cell without replication.

DR. GOLUB: Well, from rather obscure sources, in plant systems mainly, there are cases of differentiation where you have DNA synthesis going on but no replication. Also, data from Dr. Auerbach's laboratory concerning the epithelium of the developing kidney indicate again that you may have DNA systhesis and differentiation but no replication.

DR. UHR: The evidence of Drs. Howard and Sterzl is suggestive that an X cell can differentiate to a Z cell without replication. However, formal proof that this additional pathway exists demands the same kind of definitive labelling evidence which established that in the secondary response Z cells arise through replication.

The second point is that we need similar definitive evidence as to the means by which antigen affects these cellular events. Does antigen push a button and the cell goes through its paces, or does antigen affect the pathways of differentiation and the rates at which differentiation occurs?

DR. SCHWARTZ: I would just like to make one comment in regard to Dr. Uhr's remark. Dr. Tannenberg has examined, by radioautography, approximately 45,000 individual PFC and aside from some rare technical artifacts, every one of these cells was incorporating thymidine. This must mean that all the cells are proliferating. But the question is not whether or not they are or they are not proliferating; it is how they are proliferating.

DR. HOWARD: Aside from the experimental evidence, you are telling us that the cell can produce antibody without dividing. I think I would like to come to a more basic discussion. I think we may be getting into some semantic difficulty about the word "differentiation." After all, what we mean is that a cell that will not divide can get a signal and start to produce something that it was not producing before. If you call this differentiation, this is up to you. Anyhow, this situation is quite common. In the animal the action of a hormone on a target organ is an example of a signal starting production in a quiescent cell. I don't think we ought to emphasize the word "differentiation," but rather determine whether a cell can produce antibody without dividing.

DR. UHR: I think the point is that the precursor cell must become a secretory cell. Secretion, in contrast to production of cellular proteins, requires the development, as far as we know, of a very complicated system of organelles consisting of organized endoplasmic reticulum and an extensive Golgi apparatus. I believe that these extensive changes represent an indisputable example of differentiation.

DR. SISKIND: I would like to go back to the question of the effects of changes in antigen dose. Dr. Sercarz pointed out that under certain circumstances a large dose of antigen will result in a delay in the appearance of the antibody. I would like to call attention to the fact that this is not always the case; under certain circumstances quite the opposite effect can be observed, namely, that antibody appears faster after a larger dose of antigen. I think that these dose effects are pertinent to the question of how antigen concentration influences events leading to the formation of a large pool of proliferating cells. If you look at the dose-response curve of animals to DNP-BGG, you find that after immunization of a rabbit with between 5 to 50 mg of antigen in complete Freund's adjuvant a very rapid immune response follows. Anti-DNP antibody is detectable by precipitin reaction after one week and peak antibody concentrations of approximately 1.5 mg/ml are achieved after about two weeks. On the other hand, if you immunize with 0.5 mg of the same antigen after 2 weeks you find minimal concentrations of circulating antibody, while at 6 weeks antibody concentration is approximately 4 mg/ml. Thus, with a low dose of antigen one finds a slow appearance of antibody in the circulation, followed by a very rapid increase in the concentration of antibody to very high ultimate levels, whereas with antigen in a high dose antibody appears earlier but fails to reach as high a concentration. One other effect of antigen dose should be mentioned. The antibody that appears after a very high dose of antigen is of low affinity and does not increase in affinity with time after immunization. On the other hand, the antibody that appears after a low dose of antigen shows a progressive increase in binding affinity and reaches very high levels.

The situation following a high dose of antigen in adjuvants is thus operationally equivalent to the situation in a partially tolerant animal which produces a small amount of low-affinity antibody. We would suggest that when one immunizes with a superoptimal dose of antigen, one tends to induce tolerance in cells that are potentially capable of forming high-affinity antibody. It seems likely that one

of the factors involved in this tolerance induction is a
rapid terminal differentiation to antibody-secreting cells.
This results in the early production of antibody but relatively little cell proliferation. Therefore, one ends up
with low concentrations of antibody.

I think that this observation is quite similar to the
early work of Dr. Sterzl in which he showed that after a
large primary dose of sRBC, one obtains a very good primary
response, but little or no secondary response, whereas after
a low priming dose, one gets little or no antibody formed
but can elicit a very strong secondary response. I think
that antigen concentration can influence the pattern of the
immune response. A low concentration of antigen tends to
direct cells into proliferation, resulting in the formation
of a large population of antigen-sensitive cells capable of
giving a marked secondary response. On the other hand, a
superoptimal dose of antigen leads to early antibody formation but relatively little proliferation, and therefore a
small population of antigen-sensitive cells late in the response.

DR. SIMONSEN: One brief comment on the proliferative response. My question is: what does it really signify?
Could it not be that it is merely a proliferative response
to an allergic insult on the antibody-forming cells by the
antigen and complement? Has anybody observed the same loga-
rithmic phase in decomplemented animals?

DR. WEIGLE: Certainly, in the case of decomplementation one
can still obtain a sufficient antibody response, but I don't
know whether this involves an exponential increase or not.
Animals that are genetically deficient in complement still
produce antibodies to altered native thyroglobulin and
develop thyroditis.

DR. SIMONSEN: One of the reasons for my asking the question
is my own earlier findings with Dr. Nisbet that if you induce a graft-versus-host (GVH) reaction in the same genetic
system in 13-day and 17-day old embryos, you can find much
more donor cell proliferation in the older embryo, which
probably is old enough to form complement. This event occurs in spite of the fact that there is more proliferation
of donor cells in the younger embryos, which are, as far as
we know, deficient in complement. In other words, there is

an inverse relationship between the donor cell response as measured by mitotic division and as measured by GVH activity in transfer to syngeneic hosts.

DR. AUERBACH: I too would like to address myself to the question of proliferation versus differentiation. Extrapolating from embryonic studies, one can suggest that: (a) at the early stages of development one has proliferation; (b) there follows differentiation and cellular interaction usually accompanied by proliferation, but also observed without proliferation under experimental conditions; and (c) proliferation of the differentiated cells gives rise to larger numbers of such cells.

Two experimental systems with which we have been involved will point out this sequence of differentiation and proliferation events. One is the development of the leukemic cells in AKR mice. There one finds that in the preleukemic stages almost every thymus cell's phenotype is altered. If one looks later, after 6-8 months, however, one cell, or perhaps 2 or 3 seem to have become favored. Thus one sees a clonal population of tumor cells. If you were to look only at the later time, you would draw the erroneous conclusion that clonal proliferation is the explanation of tumorogenesis.

The other illustration goes back to the test system of organ versus cell culture which has already been mentioned by Dr. Bussard. The two methodologies give very different results. In the organ culture systems, such as used by Dr. Globerson and myself, antibody formation occurs with a variable cell proliferation response. In this system it does not appear that the number of PFC is directly related to the amount of antibody that is formed, and antibody synthesis increases long after the peak of PFC appears. On the other hand, in the Mishell-Dutton system, it appears that one is looking primarily at that cell population which proliferates rapidly. One can get some understanding about this difference by looking at the effect of inhibitors such as ALS. Preliminary work done in collaboration with Dr. Martin suggests that the organ culture system is vastly more sensitive to ALS than the cell culture system.

CHAIRMAN SMITH: We seem to have dealt with one possibility of the three that were mentioned by Dr. Benacerraf earlier. We have dealt with cells that are obviously not making antibodies, because that are exempt from tolerance induction even though they are presumably present. Would anybody now like to address himself to another mechanism by which, perhaps, a tolerant cell might be produced or destruction might occur?

DR. DAVIES: Figure 9 illustrates the interaction of human lymphocytes and purified soluble HLA antigen. The experiments were done by Dr. Viza. You will see that increasing

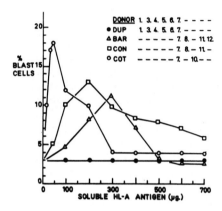

Fig. 9   Stimulation in vitro of allogeneic peripheral
         lymphocytes by soluble HLA antigen

amounts of antigen from a typed donor are plotted against cell stimulation. The antigen does not stimulate autologous cells, nor does it stimulate cells from individuals who were similar by histocompatibility typing to the donor, but it does stimulate to different degrees 3 other types of allogeneic cells. In one instance, stimulation is effected at a very small dose level of antigen. Different but larger amounts were required to stimulate cells from the two other donors. We take this to mean that the smallest amount of antigen stimulates cells from the individual who is the most histoincompatible. The typing does not reveal these differences, but then one is limited to a rather small number of typing sera. The interesting feature of all this is, I think, the question of why one gets stimulation at one particular dose level, and why increasing the dose results in diminished effects. This is not toxicity because amounts of the particular antigen preparation, too large to stimulate one culture, are stimulatory for other cultures. What is happening to the cells that meet these larger amounts of antigen?

DR. MÖLLER: I think Dr. Davies' findings are very interesting. When various substances stimulating lymphocytes in vitro, such as PHA, ALS, etc. are added to cells there is always an optimal concentration of the substances for maximal stimulation of these cells. Many of these substances interact with the majority of the cells and as the concentration of agent is increased there occurs a peak response and then a sharp diminution. The optimal concentration-effect must therefore be explained on the cellular level. For the most part, toxicity can be ruled out. We are faced with the possibility that the cell somehow knows how much of the surface has been covered by the stimulant, which does not seem to involve an all-or-none-phenomenon. This is further emphasized by studies of interactions between different stimulating processes. Let us take as an example PHA and specific antigen added to sensitized cells. At certain concentrations of the two substances, a negative interference on stimulation is observed, one substance abolishing stimulation by the other. At other concentrations a clear synergistic effect is obtained. Since the stimulants probably act on different cellular receptors, simple competition for receptors can be ruled out. This again emphasizes the possibility that a cell knows how many receptors on its surface have been triggered. The mechanism is unknown, but this certainly constitutes a model for the existence of tolerant cells.

CHAIRMAN SMITH: Dr. Möller's comment encourages me to relate an idea that is currently guiding some experimentation in our laboratory. This idea appears possibly related to the mechanism of induction of tolerance at the cellular level, involving a direct hit with antigen on a receptor on the cell surface; it concerns the consequences of this hit with respect to that single cell. The idea generates from several models with which everyone here is familiar. It involves what I shall term "antigen purging" or "receptor purging," a process by which the antigen or the receptor is removed temporarily or permanently from the surface of a living nucleated cell.

The first model involves the temporary loss of membrane antigen or membrane receptors, which is assumed to occur when the IgG of Dr. Burkitt's lymphoma patients is added _in vitro_ to various cell lines derived from this tumor. Provided the system is incubated at 37°C for 60-120 minutes, the attachment of the particular IgG preparation diminishes markedly and cannot be reattached by adding more of the serum factor. The Burkitt antigen is presumably purged from the surface of the cell by an energy-requiring process initiated by the reaction of antigen with antibody. Complement is, of course, present in the system. Dr. Osunkoya has also shown that the process is reversible, providing the IgG is removed. The receptors are apparently restored rapidly within a 12-24 hour period. "Antigenic modulation," which Drs. Boyse and Old have recently described, is an apparently similar phenomenon which can be demonstrated both _in vitro_ and _in vivo_ with respect to the TL antigen of mice.

We seem to be dealing with a general phenomenon by which cells possess the capacity to purge their membranes of specific antigen rather rapidly, and can restore these after 2-3 cell divisions. The general characteristics of this phenomenon are listed in Table 4.

TABLE 4

Characteristics of the "purging" effect

1. Short time required

2. Energy dependence

3. Reversibility

4. Recovery after 2-3 cell divisions

5. Blocking of recovery with agents that block cell division

6. Recovery requires removal of antibody

Purging requires a very short time, antigen or receptor loss can occur within minutes or hours and is dependent on energy mechanisms. It does not occur at 0-4°C and is blocked by those agents that interfere with the release of intracellular energy.

We can tentatively suggest some mechanisms by which antigen purging may occur. In the case of red cells it can be demonstrated that micropinocytosis of the complex of receptor and antibody is initiated in the presence of complement. We have some preliminary evidence that this is also the case in the Burkitt cell lines, where we employed ferritin-tagged antibody for the visualization of events. The complex seems to be purged inwardly rather than outwardly. Secondly, I want to refer to the reciprocal locus activation described by Drs. Old and Boyse in the TL system. They showed a linkage between the H-2 system and the TL antigen genes. During the repair process following purging, the TL gene locus is apparently suppressed temporarily, and the H-2 on the cell surface increases by a factor of about two compared to what it had been before, indicating that the membrane is reconstituted by increasing the H-2 component of surface antigens. In order for the cell to recover, the stimulant (antibody in this case) must be removed. As long as it is present, the phenotypic expression of the TL locus is suppressed in favor of the H-2 locus.

If I may speculate now, it would be that induction of tolerance in all antigen-receptive cells might occur by simular mechanisms; two premises may then be clearly stipu-. lated. First, the cell membrane antigen that we studied must have some equivalent in a receptor that interacts with antigen on the surface of a primitive lymphoid cell; in other words, we must postulate that antigen-sensitive cells have membrane receptors. The second assumption is that the antigen receptors on the antigen-sensitive cells are phenotypically linked with other structural components of the surface. This is a rather tenuous assumption for it says that there must be built into the surface membrane a receptor that looks at the antigen and says, "I know you." I am not aware of any direct evidence on this point.

If one accepts these premises, one can account for all known characteristics of the tolerant state by a single mechanism at the cellular level. For us it has suggested a number of experiments that are currently in progress, and regardless of its validity the concept is therefore operationally useful.

II

ANTIGEN DOSAGE IN RELATION TO
RESPONSIVENESS AND
NON-RESPONSIVENESS

Low-dose and high-dose tolerance — Tolerance *in vitro*— Induction of non-responsiveness in newborns vs. adults — Adoptive transfer of tolerance — Essentiality of antigen for the proliferation of activated antibody-forming clones — Antigen processing — Immunogenicity as a prerequisite for tolerogens — Species differences — Dependence of tolerogenicity on cell-antigen affinities — Effects of dosage on the cytokinetics of antibody-forming and memory cells.

II. EFFECTS OF ANTIGEN DOSAGE

DR. NOSSAL: My task is to discuss antigen dose, molecular weight of antigen, and antigen processing as it relates to tolerance effects.

Impressed as we were by the work of Dr. Dresser, by the very clearcut work of Drs. Frei and Benacerraf, and to a certain extent also by our own studies on antigen distribution during tolerance induction, we followed the generalization with which Dr. Benacerraf began his discussion, namely, that antigen that reaches the surface of lymphoid cells directly causes tolerance, whereas antigen that becomes associated with the RES is involved in the causation of immunity. However, we have recognized that this concept may be an over-simplification, and that really hard data to prove its validity were lacking. I hope to be able to convince you that this theory no longer explains all the facts of tolerance induction. I am going to try to achieve 3 goals in my remarks. First, I want to tell you about dose-response relationships in tolerance induction. Secondly, I want to talk about tolerance induction in vitro. Thirdly, in a completely speculative vein, I want to try to construct a tentative new theoretical framework which fits the data a little better and represents a modification of my own previous standpoint. One more preliminary announcement. I think all of you know that I am here as a spokesman of quite a large group. First, I must mention Dr. Deiner, also critically involved have been my colleagues, Drs. Ada, Shellam, Parish and Armstrong, who have been instrumental in much of this work.

Our first subject is the effect of dose-response relationships in tolerance induction. The whole nature of this work has been radically altered by Dr. Mitchison's finding of 2 zones of immunological tolerance, the well-known result that excessive antigen dosage leads to tolerance, and his newer concept of tolerance with the repeated injection of small and subimmunogenic amounts of antigen.

I want to tell you about some dose-response work that Shellam has done using flagellar antigens in newborn rats.

55

Let me say at the outset why I want to start off with the newborn. This is for two reasons. First, starting a tolerance course on the first day of life does away once and for all with the old shibboleth of whether we are dealing with a primary response or a secondary response. If we begin our experiments on the day of birth, when the peripheral lymphoid system of the animal has not yet been colonized, and manipulate the system at that age, we at least avoid the criticism that the extreme sensitivities we are dealing with are in some way related to the fact that we are causing secondary responses.

The second point is one which Mitchison has made forcefully a number of times; namely, that studies in tolerance are often complicated by concomitant antibody production, and that if we want to investigate tolerance induction without undue complications we must choose a setup where antibody production does not occur. Figure 10 summarizes the essential features of the work by Dr. Shellam. Daily injections

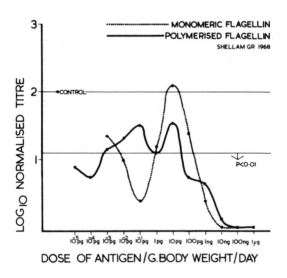

Fig. 10   Two zones of antigen dosage leading to immunological tolerance in newborn rats. Animals received daily injections for the first 2 weeks of life. The results are derived from titers 6 weeks after challenge.

(Data reproduced with permission of Immunology)

II. EFFECTS OF ANTIGEN DOSAGE

of flagellar antigens into newborn rats for two weeks were employed. It is important that one uses a daily injection schedule because this antigen is rapidly eliminated from the circulation and a twice weekly injection schedule (such as I had used prior to Shellam's arrival in our laboratory) led to misleading conclusions about thresholds. In this work we encountered considerable individual variation, and we have chosen, therefore, to be prudent and to consider only tolerance effects where geometric mean titers differed from controls at a $p < 0.01$ level. High-zone tolerance is induced by amounts of the order of 1 nanogram per gm body weight of rat per day. By the time we increase the dosage tenfold, we reach such a profound tolerance that no animal in any one group responded detectably. With somewhat lower doses the animals made antibody titers similar to control levels. With still lower doses, we come to our low-zone tolerance range, the trough of which is reached at 10^{-1} picogram per gram of body weight per day. This finding already caused us some headaches since it seemed unlikely that the free, widely diffused antigen could be involved, at these dosages, in tolerance induction.

Now let me come to Dr. Shellam's newer work which has raised the most difficult theoretical problems. This work employed the particulate antigen polymerized flagellin, a poly-dispersed preparation of aggregates of monomeric flagellin units (some being quite long strands, mimicking in size and shape the original flagella of the Salmonella bacteria, but containing also some smaller aggregates); the median molecular weight would appear to be of the order of 10^7, representing about 300 monomeric units. This antigen was given to newborn rats every day for 2 weeks; a very wide range of antigen doses was used, and at 2 weeks of age a maximally immunogenic challenge of the polymer was given. In this manner it was possible to see how such animals responded in comparison to control rats given diluent only. The polymer turned out to be a better tolerogen than we had anticipated, particularly in the low zone region. It was active in tolerance induction in amounts that really strained credulity, namely, 10^{-4} picogram (10^{-16} grams per gram body weight per day). We calculated that in this trough of low-zone tolerance the animals had received only some 200,000 monomer units during their 2 weeks of life and less than a thousand polymer particles. This in some way had modified the subsequent immune response to challenge, so that the peak was 20-fold lower than the peak of the equivalent controls, in other words, a very substantial, although partial, tolerance.

I think 2 things go out of the window because of this finding. First, Dr. Mitchison's idea of a common molar threshold for tolerance induction, around 10^{-8} molar. In any calculations you care to make, the molar concentration of this antigen is perhaps as much as 10 orders lower than in Dr. Mitchison's low-zone work. I think the second thing that goes out of the window is the idea that it is the freely diffused, freely circulating antigen that permeates the lymphoid system and causes tolerance. More of that anon.

I can understand from Dr. Landy's work, for example, how only a thousand molecules of a potent immunogen such as S. enteritidis LPS delivered into the area of a draining node can cause an immune response, but I find it difficult to understand how a thousand polymer particles can cause tolerance, bearing in mind that to achieve tolerance, at least on classical concepts, we must somehow reach the bulk of all the lymphoid cells in the body. For immunity it is enough that we should reach one lymphoid cell, that, in turn, might make 100 or a thousand progeny of antibody-forming cells; but for tolerance, it seems to me we must somehow reach a very large proportion, e.g. 95% of all the antigen-reactive cells of the body.

There are 2 things that come to mind. I hate to mention the first, and that is the question of some replicating agent. If you want to say "transfer factor" or something else, e.g. a Smithies-type virus or episome, the audience is at perfect liberty to do so. The second thing is a concentrating mechanism, and when I come to antigen processing I will be talking a bit about Drs. Ada and Parish's work in that field. They have shown that when you give the identical antigen, the H antigen of Salmonella, in a variety of molecular forms, a convincing tolerance is achieved in adult rats only with a cyanogen bromide prepared fragment of flagellin (Fragment A). However, I wouldn't like to construe this as evidence for the fact that the fragment is inherently more tolerogenic at the single cell level. I think that the other antigens, monomers and polymers, are so immunogenic that immunity escalates whereas tolerance presumably does not. Therefore, the immunogenicity of these agents in adults blinds us to whatever their possible tolerogenicity may be.

58

II. EFFECTS OF ANTIGEN DOSAGE

If you want to think in terms of human kidney transplantation, I agree that the low molecular weight helps in tolerance induction. If you want to think about mechanisms at
the single cell level, I am not at all certain that it has
been proven that an antigen's molecular weight determines
whether the cell will be turned on or turned off. That to
me remains a quite open question.

Now let us come to the second subject and that is the
question of antigen dose as it relates to the induction of
tolerance in vitro. The work is that of Drs. Diener and
Armstrong, and much of it is still unpublished. They have,
as I think most of you know, adapted the Mishell-Dutton system to the assay of antibody to Salmonella produced by
normal mouse spleen cell suspensions (Fig. 11). The modification that they and Dr. Marbrook have made is that they
have avoided the use of a "nutritional cocktail" and have
facilitated cell to cell interaction by using a small inner
vessel, which is stuck into a larger vessel, the cells
resting on an intervening dialysis membrane. The immune
response they have obtained is measured by the technique
of bacterial immunocytoadherance, adapted to produce actual
colonies of growing bacteria on agar.

The immune response obtained in vitro by Drs. Diener and
Armstrong with CBA mouse spleen cells (Fig. 11) is in all
respects similar to that which is seen in the spleen of an
intact, immunized mouse. We start off, and this is an important point, with a low background usually <1 positive
cell per million. This is followed by a rapid rise to a
peak at 4 days, and it is important to point out that auto-
radiographic studies by Dr. Diener have supported the conclusion that this is preceded by mitotic divisions; these
events are in all respects similar to what happens in the
whole animal.

Now, let us come to tolerance. If one plots the dose of
antigen that is required to achieve these immunological
effects in vitro, one sees that optimal antibody production,
as measured by antibody-forming cells per 10^6 cells, is
achieved by 2 to 20 nanogram antigen/ml of medium (Fig. 12).
There probably isn't a great deal of difference between 2,
20, and 200 nanograms. As the dose is increased there is a
sharp falling off in the degree of antibody production
(Table 5) so that with 2 nanogram/ml or more there is a

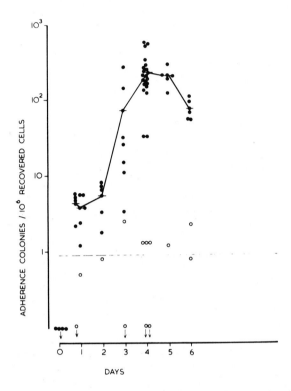

Fig. 11   In vitro immune response of mouse spleen cells to
the polymer of S. adelaide flagellin at various
periods after start of the cultures. Closed circles
show number of antibody-forming cells per test culture incubated with 0.02 µg/ml of polymer. Horizontal lines through closed circles indicate the
arithmetic mean of test cultures. Open circles indicate control cultures incubated without antigen;
interruped line represents mean background of antibody-forming cells, calculated from control cultures;
arrows indicate values less than 0.1 .

(Data reproduced with permission of Lancet)

sharply reduced number of plaques. Is this reduction due
to tolerance and not merely some kind of toxic effect? Good
evidence for the former is given in two points on Fig. 12,
which represent experiments in which both polymer and sRBC

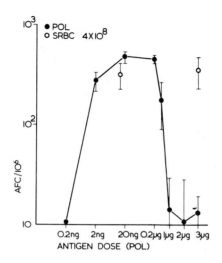

Fig. 12   Effect of increasing doses of the polymer of S.
adelaide flagellin on the in vitro immune response
tested 4 days after start of the culture. Vertical
bars indicate 95% confidence limits.

TABLE 5
Response of mouse spleen cells in vitro

Immune status of cells	Antigen dose	
	0.02 μg	3 μg
Virgin	187 ± 51	7 ± 18
Primed	1021 ± 176	167 ± 61

were given to the spleen cells involved. When Drs. Diener
and Armstrong doubly stimulated the system in this way,
using an optimal antigenic stimulus of sRBC but a supra-
optimal stimulus of the polymer, they showed that the response
to the sRBC was standard, but the response to the polymer was
greatly diminished.

The second thing that was done to see whether these cells were truly tolerant, was an "in vitro-in vivo" transfer, or an adoptive immunity type of experiment using Dr. Armstrong's modification of the Kennedy focus assay; a reasonably direct test of the actual number of antigen-reactive cells remaining in the culture. It was found that the number of antigen-reactive units in the population that had been exposed to high antigen dose was specifically reduced whereas with immunogenic lower concentrations it was elevated (Table 6). Thus, we believe that we have a model of tolerance and not a toxic phenomenon, nor some kind of temporary obscuring of the capacity of the cells.

TABLE 6

Response of mouse spleen cells made immune or tolerant
in vitro following transfer to irradiated host mice

Antigen dose in vitro (μg)	Number of viable cultured cells transferred per recipient	Specific activity per host spleen* %
none	2.5×10^6	10
0.02	2×10^6	34
3.0	2.5×10^6	1.2

* Activity of antigen-reactive cells in the host spleen as described by Armstrong and Diener, 1968.

Dr. Diener has attempted to induce tolerance in the cold. In such experiments normal CBA mouse spleen cells were mixed at 4°C with various concentrations of antigen, and were kept together for varying periods of time. After washing, the culture was stimulated with a maximally immunogenic dose of the polymer, namely, with 20 nanogram/ml. Figure 13 shows what happened when the cells were held for 6 hours with 3 μg per ml of the polymer, i.e. with a tolerogenic dose. There

II. EFFECTS OF ANTIGEN DOSAGE

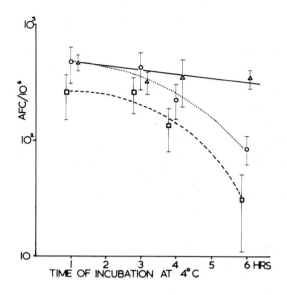

Fig. 13 Induction of tolerance in vitro to the polymer of
S. adelaide flagellin. Cells were preincubated with
3 μg or 30 μg of antigen at 37°C for 4 days. Circles
show arithmetic mean number of antibody-forming
cells/10^6 harvested cells. Preincubation was with
3 μg of polymer; boxes indicate arithmetic mean
number of antibody-forming cells/10^6 harvested
cells. Preincubation was with 30 μg of polymer;
triangles show arithmetic mean number of antibody-
forming cells/10^6 harvested cells. Preincubation
was with 0.02 μg of polymer. Vertical bars indicate
95% confidence limits.

was a time-dependent reduction in the degree to which the
cells could respond subsequently to a maximal immunogenic
challenge. It was only a 5-fold reduction, but it was quite
consistent and not as profound as would have been achieved
by holding the 3 μg of the polymer and the cells together
for a period of 4 days. When the concentration of antigen
was increased by a factor of 10, i.e. to 30 μg, a suggestion
of a reduction at the earliest possible point, i.e. one hour,
was obtained and by 6 hours in the cold a pretty substantial
reduction was elicited. When these cells were extensively
washed and held free of antigen in an effort to undo the
postulated union between antigen and cell receptor, an at

least partial restoration of an immune response was obtained, i.e. a partial reversal of the tolerance effect. I don't want to say much more about this because Drs. Diener and Armstrong are working hard on this problem at the present time. But it would seem to me to imply: (a) that the initial step in tolerance induction probably is the union of antigen with an antibody-like receptor on the surface of the lymphocyte, and (b) that the receptor is not a particularly avid or well-fitting one, because as we all know in the case of an extremely avid antigen-antibody reaction, the reversibility tends to be difficult to achieve and it is indeed pretty hard to get the antigen off the antibody without using harsh treatment such as gross changes in pH. So it would seem to me that the initial union is not a particularly tight one.

Now we come to the final point which is an attempt to integrate these findings into a theoretical framework. What do we think is going on in tolerance induction, at least in regard to the three parameters of: (1) antigen processing, (2) molecular weight of antigen, and (3) antigen dose?

Let us postulate that there is a virgin cell with receptors which we call the antigen-reactive cell. By mutual consent, Dr. Miller and I have decided that this is not the point in which we want to introduce the complexity of cell to cell interaction. I am now going to argue as though all events were occurring on one cell, not because I believe this to be true, but because I believe that it would become too complex if I were to introduce the further complexity of bone-marrow to thymus interactions at this point. So here we are back with the classical concept that there is one cell that differentiates and proliferates, but we shall modify and amplify this model after we have heard about other interactions later in our discussions.

We have good reasons to believe that there exists an antigen-activated cell, call it "Y," if you want, which is dependent upon further hits by antigen to finally achieve antibody formation. We know this for at least three reasons. First of all the work of Dr. Uhr and his colleagues has indicated the necessity for antigen to drive the system in a continuing way. Secondly, Uhr's, Möller's and Wigzell's work on the effect of passive antibody also has indicated that antigen drives the system; without antigen everything grinds to a halt permitting perhaps one or two additional mitotic divisions. Thirdly, we know that if we take a cell population that is all in the "Y" stage and transfer these cells into an X-irradiated host, we will not get antibody production without further antigenic stimulation. Next, we postulate an actual antibody-forming, dividing cell which for further proliferation is dependent on additional hits by antigen. Finally, of course, we know that we have an antibody-forming cell which is in no way dependent on antigen or for that matter inhibitable by antibody.

These are the definable stages in an antibody-forming clone. The way I am now beginning to think of tolerance is based on purely quantitative aspects, making no categorical distinction between antigen that has or has not been through a macrophage, that either is or is not attached to RNA, and that either is or is not on a lymphoid follicle or a reticular cell.

I think in normal antibody formation we have receptors not only on the virgin cell (Fig. 14), but through most of

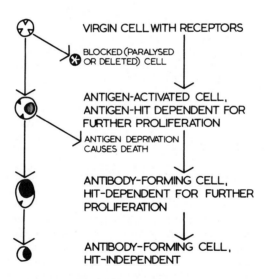

Fig. 14 Stages in the antigen-responsiveness of cells in an antibody-forming clone

the different stages of the proliferating clone. Only at
the very end of the proliferative sequence do we run out of
need for antigen to drive the system. Therefore, in immunity
antigen is going on to the cells throughout the entire process (Fig. 15). I am not necessarily implying that this
must mean new encounters between newly arrived antigen molecules and the cell. It could well be that there is enough
antigen at various receptors on the initial cell to survive
dilution and to maintain an adequate concentration for most
of the cells throughout the various stages.

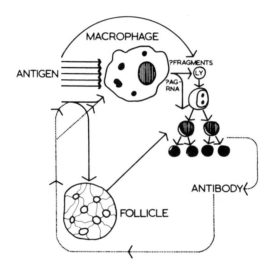

Fig. 15 Antigen distribution pattern leading to immunization

My view of low-zone tolerance, though it achieves in a
sense the same end result as high-zone tolerance, is a bit
different and is based on the suspicion that it may involve
a kind of sterile activation. I am postulating that if a
virgin cell is hit once by a very liminal concentration of
antigen and then does not see antigen again, it undertakes
the first step; it begins to change into a blast, and if
antigen, either through dilution, or pinocytosis or metabo-
lism, is not present at the surface of the cell, or if the
cell is not hit again, I am postulating that this cell either
dies or at least fades away. It is no longer a part of the
antigen-reactive cell pool (Fig. 16). We have no evidence
whatsoever for the indefinite maintenance of this particular

II. EFFECTS OF ANTIGEN DOSAGE

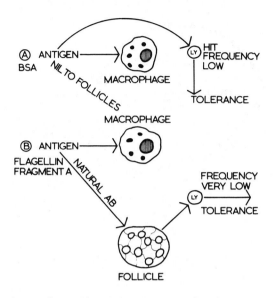

Fig. 16   Antigen distribution pattern leading to low-zone
tolerance

cell as a "Y" cell in the absence of antigen, nor do we have
any evidence whatsoever of the fact that it might revert
back to becoming an "X" cell. So I am postulating that in
low-zone tolerance the "X" cell is changed in some way; it
is activated, but in the absence of further hits it does not
get anywhere. It dies. In high-zone tolerance, we postulate a supra-optimal saturation of surface sites which im-
pedes correct clonal development (Fig. 17).

We have talked about antigen hits and so I think that the
time has come that we must say something about the various
factors that might influence the end result of a union between the postulated receptor on the lymphocyte surface and
an antigen. I am putting a lot of weight on the number of
such encounters, both in space and in time. I think that
the molecular weight of the antigen may play an important
role. There may well be an optimal size of antigenic determinants for whatever is the correct binding and the correct
perturbation of the membrane that finally leads to lymphocyte activation. At this moment I am tending to think of
the main role of the macrophage as being on this level. The
macrophage may well spew out, in a very unintelligent, non-
specific way, fragments of a varied size range so that some,

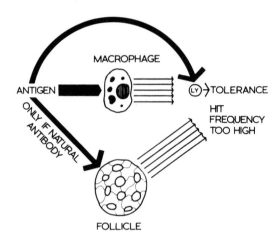

Fig. 17 Antigen distribution pattern leading to high-zone
tolerance

at least, will be of the correct size for activation of the
lymphocyte.

I think we have to pay attention to the chemical nature
of the antigen. No one has yet explained to me why there
may be 100 million-fold differences in the inherent tendency
of different kinds of chemical entities to cause antibody
production either in vivo or in vitro. This to me is still
a total mystery, why for example, flagellin or some LPS preparations can stimulate in incredibly small amounts, and
other agents can stimulate with only very large amounts.

To demonstrate that a purely quantitative approach along
the lines of little black balls hitting little white boxes
can account for the data, a graduate student of Dr. Edelman's,
Dr. Marchalonis, has compiled some mathematical formulas
that might describe the properties of the system where zero
to X antigen molecules will cause low-zone tolerance if they
hit a cell, where X+1 →Y will cause immunization, and where
Y+1→ ∞ will cause high-zone tolerance. Mr. Gledhill, our
computer expert, wrote the relevant program and constructed
a large family of curves setting wide parameters with very
wide variations for both X and Y. It turns out that in this
system of tolerance induction with monomeric flagellin, if
one sets a value for X of about 10 molecules of antigen per
cell, and a value for Y of about 1,000 to 10,000 molecules,

and temporarily forgets about the time parameter, one gets
a curve that does rather simulate the observed data.

Finally, to the role of antigen processing. Here (Fig.
15) is the antigen distribution pattern which I now believe
leads to immunization. I am no longer making a categorical
distinction between antigen that hits the lymphocyte directly and antigen that is held extracellularly in lymphoid
follicles and subsequently reaches the lymphocyte, or an
antigen that has been processed by macrophages and perhaps
hooked on to RNA. I am not persuaded that there is any
critical evidence that allows us to state whether there is
a categorical difference between these various antigen presentations. I believe the critical factor may be the amount
of antigen that hits the virgin cell and the subsequent proliferating clone. With a modest amount of antigen and certainly with amounts that occur in natural infection, the
bulk of the material ends up in the RES and encounters between antigen and lymphocyte occur with a frequency that is
between the two extremes for low and high-zone tolerance.
Lymphoid follicles, as Dr. Humphrey has shown us, only get
into the act once antibody is present; once specific antibody has been made, antigen is readily funneled into this
extracellular compartment. Alternately, antigen may "hit"
the lymphoid follicles directly from the very beginning because of the presence of natural or cross-reacting antibodies. The pattern of antigen distribution leading to high-
zone tolerance is simply conceived of as a hit frequency
that is too high. Either because the macrophage is excluded,
or because there is so much antigen released from the macrophages, supra-optimal amounts "hit" the lymphoid cells.

The difficult aspect is low-zone tolerance. I am now
going to give you a final fact, that I have withheld so far,
because I think it is the most central one of all, and that
is Ada's and Parish's discovery that in the induction of
low-zone tolerance in adult rats with fragment A of flagellin
(requiring sub-picogram amounts injected into adult rats),
all the antigen that is trapped is trapped in lymphoid
follicles. So in this system we are getting tolerance induction in the adult with very little free antigen in the circulation, without anything detectably permeating into the
thymus or into the diffuse lymphoid cortex. Most of the
antigen that one can see autoradiographically becomes associated with the reticular cells and the processes of the

lymphoid follicles. To explain low-zone tolerance, I think
we have to make a categorical distinction between the BSA
type model and this new model of the reaction of adults to
flagellin fragment A causing tolerance in ultra-low dose.
As shown in Fig. 16, I think the BSA model can be explained
on the basis that BSA may not be particularly palatable to
macrophages and has no tendency whatsoever to go to the
follicles; it is in fact reaching the lymphocyte surface by
direct permeation but at a frequency that is too low for
correct clonal proliferation. A mechanism that may be
termed "sterile activation" comes into operation. But with
flagellin fragment A, which appears to end up in follicles,
we must postulate that cells are recirculating in a continuous but slow fashion through the follicle and are somehow
being rendered tolerant.

We are puzzled by ultra-low zone tolerance, and I would
like to leave you with the thought that this one model of
tolerance induction with 10^{-4} picogram antigen per gram of
body weight has thrown our previous thinking into disarray,
but the results can't be ignored.

DR. COHN: I just want one detail of your experiment. The
fact that your material is tolerogenic at dose levels of
10^{-15} to 10^{-16} molar raises questions about interaction. I
would, therefore, like to know the meaning of the subsequent
dose for maintaining the tolerance you are talking about.
As concerns the tolerogenic fragment, wouldn't you have to
show that this fragment is free of the unchanged material
contaminating at the level of 10^{-16} molar?

DR. NOSSAL: When we initially got into this work we used an
extremely complicated protocol with one dosage for tolerance
induction and another for tolerance maintenance. In all of
Dr. Shellam's recent work, extremely simple protocols are
being used, namely, the daily administration of antigen at
a given dose per gram of body weight for 2 to 6 weeks,
followed by a challenge either with a large amount of polymer or with a large amount of monomer in Freund's complete
adjuvant. This is a straight Mitchison-type protocol and
avoids confusion regarding tolerance-maintaining dosages.

With regard to the second question, tolerance has been
induced by Parish with sub-picogram amounts of fragment A in
adult rats (Ada and Parish, Proc. Nat. Acad. Sci., in press).
Then, after 4-6 weeks of such daily injection, the whole

monomeric molecule is given in adjuvant and the response is
measured.

DR. UHR: In the additional tolerance experiments performed
by Ada et al., did they extend your response curve to lower
doses? Neither of the dose-response curves you showed
reached control levels of response at the lower doses. It
would be particularly puzzling if no injections at all produced tolerance.

DR. NOSSAL: I should make two things absolutely clear. The
work by Drs. Ada and Parish involves points in the realm of
10^{-4} picogram/gm which do return to control values.

Secondly, the controls were, of course, injected daily
with the diluent. If I didn't say this it was because I
thought all of you would realize that we would do this; the
controls are not simply animals held with no treatment for
the entire period of time. They are animals that received
the diluent daily for the same length of time as the experimental groups. Furthermore, all of the antibody titrations
are done in a completely double-blind fashion. We have been
at some pains to make sure that we are not being misled by
some form of error on the part of the observers.

DR. UHR: Polymerized flagellin did not stimulate an immune
response equal to the controls at any time over the entire
dose range. Why?

DR. NOSSAL: As soon as you get into adults, you get into
a "hump" situation, and with fragment A in adults, in a wide
span of dosages between the 2 troughs of tolerance, there
was a substantial "immunity hump," so that the animals had
preformed antibody before challenge and an elevated response
to challenge.

DR. UHR: I thought this was in newborns.

DR. NOSSAL: No. The work in newborns is with the monomeric
flagellin; polymerized flagellin does not cause a typical
immunity hump. The work in adults is largely with fragment
A.

DR. BENACERRAF: Was it previously shown by Dr. Ada that
your fragment A when injected into adult animals would lead

to paralysis without being taken up in the macrophages? If I am correct it was cleared very rapidly by the animal, and this was interpreted by Dr. Ada as being one of the reasons why it was effectively tolerogenic in adult animals. In contrast, paralysis could not be obtained with flagellin in adult animals. Now you are showing some remnants of fragment A on the surface of the macrophages. However, as far as I am concerned you showed no evidence with respect to the diffusibility of this fragment A.

DR. NOSSAL: When we talked about adult tolerance at the recent Cold Spring Harbor Symposium, no radioautographs had been done, and, in fact, we believed that fragment A because of its small molecular weight would traverse the node and would not be retained in follicles. In fact, when the radioautographs were done, it was found that only a relatively small proportion of the antigen was trapped in the lymph nodes; this trapped material ended up in the follicles.

DR. BENACERRAF: I am glad to have you make that point.

DR. NOSSAL: You ask, then, can't we still have our theory that "direct contact" may cause tolerance. I would counter that by saying that in the brief time before the fragment is excretèd the chances of a lymphocyte finding even a single antigen molecule are very small because of the extremely low dilution.

DR. LESKOWITZ: I am a little concerned with the attempt to reconcile dosages of two different antigens in respect to tolerance without knowing anything about the degree of antigenic complexity or the number of antigenic determinants of either. Is there any evidence that anyone could cite on whether flagellin is, in fact, a rather simple repeating unit?

DR. NOSSAL: We hope that Drs. Ada and Parish will generate the necessary data for us in the next year or two but at present I don't think that I can give you an informed answer. I doubt whether it will turn out that flagellin is a rather simple repeating unit.

DR. FRIEDMAN: I had essentially the same type of question. I believe you stated that the lowest dose constituted about a thousand molecules of polymer--

II. EFFECTS OF ANTIGEN DOSAGE

DR. NOSSAL: Perhaps we should not call them molecules, they are really small particles; I would rather call them "polymer units."

DR. FRIEDMAN: Alright. A thousand units of polymer made up of 200 molecules of monomer each.

DR. NOSSAL: Yes.

DR. FRIEDMAN: And if each monomer were made up of 100 antigenic determinants this would bring us up to the level of 20 million determinants. Would this now give you enough antigenic determinants per potential immunocompetent cell?

DR. NOSSAL: I think it depends on what assumptions one makes as to the number of antigenic determinants per monomer molecule. Also, bear in mind that the 200,000 monomer unit value is an integrated value of two weeks of injections. Over this period, the animal is continually excreting the monomer. Consequently, there are never 200,000 molecules present at a single point in time. There is at most about a twentieth of that amount present at a single point in time. Therefore, the maximum concentrations that are reached are very low.

DR. FRIEDMAN: These animals are challenged at two weeks of age. What is the response of the normal control rat to challenge at that age?

DR. NOSSAL: The antibody titers are in the vicinity of 1:100 to 1:400.

DR. FRIEDMAN: As regards the second part of the question, we have tried to induce tolerance to flagella in mice with no success whatsoever. Could you let us have your views on this?

DR. NOSSAL: I am very glad you asked that because we have been relatively unsuccessful in inducing tolerance in mice. Also we have had much less luck with the Lewis strain of rats than with the Wistar strain. If any one here can provide me the reasons for these differences, I would be grateful!

73

DR. SMITH: Did you do the experiment involving the incubation with large doses and washing at 4°C and varying the time of incubation in such a way that at 6 hours the temperature was varied? What was the temperature variance?

DR. NOSSAL: Dr. Diener held the cells and the antigen together for varying periods of time, and then with two standard washes monitored the amount of antigen carry over using I_{125} polymer. He found that under these circumstances something like 0.3% of the total dose was carried-over. The amount that was transferred into the final immunogenic mixture was not enough to convince us that it would cause tolerance after subsequent heating to 37°C.

DR. SMITH: But what were the controls that were incubated at 37°C rather than 4°C or some other temperature? What happened to them?

DR. NOSSAL: Cells that were incubated at 37°C for 6 hours, of course also became tolerant. This effect was marginally more so at 4°C, not dramatically but moderately more so. I, therefore, think there must be a step after the initial union which is a metabolic step. I don't think anyone would deny that.

DR. SIMONSEN: Have you made sure, by passive transfer of serum or cells, whether the state of ultra-low zone tolerance is transferable? It just might be that you are producing by these minute quantities of antigen a special kind of enhancing antibody so that, in fact, what you are studying is ultra-low zone immunity.

DR. NOSSAL: I don't believe that we have done quite that. We have taken serum from high-zone tolerant rats to see whether it has antibodies as judged by its capacity to induce accelerated follicular localization of antigen, and some sera were positive. We have not tested low-zone sera in a similar manner.

DR. BENACERRAF: I want to add a point of clarification. My earlier remarks when I was speaking of tolerogenic properties of the free diffusable antigen applied only to adult animals. I find nothing in what you have said that is not consistent with the correctness of this concept. I say this because when you work with adult animals, you have to inject fragment A, which is far less arrested in the lymph nodes, in order to achieve tolerance.

In your presentation, I am far more impressed by the differences between the behavior of adults and newborns, which I find are not accounted for in your theory; I would hope that you can do so.

The third point I would like to make is: you are concerned with the fact that the 99% of the antigen that diffuses passes through the lymph node and equilibrates in the animals, thus not having a change to hit all of the lymphocytes. I, however, am even more concerned that the 1% that is attached to macrophages in the lymph nodes has even less of a change to do so, and, therefore, could not be responsible for the observed paralysis.

DR. NOSSAL: Taking these points in order, what perturbs me most is not so much the question of whether antigen encountering cells directly can or cannot cause tolerance (because I believe, as I think my data showed, that it can cause tolerance); I am concerned about the previous idea, namely, the idea that antigens that are palatable to the RES, and which have a profound tendency to go to the follicles exclusively and obligatorily, cause immunization. It is this latter assumption that is now weakened in view of the results of Drs. Ada and Parish. Previously we had conceived, and documented with many materials, a direct relationship between those antigens that the RES likes and those antigens that cause immunization in the adult. Now we have an antigen that the follicles like very much but which does not readily cause immunization. I think your point is quite right. I don't know whether the actual tolerance effect is caused by materials being free in the circulation or present in the follicle. However, I think that because of the extraordinarily small amount one ought at least to think about a concentrating mechanism that brings antigen molecules closer together.

DR. BENACERRAF: I quite agree with you that for an antigen to be tolerogenic it generally has to be immunogenic. To that extent, I never felt, nor do I presently feel, that a particulate antigen is different from one which does not have the cytotactic characteristic that allows it to be diffusible. But practically speaking, when you deal with an adult animal possessing a trapping mechanism and when

75

you deal with particulate antigens, or with antigens that have properties that allow them to be trapped, you have to contend with these facts in respect to encounters of cells with these antigens. You also must consider when the cell encounters the antigen and whether they are in an environment that makes for adjuvant characteristics.

DR. NOSSAL: Then may I ask you why on preliminary data from Dr. Diener fragment A does not appear to be tolerogenic in vitro? This is another thing that puzzles me; it should be.

DR. BENACERRAF: I agree. It should be.

DR. CINADER: Dr. Nossal, you gave us some very complete data on responses in the newborn rat and your hypothesis is based on it. Now, a further test of this, as of all other hypotheses, would depend on its predictive capacity for somewhat different circumstances. In the case before us, one would imagine that such a situation of different circumstances would be available in the dose-response relationship of another species. In fact, you have relevant information in the mouse. The question now is: how does your hypothesis fit the data obtained in the mouse?

DR. NOSSAL: What happens in the mouse is that with any injection protocol you tend to get rather marginal tolerance effects. As I think Dr. Mitchison has recorded a number of times, and as we have ourselves documented at the single cell level, we have to think of tolerance and immunity as in a sense competing functions. The trouble with tolerance is that once you have made a cell tolerant, there is, at least as far as I know, no evidence that it can be a replicating event. However, once we make a cell immune we start a proliferative process which results in the production of a large number of cells from the one cell. Therefore, the events of immunity, when they occur, may obscure concomitant tolerance effects. This is what I belive is happening in the mouse, and quite frankly if you are in that ultra-low zone, I don't consider that negative results such as those presented to us by Dr. Howard are very compelling. I can think of many good reasons why the tolerance events that are occurring at the single level are never detected by the investigator, because the picture is obscured by immunization.

II. EFFECTS OF ANTIGEN DOSAGE

DR. CINADER: To clarify it in my own mind, you postulated a low-zone mechanism in which an antigen was engaged by a cell, but where there was not enough antigen available for the cell to go on. Accepting this model I still don't understand why this does not work in the mouse. If it is a general mechanism, it must surely operate in the mouse as well as in the rat.

DR. NOSSAL: I can't answer your question. I don't myself understand the immense influence of species, strain, route of immunization and the many other parameters that influence tolerance experiments. I can only recognize the possibility that it does not work in another species because of concomitant immunization obscuring the tolerance effect.

DR. LESKOWITZ: I think you should remember in this connection the work that both Drs. Benacerraf and Siskind presented earlier in our discussions, that tolerance to a carrier can impose a diminished response to the immuno-dominant hapten "tip" and this process may well be operating in the system you are talking about.

DR. EDELMAN: If I assume your antigenic unit is 10^5 molecular weight, then I calculate that there is roughly a factor of 10 logs difference between your range and Dr. Mitchison's. Is that right?

DR. MITCHISON: That's right.

DR. EDELMAN: It seems to me that the essential question is not that difference, because I think Dr. Leskowitz pointed out that the way the antigens may be processed may be different. What I think is worth calculating is how many cells could possibly collide with that number of particles within the time period involved.

DR. NOSSAL: Exactly.

DR. EDELMAN: Couldn't we make that calculation, since you know the time and the number of cells?

DR. NOSSAL: That is just what Drs. Gledhill and Marchalonis have attempted to do, using the assumption that an animal has 10^8 lymphoid cells at the time of its birth, and using the equally hazardous or unproven assumption that about one in 10^4 of those can react with the antigen concerned. It was on this basis that many families of curves of predictability were constructed in an extremely simplistic manner, and the theoretical curves that I showed you were obtained.

DR. EDELMAN: What I wanted to know was not that question but the encounter frequency; that is to say, how often would I expect, without a concentrating mechanism, to have a collision?

DR. NOSSAL: That was one thing that I asked your student to calculate, and that was the one thing he didn't think he knew how to do. Consequently, this is what led us to consider an involvement of replicating mechanisms.

DR. GOOD: Dr. Nossal, there are many parallels between tolerance and immunity in your model especially with respect to the very low-dose tolerance. Immunity involves cells which at a stage of their differentiation can achieve upon contact with antigen: (1) proliferation, and (2) secretion, as your model indicated. But these cells before differentiating might be extraordinarily vulnerable to other immunological influences, namely, complement as the amplification system of the immunological apparatus. Dr. Azar and I have obtained indirect evidence in mice that complement may be required for the development of certain types of tolerance. The real question arising from the observations you presented is whether or not, in your isolated cell system, you have demonstrable complement or complement components.

DR. NOSSAL: The isolated cell system involves the use of heat-inactivated fetal serum, which I would not consider a good source of complement. However, I suppose there exists a remote possibility that the heterogeneous spleen cell population used is actually synthesizing complement components during the incubation period, and on that I have no evidence one way or another. It is not very likely.

DR. GOOD: It seems to me that the cell population you are using could be either carrying or synthesizing complement components. I wonder if it wouldn't be worthwhile to try some indirect measures to interfere with the development of the complement system and thus with tolerance in vitro.

II. EFFECTS OF ANTIGEN DOSAGE

DR. HUMPHREY: In guinea pigs, C'1, according to Drs. Colten, Borsos and Rapp, is made solely by the epithelial cells of the gut mucosa; they find a similar origin in man, and I suppose that the finding may be valid for other mammals as well. If so, it seems unlikely that any cells making C'1 are present in the spleen.

DR. GOOD: To me the work of Drs. Borsos and Colten shows that at least one complement component can be produced by the epithelial cells of the gut--not that it is the only site where it can be produced.

DR. HUMPHREY: They tell me that they have looked at very many other tissues; these all proved negative.

DR. LANDY: May I get one point clear, Dr. Nossal. Did I understand you correctly to say that the background values for flagellin in adult mice and rats were consistently very low? This strikes me as remarkable in view of the environmental antigenic stimuli in all probability operative in rodent populations; this is evidenced by the rather appreciable level of cells reactive with other natural enterobacterial antigens. I would therefore have thought background would be low only in the newborn or young animal.

DR. NOSSAL: The backgrounds are always very low, usually 1 per 10^6 cells. This low value may be a reflection of the sensitivity of the method being used, but I doubt it.

DR. SILVERSTEIN: Dr. Cinader raised the question of species differences between mice and rats, and why Dr. Nossal's experiment worked in the rat and didn't work in the mouse. Insofar as one knows at this time, an animal has to be immunologically competent to permit the induction of tolerance. Dr. Nossal tells me that the rats he has used are not capable of responding to an optimally immunogenic dose of this antigen until about 7 days after birth. Dr. Friedman, on the other hand, tells me that the mice that were used are not susceptible to the induction of an active immune response with this antigen until about 4 weeks after birth. Dr. Nossal may, therefore, have been using a newborn mouse that was actually immunologically incompetent. Along these same lines, one wonders whether the antigen that he gave the newborn rats over the first 7 days really served any purpose at all.

DR. NOSSAL: I agree with half of what Dr. Silverstein said
and I disagree with the other half.   I think it is quite
possible that during the first 5 or 6 days the injections
into the rat didn't really add very much.   This has been
investigated systematically only in the high zone; here it
is true that one can achieve very satisfactory tolerance by
beginning at day 7 of life.

I disagree with the first half of what you said if you
imply that the animal must be able to form antibody in order
that tolerance might be induced.   We get no detectable antibody in newborn rats with a single challenge on the day of
birth.   That is universally true; if we inject them with any
flagellar antigen on the day of birth and do nothing more to
the animal except bleed it, we will never get antibody formation.   The first time at which we will get antibody formation
as the result of a single injection is following an injection
at 7 days, but this is very, very far from being the optimal
time for antibody production in the rat.   I would say that
the optimal response does not occur until about 6 or 8
weeks, so that the 7 day old animal is at best a "marginal"
responder.

I don't have nearly as many data in regard to the mouse,
but if I had to make a guess I would say, in contradistinction to the claim that you made, that immunologically speaking the mouse was not less mature but rather more mature at
birth and that had one systematically investigated the point,
one might have been able to get antibody formation slightly
earlier in the mouse than in the rat.

CHAIRMAN MILLER: I think we should now turn to another
antigen and another system of in vitro tolerance induction,
to be described for us by Dr. Britton.

DR. BRITTON: I would like to tell about the possibility to
induce paralysis to bacterial endotoxins (LPS) by exposing
normal lymphoid cells for a brief period to high doses of
LPS in vitro.   The LPS endotoxin has been detoxified with
alkali and if you study the paralysis induced in vivo with
such material you will find that only high-zone paralysis
can be demonstrated.   The ultra-low doses that have been
described by Dr. Nossal have not been tried in this work,
but I am currently doing that.   The state of paralysis induced in vivo is finite and it is strictly dose-dependent.

II. EFFECTS OF ANTIGEN DOSAGE

Actually, the range between the doses that induce paralysis and those that induce immunity is comparatively more narrow than that described for protein antigens.

The experiments that I refer to involve normal mouse cells that have been exposed in vitro to various doses of detoxified endotoxin for periods of time ranging from 12 to 120 minutes. Thereafter, the cells have been carefully washed and reinjected into irradiated syngeneic recipients. Twelve hours later these recipients have been challenged with the homologous antigen in the form of bacteria and the immune status of the recipients was tested. I would point out that similar experimental designs have been used unsuccessfully by several other investigators seeking to induce paralysis to protein antigens in vitro. In this system, however, it turned out that cells exposed to higher doses of LPS under appropriate conditions could be shown to become truly paralysed. The kind of paralysis obtained is strictly dose-dependent, and naturally it is also specific, because exposure of the cells to high doses of LPS, followed by their transfer into irradiated animals later challenged with sRBC, results in a perfectly normal response to sheep cells, whereas these animals are unresponsive to subsequent challenge with homologous bacteria. As indicated in Table 7 the induction of paralysis is dose-dependent, so that 10^6 cells exposed to a concentration of 100 µg of LPS become completely paralysed, as measured by the number of antibody-forming cells in spleen as well as the antibody titers of the antigen-injected secondary hosts. With the lower concentration of antigen, a decreasing state of paralysis occurs.

A very important issue is the quantity of antigen transferred via cells to the secondary hosts. If much antigen is transferred to recipients the observed induction of paralysis may be taking place in vivo rather than in vitro. We have made several assays to estimate the amount of antigen retained on the cells after the antigen treatment in vitro. The most appropriate of these involves the use of C_{14}-labelled LPS, i.e., LPS obtained from bacteria grown in a synthetic medium with C_{14} glucose as the carbon source. With this LPS we can estimate fairly accurately the amount remaining on the cells injected into the irradiated recipients. This corresponds to 0.2% of the initially added LPS, which suggests that with the cells exposed to a paralysing concentration of antigen there is 5 to 10 µg transfer to the secondary

81

TABLE 7

The effect of dose on the ability of endotoxin to paralyse lymphoid cells in vitro

Dose of endotoxin added in vitro	Arithmetic mean number of PFC/10^6 spleen cells +SE	Mean $\log^2$ agglutinin titer +SE
100 μg/10^6 cells	1.5 + 1.2	0
10 μg/10^6 cells	86.4 + 32.4	3.4 + 1.6
1 μg/10^6 cells	450 + 212.4	3.6 + 0.8
0.001 μg/10^6 cells	134.5 + 58.4	4.4 + 1.8
None*	121.1 + 72.3	5.6 + 1.8

The cells were incubated 2 hours at 37°C, washed 5 times and 40 x 10^6 cells transferred to secondary irradiated (750 r) hosts which were immunized with 75 x 10^6 heat-killed bacteria 12 hours after cell transfer. Tests were made at day 7 after immunization (4-5 mice/group).

*Cells incubated without antigen for 2 hours at 37°C.

host. This is a dose that is clearly immunogenic in vivo.
Other methods were also employed to find out whether the
induction was taking place in vitro or in vivo. This included varying the conditions of incubation, mainly the
time of antigen exposure and the temperature at which the
cells were exposed to LPS. It should be noted that in the
situations where paralysis was obtained exposure was of the
order of 2 hours.

As can be seen in Table 8, when cells are exposed to
paralytogenic concentrations of antigen for 2 hours at 37°C,
complete paralysis occurs. However, exposure to the same
concentration of antigen for the same time at 4°C leads to
a less pronounced state of paralysis. Exposure at 37°C
and 4°C, respectively, for only 12 minutes yields no sign
of paralysis.

It is thus evident that for paralysis to develop, a
finite period of time and appropriate metabolic conditions
are required. Since the state of paralysis is specific, it
was considered that the inactivating binding between LPS
and the reactive cell must occur via an "antigen-specific
receptor" and that this receptor probably was of an immunoglobulin nature. If this recepter could be destroyed by
enzymatic tréatment, the induction of paralysis by in vitro
treatment with antigen would then be abolished. In Table 9
it can be seen that cells that have been trypsinized and
immediately thereafter exposed to LPS in vitro for 2 hours
do not develop any degree of paralysis, whereas cells that
have not been trypsinized but incubated with the same antigen concentration for the same time are paralysed.

It seems that whatever effect trypsinization has it prevents cells from being targets for the paralytogen when exposed to antigen in vitro. Other explanations for the
effect of trypsinization have also to be considered. One
question, still left unresolved, is whether trypsinized
cells transfer to the irradiated host less antigen than non-
trypsinized cells. We are fairly well convinced that the
amount of antigen transferred to the secondary host is,
from the point of view of paralysis, rather negligible.

DR. LANDY: I think it is hardly coincidental that the
alkali-treated polysaccharide that Dr. Britton found so
effective in inducing tolerance is the very product that
has the greatest capacity to adhere tenaciously to cells.

TABLE 8

The effect of time and temperature of incubation on the ability of endotoxin to paralyse normal lymphoid cells in vitro

Time of incubation (minutes)	Incubation temperature	Arithmetic mean number of PFC +SE	Mean $\log^2$ agglutinin titer +SE*
120	37°C	3.8 + 1.8	0
120	4°C	27.9 + 8.2	1.6 + 0.6
12	37°C	98.8 + 12.0	4.4 + 1.2
12	4°C	112.0 + 24.8	5.0 + 2.4

*Tests were made 7 days after injection of 75 x 10^6 heat-killed bacteria (8 mice/group).

84

TABLE 9

The effect of pretreatment with trypsin on the ability of endotoxin to paralyse lympoid cells $\underline{in\ vitro}$

Trypsinization	Endotoxin* treatment	Arithmetic mean number of PFC/ 10^6 spleen cells $\pm$SE	Mean $\log^2$ hemolytic titer $\pm$SE
Yes	Yes	137.2 ± 48.2	8.6 ± 2.4
Yes	No**	80.0 ± 24.6	8.6 ± 0.8
No**	Yes	4.0 ± 2.6	1.8 ± 0.8
No**	No$^+$	72.9 ± 18.6	6.0 ± 2.8

Cells (40×10^6) were transferred to secondary irradiated (750 r) hosts, which were injected with 75×10^6 heat-killed bacteria 12 hours later. Tests were made 7 days after immunization (8 mice/group).

*100 μg endotoxin/10^6 cells for 2 hours at 37°C; cells washed 5 times.

**Incubated without trypsin for $1\frac{1}{2}$ hours at 37°C; washed 3 times.

$^+$Incubated without endotoxin for 2 hours at 37°C; washed 5 times.

I would point out that the amount of antigen that adheres
is remarkably high; one can make estimates of this by various means.

In the context of Dr. Britton's work, I think it would
be of particular interest to extend this experiment to "detoxified" endotoxin, i.e. products whose physiological
effects have been minimized by various other means now available, in order to ascertain whether the tolerance-inducing
effects are still evoked.

DR. BRITTON: Yes, that's right. It is not known what the
alkali treatment does to the molecule other than that it de-
creases the molecular weight and also the toxicity. This
type of experiment works equally well with heat-treated
polysaccharide, and though a large amount of the material
gets stuck on the cells, the amount of material that is
transferred to a secondary host is insufficient to account
for the rate of paralysis that is seen.

DR. UHR: I think that the data presented by Dr. Britton are
still compatible with the induction of tolerance in the recipient animal. The lymphoid cells that are transferred to
the irradiated recipient certainly "home" to lymphoid organs
primarily to the spleen and lymph nodes. Therefore, the
antigen on those cells may be particularly effective, though
in very low concentrations, because of its location in the
initial areas in which the issue of tolerance versus immunity
is decided.

The trypsin data can be explained in one of two ways.
There may be a diminished uptake of antigen, as was earlier
suggested, or even if the same amount of antigen is taken
up, Dr. Gessner has shown that trypsin-treated lymphocytes
home initially in large numbers to the liver. Many hours
later, they leave the liver and go to the lymph nodes and
spleen. During their residence in the liver, however, the
antigen could be stripped off and catabolized.

DR. MITCHISON: I want to make two comments of a general
nature concerning dosage and the different antigens which
we have been hearing about in this discussion. First of
all, to the matter of low zones and ultra-low zones. In the
flagellin data, the upper zone corresponds pretty well to
the low zone observed with a variety of proteins, such as

serum albumin, ribonuclease, and diphtheria toxin. I think
the fact that there is agreement in dose thresholds for this
low zone of tolerance is itself one of the strongest arguments against a processing mechanism at that stage, and in
favor of direct interaction with the critical receptor. I
think that we should not try to reconcile Dr. Nossal's
ultra-low zone for flagellin with low zones obtained with
other proteins, but rather we should try to find some special and additional mechanism that can account for the ultra-
low zone. The message which I shall take away from this
discussion is: (1) perhaps something glues the antigen in
the right place for cells to brush past it in order to
account for the ultra-low zone, and (2) a shadow of a doubt
whether this phenomenon is at all comparable with other
kinds of tolerance.

The second point I wish to make concerns the effects of
brief exposure to antigen _in vitro_ or _in vivo_. Here again
I want to make a distinction. The serum protein antigens,
which have been looked at by Drs. Waksman, Thorbecke, Smith
and myself, and where we fail to find induction of tolerance
in vitro, are nevertheless effective as inducers of tolerance through brief exposure _in vivo_, at least in the case
of bovine serum albumin. For example, a population of
lymphocytes can be recovered from animals injected with
large doses of serum albumin 2 hours after injection, and
these are tolerant when challenged after transfer. Now,
what are the doses which are required here? Apparently,
they are well above 1 mg per mouse or per ml. We are thus
in an entirely different dose range from what Dr. Nossal's
colleagues have used with flagellin and from what Dr.
Britton uses with LPS. I think the indication is that we
are dealing in Dr. Nossal's case and in Dr. Britton's case
with antigens that are in some way sticky and so able to
increase their effective concentrations at the cell surface,
whereas with the serum proteins we have to be at a level of
concentration in the medium which would be expected from
simple thermodynamic considerations.

DR. NOSSAL: I want to reply briefly not to the second part
of the argument with which I agree, but to the first part
of the argument with which I disagree profoundly. Obviously,
the definition of high and low-zone tolerance can at this
stage be only operational. What are the antigen doses needed
to achieve certain effects that we have described. From

Dr. Mitchison's work, high-zone tolerance means to me 3
things. First of all, we have tolerance that is relatively
rapidly induced; secondly, we have tolerance which usually
has an "immunity hump" underneath it; thirdly, we have tolerance which does not have an immunity hump to its "right,"
i.e. with still higher antigen doses. In the case of the
flagellin system the nanogram dosages used obey in the main
all of the criteria for high-zone tolerance. There is,
under some circumstances, particularly in the adult rat
immunized with fragment A an "immunity hump" underneath
extending over many log increments of antigen dose.

Although the time parameter has not been as extensively
investigated by us as it has by Dr. Mitchison, our higher
zone appears to be induced relatively rapidly; certainly,
some effects are seen within a week or so. This is an area
which we must extend.

Finally, and perhaps most importantly, our higher dosage
zone is not "low-zone tolerance" because there is no vestige
of an "immunity hump" to its "right." This is something
that I can document now over a range of 6 additional logs
above the threshold of what I am calling the high zone. You
can give 6 logs more of antigen and not get immunity. So,
I think that by all of the operational criteria that you,
yourself, have set up, Dr. Mitchison, to define these zones,
our one nanogram/gm threshold zone is high-zone tolerance.

DR. BENACERRAF: I am in agreement with what Dr. Mitchison
said, and it is relevant to point out that when one attempts
to make low-zone tolerance in mice and in rabbits, exactly
the same dosage level per unit weight of animal is required.

The other point I want to make, which I think is a relevant one is that in low-zone tolerance, as was described
orginally by Dr. Mitchison, we are dealing in every case
with adult animals. In the work which you are discussing,
Dr. Nossal, when you refer to low-zone tolerance, you are
dealing with newborn animals. I am not certain that the
host situations are comparable because it is possible that
newborn animals become tolerant through pathways that do
not exist in adult animals.

DR. NOSSAL: To correct any misimpressions, we are getting
with fragment A in the rat, the 2 zones in the adult and the
threshold for the lower zone; actually the trough of the

lower zone, is to be found at a dosage of around 10^{-3} picrograms.

DR. MITCHISON: Are the troughs separated by a hump?

DR. NOSSAL: A very wide hump exists in the adult system.

DR. MITCHISON: You told us fragment A was non-immunogenic?

DR. NOSSAL: When given as a single dose without adjuvant. I tried to make the point that I believe that once the first few molecules of antibody have been formed, the whole picture changes.   On repeated administration, fragment A can, in fact, become very immunogenic, as Drs. Ada and Parish have shown and published.

DR. WAKSMAN: I would like to present some relevant data of one of our graduate students, Mr. David Scott.   We are concerned here with the production of high-dose zone tolerance to BGG in adult rats with the additional complication that we are using deaggregated material which is not immunogenic in these animals.

Table 10 shows that soluble BGG (the designation A indicates that it was obtained from Armour) given in a dose of 20 mg to an intact or thymectomized adult Lewis rat produces more or less complete tolerance, whether one is measuring an Arthus skin reaction, a delayed skin reaction, or hemagglutination titer.   The Armour preparation has a contaminating γA-globulin, and it is probable that most of the titer in the tolerant animals is, in fact, antibody against the contaminant rather than against BGG itself.   With 500 μg, a moderate degress of tolerance is produced as well, but with the lower doses tested there is no sign of tolerance.

These animals were challenged via the foot pad with a dose of 100 μg of BGG in adjuvant, and the skin test reactions were measured at 10 and 20 days and the hemagglutination data after 10 days.   The gel precipitins were measured at the end of the immunization period at 32 days.   Thus, with a single dose of soluble material given to the adult, there is no sign of low-dose zone tolerance.   We have tolerance only with doses of 500 μg or better.

TABLE 10

Suppressive effect of various doses of soluble BγG-A on the immune responses
of thymectomized, non-irradiated Lewis rats

Soluble BγG-A Injected	Arthus reactions to BγG	Delayed Skin reactions to BγG	Average HA titer vs BγG-A	Gel Precipitins
	mm	mm	$\log_2$	pos./total
20 mg[a]	2.0	6.0	1.3	0/3
500 µg	6.3	10.5	0.0	2/4
5 µg	9.5	17.8	5.0	4/4
50 ng	11.0	19.0	6.0	4/4
500 pg	11.5	18.8	6.0	4/4
5 pg	11.2	19.3	7.0	4/4
0	10.8	18.3	6.0	5/5

[a]
Rats in this group were challenged, five days after iv injection of antigen, with 100 µg
BγG-A in adjuvant; all others were challenged with 100 µg purified BγG in adjuvant.

(Data reproduced with permission of Journal of Immunology)

Table 11 shows that if one transfers normal lymphoid
cells from untreated adult rats to recipients that have been
thymectomized at the age of 5 weeks and given 900r of whole
body irradiation at the age of 8 weeks, these animals are
restored to complete immunological competence. If you
challenge them 5 days after irradiation and cell transfer
in the usual way, with BGG, the responses are comparable to
those in normal animals. When BGG was given to similar recipients, 20 mg again produced more or less complete tolerance and 500 µg a moderate degree of tolerance, while 50 µg
produced no sign of tolerance. This experiment seemed to us
to establish that the cells of such a suspension as those
transferred provide a suitable target for the induction of
tolerance. It also showed that transfer of this number of
cells ($5\text{-}10\text{x}10^8$) to this type of recipient could be used as
a suitable test for tolerance or immunocompetence.

TABLE 11

Suppressive effect of various doses of soluble BγG-A on immune responses of thymectomized, irradiated rats restored with normal lymphoid cells

Soluble BγG-A Injected	Delayed Skin Reactions to BγG	Average HA titer vs BγG-A	Gel Precipitins
	mm	log_2	pos./total
20 mg[a]	0.0	2.5	1/7
500 μg	5.6	1.9	2/6
50 μg	12.8	4.8	6/7
0 (or 20 mg Ea)	14.2	4.9	5/5

[a] These rats were challenged with 200 μg BγG-A in adjuvant, while all others received 100 μg BγG-A in adjuvant five days after cell transfer and antigen iv.

(Data reproduced with permission of Journal of Immunology)

In Mr. Scott's final experiment, the transferred cells were exposed in vitro to antigen by one of two techniques. In the first, the spleen and several lymph nodes were placed in a petri dish and injected by means of a syringe and needle with soluble BGG or with soluble egg albumin, taking care to expose every part of the organ. They were then incubated at $37^{o}C$ for 2 hours, and at the end of this time the cells were teased out, washed thoroughly, and transferred. Five days later the recipient was challenged, as already described, skin-tested at 10 and 20 days, boosted with antigen at 25 days, and bled at various times, the last bleeding being at 32 days. Labelled antigen was found to be uniformly distributed in different parts of the injected spleen. Table 12 gives data obtained in this way. As you see, in the experimental group there was a marked suppression of delayed sensitization to BGG, of hemagglutinin formation, and of the formation of gel-precipitating antibody against the γG component of the BGG preparation. Reactivity to PPD in these animals was not diminished. When pre-treatment was with ovalbumin instead of BGG, there was no suppression of reactivity to BGG. Thus, the phenomenon appears to be entirely specific.

91

TABLE 12

Attempted induction to BγG in lymphoid cell suspensions or
intact organs in vitro

In vitro treatment of transferred cells	Delayed Skin Reactions BγG	PPD	Average HA titer vs BγG-A	Gel Precipitins Anti-γG	Anti-γA
	mm	mm	$\log_2$	pos./total	pos./total
None (non-irradiated controls)	16.8	10.8	5.5	7/7	7/7
100 mg Sol-BγG-A into intact lymphoid organs	5.9	10.0	2.1	6/12	11/12
100 mg Sol-Ea into intact lymphoid organs	14.5	10.5	4.9	11/12	12/12
100-500 mg Sol-BγG-A incubated with lymphoid cell suspensions	15.0	11.3	5.0	13/14	14/14
100-500 mg Sol-Ea incubated with lymphoid cell suspensions	15.8	11.1	5.2	14/14	14/14

(Data reproduced with permission of Journal of Immunology)

An interesting fact, to which Dr. Britton has already alluded, is illustrated as well. If the same cells were incubated as a suspension with the same antigen at comparable concentrations for the same length of time, no tolerance was observed in the recipients. The induction of tolerance, thus, appears to depend on some aspect of the interaction of antigen with lymphoid cells within the intact spleen and lymph nodes.

Fig. 18 merely establishes the point already mentioned about the hemagglutinins. When we used whole BGG obtained from Armour to sensitize the red cells, you can see that at 10 days there was considerable difference between the titers in recipients of cells from organs pretreated with BGG and from organs pretreated with ovalbumin. However, by 20 days this difference had almost disappeared. When titration of the same sera was carried out with a BGG preparation (obtained from Immunology, Inc.) that did not contain contaminating γA-globulin, there was a quite striking reduction in titer throughout the period of observation in the challenged recipient.

II. EFFECTS OF ANTIGEN DOSAGE

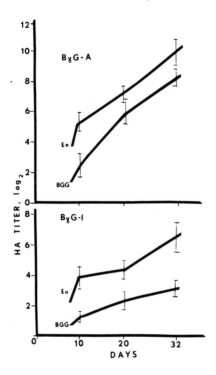

Fig. 18 Hemagglutination of cells sensitized with BGG
obtained from Armour (BGG-A, top) or from Immunology
Inc. (BGG-I, bottom) by sera from thymectomized,
irradiated rats restored with cells from organs
injected in vitro with soluble BGG-A (BGG) or soluble ovalbumin (Ea). Bars indicated standard error
of the mean.

(Data reproduced with permission of Journal of
Immunology)

Now the question of the amount of antigen transferred is,
of course, a very central one. As you see from Table 13,
cells from organs that had been directly injected carried
with them into the recipient an amount of BGG of the order
of 200-500 µg. About one tenth of this amount was present
free in the fluid accompanying the cells. Exactly comparable
amounts of BGG accompanied cells which were incubated as a
suspension with soluble BGG.

93

TABLE 13

Uptake of I_{125} BγG by cells from intact organs or suspensions exposed to
soluble BγGA—A in vitro

Treatment group	Number of Experiments	Calculated BγG in supernatent from last wash (mean)	Calculated BγG remaining associated with final cell pellet	
			Range	Mean
		µg	µg	µg
100 mg Sol-BγG-A into intact lymphoid organs	6	37	220-510	353
100 mg Sol-BγG-A incubated with lymphoid cell suspensions	5	55	500-1000	690

(Data reproduced with permission of Journal of Immunology)

There are several important questions to which we must now address ourselves. One was suggested by Dr. Uhr. What is the possibility that free transferred antigen produces tolerance in the recipient. The amount of free BGG transferred here is not sufficient to induce tolerance in the recipient, as shown in the titration illustrated in Table 10. It takes 500 µg or more of free BGG to induce tolerance in the recipient. At the same time, the fact that tolerance was not seen in recipients of cells that had been incubated with BGG as a suspension, although exactly similar amounts of BGG were transferred, suggests very strongly that it is not antigen transfer that produces tolerance in this experiment.

Another possibility is that we may be dealing with transfer of some type of membrane-bound antigen. Work published by Dr. Battisto and his colleagues a number of years ago suggested that membrane-bound antigen may be more effective in inducing tolerance than free antigen. I think he used BGG as one of the antigens with which he demonstrated this point. Again, the second group of data here militates strongly against this interpretation. Mr. Scott carried out a further experiment, which is shown in Table 14, which also seems to disprove this possibility. Here again transfer involved cells from organs injected in vitro and resulted in the appearance of a moderate degree of tolerance in the recipient. You see that other recipients injected with these

94

TABLE 14

Failure of "tolerant" cells to transfer tolerance to thymectomized, irradiated
rats restored with normal lymphoid cells

| Cells Transferred (x 10^8) | | Delayed Skin Reactions | | Average HA | Gel Precipitins |
Normal	"Tolerant"	ByG	PPD	titer vs ByG-I	
		mm	mm	$\log_2$	pos./total
0	8	6.7	10.5	2.2	2/4
8	8	14.0	10.8	4.8	4/4
8, 16^a	0	15.8	11.0	5.1	7/7
8^b	0	4.8	10.8	2.0	1/3

a

Four animals received 8 x 10^8 normal lymphoid cells; three rats received 16 x 10^8 normal
lymphoid cells.

b

These rats were injected iv with 500 μg Sol-ByG-A within an hour of cell transfer.

(Data reproduced with permission of Journal of Immunology)

same cells, but at the same time given a complement of untreated cells, showed no signs of tolerance. So membrane-
bound antigen could not induce tolerance in untreated cells.

There is one additional point which is of importance. It
seemed possible that antigen injected into the spleen and
lymph nodes might be taken up by a phagocytic cell or some
unidentified processing cell and that what we were transferring was, in fact, antigen at some stage of a processing
event. We therefore fractionated the cell suspension, before transfer, on glass bead columns (Rabinowitz). In the
effluent we obtained an almost pure suspension of lymphocytes; other cell types were eluted in subsequent fractions.
Figure 19 shows that in the two types of experiment, those
in which intact organs were injected, and those in which
cell suspensions were incubated with BGG, antigen uptake was
almost entirely on or in cells that behaved like small- or
medium-sized lymphocytes. The lymphocyte fraction, incidentally, had less than one in a thousand cells that would
take up neutral red in the manner of the conventional mono-
cyte. It appears then that the antigen employed becomes

95

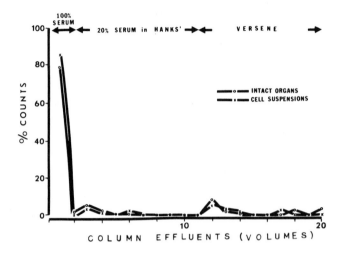

Fig. 19 Separation of labelled cells on glass-bead columns.
Washed cells from intact organs injected with I125-
labelled soluble BGG-A (—o—) or from suspensions
incubated with the same antigen (—x—) were placed
on modified Rabinowitz columns in fresh whole serum
and after 30 minutes, eluted with the materials indicated. Only lymphocytes were eluted by whole
serum in the first fraction.

associated with lymphocytes. We were able to show that this
cell fraction transferred tolerance as effectively as the
whole suspension.

We conclude tentatively that we have effectively produced
tolerance in lymphocytes in the 2 hour incubation period in
vitro, or at least that we have initiated a process which
then continues in the recipient in such a manner that he
becomes tolerant by the time of challenge 5 days later.

Obviously, we are dealing here with very large amounts
of antigen. When experiments were carried out with 20 mg
or 5 mg, a much lower degree of tolerance was produced, so
this really is a high-dose zone tolerance. As to the matter
of mechanisms we have no evidence at all. It seemed to us
that any of several possibilities may be operative. One is,
of course, the phagocytic cells, which can not take up so-
called soluble BGG phagocytically, nevertheless, may be
taking it up pinocytically. Perhaps, a different type of

processing occurs in the same cells that take up particulate
antigen in the production of an immune response. Another
possibility, of course, is that the environment in the intact organ is in some way more favorable towards the sticking process than that in cell suspensions. We have no evidence on this point since cells in suspension are not made
tolerant by antigen and yet, when injected into the recipient, can be made tolerant by the injection of antigen
immediately afterwards. It is hard to believe that they
have been damaged by the suspending process in any important
way. The issue, then, may be one of environment. A third
possibility is that the processing cell simply alters the
antigen slightly and makes it more sticky, so that it resembles, for example, the LPS. To make a distinction among
these possibilities requires further work.

DR. THORBECKE: Two technical questions. After the fractionation of the cells, did they still transfer the immune
response? When you were investigating whether there are 2
zones of tolerance to BGG, was that in thymectomized rats?

DR. WAKSMAN: To the first question, the answer is yes.
These cells restored immunocompetence perfectly well. One
would have expected this, of course, since Dr. Gowan's
earlier experiments showed that highly purified lymphocytes
will restore lymphopenic animals. In the experiments shown
in Table 10 thymectomized animals were used. They were not
irradiated but were immunocompetent animals to whom we gave
doses of BGG.

DR. THORBECKE: Did you also do that with intact rats?

DR. WAKSMAN: No. But I doubt that there would be any
difference.

DR. THORBECKE: In adult mice, with a similar single injection of BSA, you get good low-dose tolerance as shown in
Table 15. This work was done by Drs. Theis, Siskind and
myself. It seems that with respect to low-dose tolerance
to serum protein antigens, rats and mice show a response
that is in the opposite direction from that obtained on
induction of tolerance to flagellin.

TABLE 15

Effect of a single intravenous injection of soluble BSA in adult CAF_1 mice
on the subsequent immune response to alum-precipitated BSA*

Initial i.v. Dose of BSA (μg)	Day of Immunization after i.v. Injection	# Mice Tolerant[+] / # Mice Tested	Percent Tolerant
100,000	2	0/10	0
	7	0/8	0
20,000	2	0/3	0
	7	0/5	0
1,000	2	0/3	0
	7	0/5	0
100	2	1/13	7
	7	6/14	43
35	1	3/7	42
	2	3/10	30
	7	10/10	100
10	2	0/13	0
	7	14/16	88
1	2	0/6	0
	7	5/15	33
0.1	2	1/7	14
	7	0/7	0
0	-	0/16	

* 1 mg alum-precipitated BSA i.p. followed 9 days later by 1 mg soluble BSA.

+ Mice were considered "tolerant" if the reciprocal of their serum antibody titer remained < 40.

DR. MITCHISON: The first and the third possibilities that you raised, Dr. Waksman, seem unlikely in the light of the findings with peripheral lymphocytes--would you not agree?

DR. WAKSMAN: Yes.

DR. MITCHISON: May I return to the relation of high-zone tolerance to immunization. The shift from low zone to high zone is normally associated with immunization. For example, radiation, or treatment with immunosuppressive drugs, or antigen administration on a tolerance-maintaining schedule rather than on a tolerance-inducing schedule, all reduce the dose of antigen required for tolerance. Therefore, in accounting for the difference between high and low zones, one must take into account this relationship to immunization. It is for this reason that I would query Dr. Nossal's purely kinetic account of events. A further objection is that if

you compare a number of different proteins with very different thresholds for immunization, and, therefore, must make
entirely different predictions on the purely kinetic model,
these proteins tend to elicit roughly the same amount of
antibody. This is compatible with a shift to the high zone
being attributable entirely to antibodies, and can account
for the constancy of the high zone.

If you compute the number of binding sites of antibody
present in the mouse in relation to the high-zone threshold,
there is pretty good agreement. A well-immunized mouse
makes of the order of 1 mg of antibody, and this is approximately the dose of antigen at the high-zone threshold.

DR. SELA: Concerning the role of molecular weight, Dr.
Mitchison mentioned earlier that one usually does not
succeed in inducing tolerance with the free hapten; one
possibility is that this is due to the fact that the hapten
used was smaller than a complete determinant.

On the other hand, we know that we can induce tolerance
to a polypeptide determinant, the poly-DL-alanyl group just
by injecting into rabbits at birth the branched poly-DL-
alanine which by itself is a very weak immunogen (Bauminger
et al. Immunochemistry, 4, 169, 1967). Now, is this due
to the macromolecular character of this polymer, or to the
fact that it contains complete determinants? Maybe I should
clarify that when I say "induce tolerance" with polyalanine,
I refer to tolerance to ultimate immunization with polyalanyl
proteins.

From the successful induction of tolerance in newborn
rabbits with multichain poly-DL-alanine, we may draw the
conclusion that there is no direct correlation between
immunogenicity and the capacity to induce tolerance. I already mentioned earlier that there is also no direct correlation between the specificity of cross-tolerance and the
specificity of antigen-antibody cross-reactions.

In view of what I said, we asked ourselves whether we
can induce tolerance with a tetrapeptide of alanine. In a
study with Dr. Bauminger (Israel Med. Sci., in press), we
tried to induce tolerance to the poly-L-alanyl determinant
with tetra-L-alanine, and to the poly-D-alanyl determinant
with tetra-D-alanine. We also did the appropriate controls,
namely, to inject into newborn rabbits tetra-L-alanine and
immunize them later on with poly-D-alanyl proteins, and

vice versa. The results are shown in Table 16. The injection of tetra-D-alanine did not induce any tolerance, and
this may very well be due to the particular regimen of injections (what we did was to inject, in the first 24 hours
after birth, 10 mg of this tetrapeptide, and then for some
10 weeks 10 mg weekly). The reason for showing the table
is that as the result of initial injection of tetra-L-
alanine, the immunization with poly-L-alanyl protein led to
a sharp decrease in antibody production. You could think
that this represents specific tolerance, but a closer look
shows that when you inject tetra-L-alanine into newborn
rabbits and immunize them with poly-D-alanyl protein, the
crop of antibodies to poly-D-alanyl, which is a non cross-
reacting determinant, has also decreased, and so did the
amount of antibodies to human serum albumin. Therefore, in
this case tetra-L-alanine was somehow instrumental in depressing the immune response in a non-specific way. I don't
know the reason, but there is a distinct difference between
the two peptides: tetra-D-alanine is not digested by proteolytic enzymes of serum, whereas tetra-L-alanine is converted into free L-alanine, and this may be somewhat related
to experiments in which injecting a lot of an amino acid
interferes with protein synthesis. Certainly, if it were
not for the controls, we would have believed erroneously
that we were successful in inducing specific tolerance with
tetra-L-alanine.

I would like to ask Dr. Nossal what he means by "antigen
processing?" I tend to worry about what this means. Personally, I do not believe at all that there is any proteolytic digestion between the moment of immunization and the
moment of recognition, whether for making antibodies or for
inducing tolerance. The reason for making this statement is
that almost all the determinants of the proteins are dependent on their higher order structures. Such determinants
would be completely destroyed by any proteolytic enzyme digestion, and experiments which I won't describe here (Sela,
et al., Cold Spring Harbor Symposium on Antibodies, 1967)
show that with synthetic antigens which are originally
helical, immunization yields exclusively antibodies to conformational determinants. So, I believe that the recognition is immediate and there is no proteolytic digestion at
this stage.

TABLE 16

Production of antibodies in rabbits injected after birth with tetra-D-alanine or tetra-L-alanine

Group No.	Tolerogen	Immunogen	No. of animals tested	Precipitant			Ratio of anti-poly-alanyl to anti-HSA[a]
				HSA	pDAlaRSA (mg/ml serum)	pLAlaRSA	
				average $\pm$ standard deviation (S. D.) value			
1	Tetra-D-alanine	pDAlaHSA	8	1.24 ± 0.49	0.78 ± 0.45		0.65 ± 0.33
2	Tetra-L-alanine		5	0.42 ± 0.1	0.29 ± 0.06		0.77 ± 0.28
3	Tetra-L-alanine	pLAlaHSA	5	0.7 ± 0.53		0.23 ± 0.08	0.57 ± 0.42
4	Tetra-D-alanine		5	1.39 ± 0.95		$.57 \pm 0.44$	0.52 ± 0.37

[a] Average $\pm$ S. D. value of ratio in individual animals.

101

On the other hand, I believe the proteolytic digestion is necessary to get rid of the antigen after it has been recognized because otherwise its intact presence suppresses antibody production (or is it detection?) as in the case with some polysaccharides, also with polymers composed exclusively of D-amino acids, as well as with other polymers containing L-amino acids, but built in such a way that it is impossible for the animal to digest them (Jaton and Sela, J. Biol. Chem., in press). In every single case you get paralysis, I don't know whether it should be called tolerance, but antibodies can be obtained only when you immunize with a low dose.

Therefore, I come to the question of what is "antigen-processing?" If one assumes that, e.g. RNA has an influence on keeping antigenic fragments from falling apart, I would have no quarrel, but we are using it mostly in such a mysterious way that I would like to see it better defined.

DR. NOSSAL: I agree completely with Dr. Sela. I believe that in many cases of infection antigens may indeed be taken up by macrophages, lysosomal enzymes will be activated, digestion will take place, and to my way of thinking, in a completely non-informational manner fragments of a large spectrum of sizes and chemical natures may leave the macrophage. I think we know that something must leave because even in the case of polysaccharides the amount of material captured declines, albeit slowly. We don't know the molecular weight of a polysaccharide when it leaves the macrophage; it may well be too small to be immunologically active. I think by sheer chance it will sometimes be that fragments leaving the macrophage are of appropriate molecular size and shape to act as immunogens. Whether they need to be stabilized by RNA, whether the concept of an antigen-RNA fragment is purely a laboratory artifact or really of vital importance in vivo--I don't know. But I would very strongly resist at this point any concept claiming that the RNA is an information-bearing molecule.

I would still say to Dr. Benacerraf that I don't believe we have any concrete evidence, any firm evidence, any evidence other than inferential, of a categorical distinction between antigen that has been processed and antigen that has not been processed.

II. EFFECTS OF ANTIGEN DOSAGE

DR. UHR: In answer to Dr. Sela's question, I think there is one possibility that can be clearly presented, and which has precedence. A number of workers such as DeDuve have shown that secondary lysosomes (which have already engaged in digestion) tend to be leaky. Dr. Weissman and I followed the fate of bacteriophages in subcellular fractions of rabbit spleen and liver and found that some of the lysosomal acid hydrolases escaped from secondary lysosomes into the cell cytoplasm and eventually into the serum of the animals. We also observed that some of the bacteriophage particles, even 48 hours after their i.v. injection, were still capable of plaque formation.

The point is that a bulky phagolysosome may leak out macromolecules that retain their native tertiary structure. Therefore, one can conceive of the possibility that in the lymphoid organs a system to regulate this leakage evolved, so that a small proportion of antigen which enters the usual digestive apparatus could be channeled to escape routes to the surface of the cell in order to be available for the stimulation of precursor cells.

DR. SISKIND: I would like to add one comment to the question of the binding of hapten as compared with antigen. Such considerations would relate to questions dealing with the ability of hapten to interact with immune cells and to the ability to reverse cellular reactions by washing off the antigen after its interaction with cells.

I think one must be careful in considering such questions since when you bind a hapten to an antibody molecule, be it on a cell or elsewhere, it binds by only a single site and of course can be dialyzed off fairly readily. However, when a multivalent antigen binds to an antibody molecule, it has the opportunity to bind by multiple sites and if the reaction is taking place on a cell surface is bound by more than one antibody molecule. With a multivalent antigen molecule bound by several equivalent sites of interaction, all sites would have to be dissociated simultaneously in order to disrupt the antigen-antibody complex. Such a dissociation would be relatively unlikely and therefore binding at multiple sites offers a great energetic advantage for the maintenance of the antigen-antibody complex.

103

DR. FRIEDMAN: I would like to present some information
relative to the effect of antigen dosage on the cytokinetics
of the response of mice to primary and secondary injections
of sRBC. This may have relevance to some of the problems
encountered in tolerance studies since it appears that mice
"primed" with a very large dose of antigen are unresponsive
when challenged subsequently with a lower dose of antigen.
However, a good secondary type of immune response may occur
when such mice are injected with a larger concentration of
antigen the second time, or when a longer time interval
elapses between the two antigen injections.

We have followed in detail the cytokinetics of the immune
response of mice to sRBC and the somatic polysaccharides of
Shigella and Escherichia. We have also used in some of
these studies the Forssman antigen derived from sRBC, and
have observed a tolerance-like effect. Fig. 20 indicates
the cytokinetics of the immune response of mice to 7 different dose levels of sheep erythrocytes. There is a marked
dose-dependent effect on appearance of both high efficiency
IgM and lower efficiency IgG PFC in the spleens of 8 week
old mice injected once with different doses of sRBC. Four
to 5 mice per dosage group were tested at closely spaced
intervals within 9 to 15 weeks. A dosage of 10^4 sRBC i.p.
resulted in a minimal response. A concentration of 10^8
sRBC resulted in an optimal response, whereas 10^{10} sRBC resulted in a suboptimal response. The dose effect seemed
most marked in reference to 7S PFC. It should be noted that
63 days after immunization there were similar numbers of PFC
in the spleens of all mice, regardless of the initial low
concentration of sRBC used for immunization. Six months
after immunization there was an average of almost 400 - 500
PFC per spleen, generally 4-fold above the background of
normal non-immune mice, regardless of the initial antigen
dose.

It seems probable that "feedback" or homeostatic mechanisms regulate the eventual number of specific PFC in a mouse
spleen during a long period of time, regardless of the initial immune response. The composite data in Fig. 21 indicate
the actual number of PFC both per 10^6 and for the entire
spleen, as well as serum titers, as a function of antigen
dose and time at which the mice were sacrificed following
immunization. The effect of dose indicates a minimum response with 10^4 sRBC and a maximum primary response with

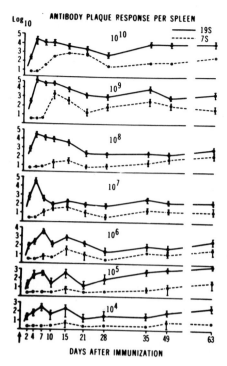

Fig. 20 Cytokinetics of the antibody response in mice that
received varying doses of sRBC. Groups of 100 to
200 mice each were immunized i.p. at 8 weeks of
life and 4-8 animals from each group were tested
at intervals thereafter. Solid line represents 19S
PFC and dotted line represents 7S PFC.

10^8 sRBC. However, the time of assay is important since the
higher dose results in an elevated response for some time.
Analysis of serum titers indicates a continued increase with
increase in dosage. There is little agreement between the
number of PFC and the serum titers once an "optimal" response
occurs.

Mice in these difference dosage groups were injected at
various times with a second inoculum of sRBC. Fig. 22 shows
the effect of the time interval between the first and second
injections of sRBC on the secondary response characterized
by large numbers of 7S PFC. The optimum number of PFC occurs
when the second dose of sRBC was administered between 3 to 5

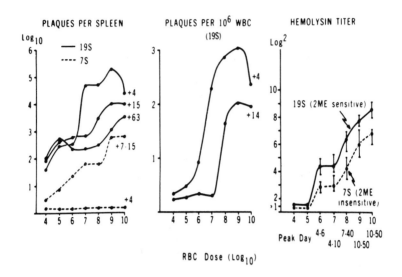

Fig. 21   Comparative PFC and hemolysin titers at various
intervals after the immunization of mice. Solid
line indicates peak 19S PFC response at various
intervals after immunization with indicated dose
of sRBC. Dotted line indicates 7S PFC response of
the same mice during first 2 weeks after immunization. Hemolysin titers indicate the average peak of
ME-sensitive and -resistant antibody activities of
pooled sera.

weeks after the primary inoculum. There was a marked booster
effect, especially for 7S PFC, only when an interval of
several weeks occurred between the 2 injections. A markedly
diminished response occurred when antigen was administered
the first or second week after the primary injection. As
time passes, e.g. 7 to 15 weeks, the ability of the mice
to respond with heightened 7S PFC formation diminished.
These results may indicate the accumulation and then disappearance of "memory" cells. However, they may also indicate the important regulatory role of serum antibody. Each
of the various primed groups of mice had different levels of
serum antibody. The amount of serum antibody was maximal in
the first few weeks after immunization and then diminished.

Similar experiments have been performed with other concentrations of sRBC for the second injection. As seen in

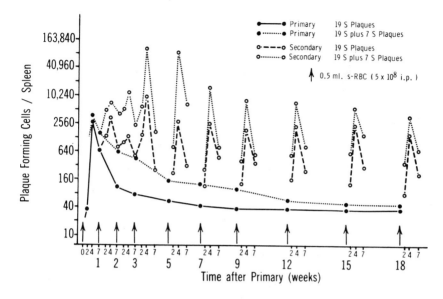

Fig. 22   Cytokinetics of the response of mice to a primary
and to secondary injection (arrows) of 5 x 10^8 sRBC.
Solid line shows the number of 19S PFC per spleen
at various times after a single injection of sRBC;
dashed line (closed circles) indicates the total
number of 19S and 7S PFC response of groups of 10
to 15 mice primed at day "0" with antigen and injected for a second time with the same dose of sRBC
at the indicated time interval. Four to 5 mice were
tested at each time interval after secondary immunization.

Fig. 23, the solid line indicates the primary peak of cellular responses to sRBC with varying doses of antigen, ranging
from 10^4 to 10^8 sRBC. The response to the primary dose
markedly influenced the level of the secondary response.
For example, initial treatment of mice with 10^6 sRBC followed
by a second injection several weeks later with 10^6 sRBC resulted in a much better secondary response than in mice
primed initially with 10^9 sRBC which were injected the second
time with 10^6 sRBC.

In contrast, when the dosage of sRBC was low, e.g. 10^4
or 10^5, a good secondary response was elicited with any of
the larger concentrations of antigen.

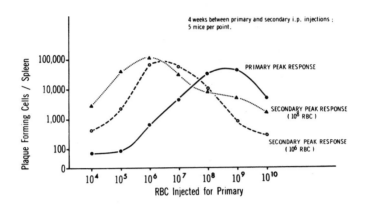

Fig. 23   The average number of PFC to sRBC in spleens of mice as a function of antigen dose in the primary and secondary response. Each curve is based on the average peak response of groups of mice receiving different doses of sRBC as a primary immunization at 8 weeks of life. Solid line is peak 19S PFC response of mice receiving various concentrations of sRBC after primary immunization. Dashed lines represent peak 19S and 7S PFC responses of groups of mice receiving either 10^6 or 10^8 sRBC as a secondary immunization 4 weeks later.

In a further series of experiments attempts were made to immunize hamsters with Forssmann polysaccharide antigens derived from pneumococci. Although few PFC could be elicited with this antigen, the hamsters became tolerant to the sRBC since subsequent attempts to elicit a response with intact sRBC resulted only in moderate number of PFC. This suggests that the major response of hamsters, which are Forssmann-negative, is to this antigen. The polysaccharide alone appears to be non-immunogenic and also seems to induce tolerance to the native erythrocytes.

DR. SISKIND: One comment regarding the data that Dr. Friedman presented. Drs. Paul, Benacerraf and I looked at the ability of antigen to stimulate thymidine uptake by cells in the tissue culture. The cells were taken from animals that had been primed with varying amounts of antigen and a dose-response curve was obtained for the stimulation of thymidine uptake by antigen in vitro. With lymph

node cells from animals primed with a large dose of antigen
we obtained a population of cells that was not stimulated by
low concentrations of antigen in tissue culture, but it did
respond to high concentrations of antigen. On the other
hand, when one primed an animal with a low dose of antigen,
one obtained a population of cells that, in tissue culture,
was sensitive to very low concentrations of antigen and
showed increasing stimulation over a large range of antigen
concentration. In other words, the population of cells present differed depending upon the dose of antigen used for
immunization. Following a high dose of antigen, which
elicited low-affinity circulating antibody, the cell population present behaves as if it is of low avidity for the
antigen in that it can be stimulated in tissue culture only
by high concentrations of antigen. On the other hand, animals stimulated with low doses of antigen, which elicited
high-affinity circulating antibody, have a population of
lymphoid cells that is sensitive to very low concentrations
of antigen; they behave as if they had binding sites of
high avidity for the antigen. I think that considerations
of this sort can account for the data presented by Dr.
Friedman in which he showed that following a high primary
dose of antigen, elicitation of a secondary response required a relatively high second dose of antigen.

DR. BUSSARD: This is a request for information. Is it
possible to induce tolerance specific for the class of antibody, i.e., can you induce tolerance to 19S antibody while
keeping immunity involving 7S antibody, or vice versa?

DR. SCHWARTZ: Yes, with immunosuppressive agents you can
produce a situation where the animal makes only 19S antibody.

DR. BUSSARD: Then you may induce a 19S tolerance while the
portion of the response involving 7S is able to go on.

DR. SCHWARTZ: Dr. Borel has shown that under certain circumstances animals producing circulating antibody are tolerant in their delayed hypersensitivity responses.

I want to give another fact in reference to something
that Dr. Mitchison brought up regarding immunological tolerance in animals treated with immunosuppressive drugs. We
are now studying a system in mice that is remarkable in that

specific tolerance to sRBC can be induced with a single injection of cyclophosphamide. The minimum dose of antigen that is required for tolerance in the drug-treated animals is the minimum dose of antigen that is needed to evoke a primary response in a normal animal. The data indicate that the tolerance is imposed on a system which, after antigen exposure, has been stimulated to enter a primary immune response.

I would like to bring up again the question that was raised by Dr. Möller, and which I think is very important. He asked Dr. Nossal whether or not he believes that a cell-- and I presume he means the lymphocyte--can "tell" how many antigen units or antigen molecules are on its surface, and Dr. Nossal said, "Yes, I believe that the lymphocyte can tell this." What I would like to know is: What is behind this belief? Is there any evidence to indicate that the cell does have a system for enumerating how many antigen molecules there are on its surface?

DR. NOSSAL: I think the best response is the evidence that is now being provided for us by Drs. Davies, Britton, Diener and Armstrong.

DR. SCHWARTZ: That is indirect evidence.

DR. NOSSAL: It will be direct evidence as soon as this is accompanied by appropriate labelling experiments and autoradiography. I am sure that a further 1 or 2 years of this kind of work will give you the answer, but at the moment we have to restrict ourselves to speculation.

DR. SCHWARTZ: The other point to think about in terms of your hypothesis is this: we can construct a different series of curves in which the lymphocyte could have anywhere from one to as many antigen units you wish on its membrane. These various numbers have important implications because even though antibody-forming cells are dividing, the antigen unit on the cell is not. The antigen unit is literally "dead." If, for example, only one antigen unit is on the cell membrane when the cell divides, one daughter cell will run out of antigen. If there are two antigen units, then it will take two cell divisions for one of the daughters to run out of antigen and so on. This seems to me to be of critical importance if we are to accept your statement that there is a stage in the differentiation of antibody-forming cells that is antigen-dependent, since as you suggest, when the cell runs out of antigen it dies.

DR. NOSSAL: I think the diagrams were an attempt to interpret certain dose-response information. At this moment I can't tell you how many receptors for antigens there are on lymphoid cells, and how heavily they tend to become saturated with defined antigen dosages. This is the very area of work that Dr. Ada now is pursuing.

CHAIRMAN MILLER: I would like to ask Dr. Mitchison whether he thinks that at the cellular level there is no difference in the mechanism of induction of tolerance at low and high zones.

DR. MITCHISON: I want first, to reenforce Dr. Sela's point. It is not only a matter of antigens being broken down and losing determinants, I think it is also inconceivable that a protein which is broken down will fail to gain determinants. So, in Dr. Nossal's scheme of things, there should be some determinants which will immunize but for which tolerance will be impossible.

As to the more general point, I do not feel at present that the cellular mechanism of high-zone and low-zone induction are different.

III

CELL POPULATIONS INVOLVED IN
IMMUNE RESPONSES

Involvement of two cell types – Roles of lymphocytes and macrophages – Antigen-concentrating mechanisms – Cell-associated IgX – Roles of bone-marrow and thymus – Restoration phenomena in irradiated and/or thymectomized animals – Sites of differentiation of thymus-independent cell populations – Clonal distribution of antibody-forming cells – Separation of hapten- and carrier-reactive cell populations – Delayed hypersensitivity phenomena – Restoration and transfer of immunological responsiveness by thoracic duct lymphocytes.

III. IMMUNOCOMPETENT CELL POPULATIONS

DR. MITCHISON: The types of cell interactions that we shall now discuss are shown in Table 17. First, we have an interaction in which macrophages are involved in stimulating lymphocytes. This is a matter which was dealt with at some length previously. Let me mention the reasons why I believe that specificity in this interaction resides solely in the lymphocytes, while the macrophage plays an entirely non-specific role. The strongest evidence for this is that in some types of immunological reactions macrophages are apparently not involved. The classical examples come from

TABLE 17

Cell-cell interactions

1. Macrophage → Lymphocyte

    (antigen presentation; non-specific activation)

2. Lymphocyte → Macrophage

    (inhibition of migration; accumulation)

3. Thymus-derived lymphocyte → marrow-derived lymphocyte

    (? antigen presentation

    ? maturation

    ??? sub-cellular transfer)

4. Anti-carrier producer → hapten-sensitive lymphocyte

    (antigen presentation)

transplantation immunity, where transplantation antigens, located presumably on the cell surface, appear to provoke reaction in "clean" populations of lymphocytes obtained from the thoracic duct. Recently, Drs. Gowans, Boak and I have been exposing thoracic duct lymphocytes from immunized animals to protein antigens in vitro. Upon transfer to irradiated recipients the lymphocytes given rise to reasonably high levels of serum antibody. These experiments again suggest that lymphocytes can interact directly with antigen, without the participation of macrophages.

The argument from these experiments is simply this: if under any circumstances lymphocytes can be shown to react specifically to antigen, then anyone who wants to argue that macrophages are capable of specific reactions as well has to bring very secure proof.

There are other arguments of a more negative character. Our own experiments with extracts prepared from macrophages which might be expected to contain "super-antigen" or "messenger" have never given convincing results. Indeed, I have found that the circumstances where others have demonstrated "super-antigen" (the response of primed cells to protein antigens) are just those where antigen taken up by viable macrophages is least strikingly effective.

Finally, our experiments on the transfer of cells into or out of mice tolerant to protein antigens have yielded no evidence of altered reactivity on the part of macrophages in tolerant animals, although altered reactivity on the part of lymphocytes can readily be demonstrated.

The other point to be made about the presentation of antigen by macrophages is that recent work lends support to Dr. Talmage's idea of non-specific activation. Irradiated mice can be given lymphocytes from one donor and macrophages from another. Drs. Unanue, Askonas and Spitznagel, have shown that exposure of the macrophages to a non-specific adjuvant such as endotoxin enhances the response. This shows that the non-specific activation proceeds via the macrophage. Drs. Allison and Spitznagel have investigated the role of lysosomes in this activation, and have found a rough working correlation between adjuvant activity and lysosome activation. Exactly what this means remains to be established.

III. IMMUNOCOMPETENT CELL POPULATIONS

Table 18 brings together the details of experiments that were considered in our earlier discussions. A series of proteins are listed in the left-hand column in order of their activity in inducing a primary response. According to this criterion, BSA and HSA are weaker antigens because relatively large doses are needed in order to immunize mice, which are what these figures refer to. The next column refers to the outcome of experiments in which immunization is performed by transfer of macrophages that have taken up protein. By means of radioactive markers the potency of antigen in this form can be compared with that of free antigen, and the factors in the table refer to this relative potency. This macrophage-bound BSA is of the order of one thousand-fold more potent in immunization than free BSA. The figures refer either to primary immunization or to sensitization for a boost.

It is immediately evident that the strongest macrophage effect is found with the weakest antigens, which suggests that only the weaker antigens require the help of macrophages.

The third column refers to the Gallily and Feldman effect, the ineffectiveness in immunization of macrophages harvested from irradiated mice. The effect can be found only with those proteins that manifest a drastic macrophage requirement, at the head of the column. Possibly this inhibition is a consequence of blockade by the breakdown products of whole-body irradiation. The inhibition is of some interest because it suggests that something more than mere uptake is involved in the macrophage, for immunogenic activity is affected much more strongly by radiation than uptake. This provides us with a tool, which Dr. Kolsch and I have been exploiting, to study the pathways which protein antigens follow through the macrophage.

The second part of Table 18 refers to the high and low-zone paralysis thresholds which we have already gone into at great length. Ultra-low zone paralysis, and in vitro induction of paralysis both occur low down the columns.

Obviously, there are limitations in the interpretation of this kind of compilation. However, there is a suggestion of a constellation of alternative characteristics in antigens which can be summarized as stickiness or non-stickiness. The proteins lower down the list, the sticky ones, are potent immunogens, don't seem to require macrophages, and

117

TABLE 18

The antigen-concentrating hierarchy

Antigen	Immunity			Paralysis		
	Threshold for 1° response/g. body weight	Potency of macrophage-bound antigen relative to free form	Inhibition of macrophage effect by radiation	Paralysis thresholds — Low-zone	Paralysis thresholds — High-zone	In vitro paralysis
BSA, HSA [1]	10^1 µg	$\times 10^3$	Yes	10^{-1} µg	10^3 µg	No
Lysozyme, OA [1]	10^{-2} µg	$\times 10^1 - 10^2$	-	10^{-1} µg	10^3 µg	-
MSH [2]	10^{-3} µg	$\times 10^1$	No	-		-
KLH [3]	$<10^{-3}$ µg	<1	-	-		-
Flagellin [4]	10^{-7} µg	-	-	10^{-3} µg Ultra-low zone 10^{-7} µg		Yes
E. coli lipopolysaccharide [5]	-	-	-	-		Yes

OA = ovalbumin; MSH = Maia squinado haemocyanin; KLH = keyhole limpit haemocyanin.

[1] - [5] = references (see J.L. Boak, E. Kölsch and N.A. Mitchison - Antibiot. et Chemother.,Basel, in press 1968)

do seem to be able to interact with lymphocytes in vitro.

Next, we must consider thymus-derived cells as another possible mechanism for presenting antigen to sensitive cells. When we do so, we ought to expect the "non-sticky" proteins to be thymus-dependent, and the "sticky" ones to be thymus-independent. This expectation is at least partially supported by available data summarized in Tables 19 and 20.

Table 19 provides a classification of antigen-presentation mechanisms. It includes the intramolecular mechanism discovered by Dr. Mäkela and his colleagues, who have shown that a given concentration of antigen tends to activate IgM

TABLE 19

Local antigen-concentrating mechanisms used by the
body to facilitate antigen-recognition

(A) INTRAMOLECULAR

　　　Multiple binding sites:　low affinity

　　　yields high avidity, especially with IgM

(B) INTERMOLECULAR (? INTERCELLULAR)

　　　(i) Specific

　　　　　a.　Secreted IgM concentrates antigen

　　　　　　　for IgM receptors.

　　　　　b.　Cell-bound immunity ("IgX")

　　　　　　　concentrates antigen for IgG

　　　　　　　receptors.

　　　(ii) Non-specific

　　　　　Macrophages

TABLE 20

Relationship of IgX to recognized classes of Ig

Genes	Chains	Proteins	Stimulation	Anatomy
Subject to generator of diversity	μ	IgM	(-) (+)	Marrow-derived; mainly sessile
"	γ	IgG		
"	α	IgA	(+)	Export areas (gut & glands)
"	?	"IgX"		Thymus-derived; migrant

receptors of lower affinity than IgG receptors. It includes also macrophages, taking the non-specific role which we are assigning them. It includes the enhancing effect of passively transferred IgM antibody, discovered by Drs. Jerne and Henry. And, finally, it includes a position into which the thymus-marrow interaction fits. Indeed, the only merit claimed for this scheme of classification is that it encourages us to regard this interaction as one among several mechanisms which have the same goal and which can supplement and act as alternatives to one another.

Obviously, these concentrating mechanisms will not be required if the antigen is capable of sticking to the lymphocyte cell surface in such a manner as to concentrate itself spontaneously. This is the force of the antigen listing in Table 18; according to this point of view, self-concentration is the basis of the distinction between thymus-dependent and thymus-independent antigens. Obviously, also the need for concentrating mechanisms depends ultimately on affinity: presumably the need is not absolute, but the mechanism provide a method of generating antibody of lower affinity than the actual concentration of free antigen deserves. This is a point that I have discussed in detail before.

III. IMMUNOCOMPETENT CELL POPULATIONS

Finally, Table 20 indicates that the specificity of a hypothetical IgX antibody generated by thymus-derived cells should cover the same range as other antibodies, since the distinction between IgX and IgG is essentially the same as the distinction between other Ig classes. The anatomical basis of IgX production, according to the evidence at present available, is unusually strictly segregated. However, anatomical segregation is already familiar to us in the context of IgA production, and need not therefore come as a surprise.

Perhaps, at this point I should insert a historical capsule about thymus-derived cells, by way of introduction to Dr. Miller's data. It was first shown conclusively by Dr. Taylor that the cells which leave the thymus and enter the lymph nodes and spleen, multiply in response to antigenic stimulation. This experiment suggested, erroneosuly as it has turned out, that these cells then go on to synthesize normal antibodies. The thymus-derived cells are, however, required for a full response to sRBC, as Drs. Claman and Talmage, Dr. Davies and his colleagues, and Dr. Doria have shown. Drs. Mitchell and Miller have now shown that in this response the majority at least of antibody-producing cells are actually other cells, of marrow origin, which in some way cooperate with the thymus-derived cells.

May I now introduce two recent experiments of Dr. Taylor's, which throw light on the location of the cellular lesion in mice tolerant of BSA? They confirm and extend the earlier work of Waksman and his colleagues on adoptive immunity conferred by cells obtained from the thymus and bone-marrow of rats pretreated with BGG. In Dr. Taylor's first experiment (Fig. 24), cells were transferred into thymectomized, irradiated, syngeneic recipients from mice pretreated one day earlier with various doses of BSA; the recipients were then immunized with BSA, and clear evidence was obtained of unresponsiveness among the cells from thymus. Cells from lymph nodes displayed some evidence of paralysis at low doses of antigen, but the effect was lost at the 1 mg dose, possibly because of concomitant immunization. In this experiment the recipients also received a relatively small number of cells from the bone-marrow of normal syngeneic donors.

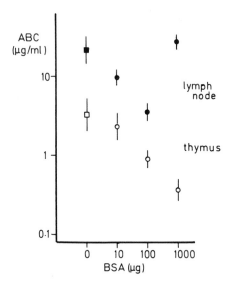

Fig. 24 Anti-BSA antibody titres 28 days after immunization
with BSA and adjuvant by mice thymectomized in
adult life and irradiated (900r) immediately before
intravenous transfer of 1/6 donor-equivalent (about
4 million) normal bone-marrow cells, and either 180
million thymus cells or 30 million lymph node cells
from normal donors (squares) or donors pretreated
one day before transfer with a single dose of 10-
1000 μg BSA (circles). Geometric mean and standard
error

In the second experiment (Fig. 25), Dr. Taylor explored
more systematically the relationship between thymus and bone-
marrow, by transferring combinations of cells from normal
paralysed (10 mg BSA one day earlier) donors. Evidently,
cells from the thymus but not from the bone-marrow become
unable to participate in the response. This experiment includes a group in which cells from normal and paralysed
donors were mixed, in order to be able to detect the effect
of antigen-carryover: some evidence of an effect was obtained, but in other experiments this could not be confirmed.

No evidence of paralysis in the bone-marrow population
was obtained in these experiments. Another experiment,
however, in which mice were subjected to a more systematic

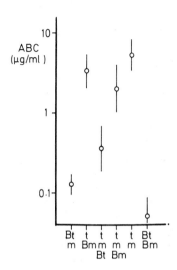

Fig. 25   Anti-BSA antibody titres 35 days after immunization
with BSA and adjuvant,by mice irradiated (900r)
and injected intravenously on the same day with
bone-marrow (m) and thymus (t) cells. The six groups
received different combinations of cells from donors
pretreated one day before transfer with 10 mg BSA
(B) and from untreated donors. Numbers of cells
transferred (x 10^{-6}) t, 92; BT, 89; m, 17; Bm, 18.
Circles indicate geometric mean;bars show the
standard error

treatment with BSA (5 mg/week for 10 weeks post-600r),
yielded a hint of paralysis in the marrow population.

Dr. Taylor's experiments clearly establish that thymocytes
which have been exposed to adequate concentrations of BSA
become unable to mediate a response to this antigen.   Further
experiments have shown that this unresponsiveness is specific.
If we can generalize from the Mitchell and Miller results,
the antibody produced in the recipients was not produced by
descendents of the thymocytes but by other cells from the
marrow.   The experiment, therefore, indicates not only that
cells are sensitive to antigen while still inside the thymus,
but also that responsiveness can be abolished by a specific
lesion among cells that do not themselves normally make

123

antibody or give rise to antibody-producing cells. One could still argue that one population of cells which mounts a specific response could help, in a non-specific manner, another population to respond at the same time (e.g. by feeding, by liberating mitogen, or by providing stroma), but this possibility seems far-fetched. On the whole these experiments lend support to the scheme of antigen-concentration outlined above.

A question mark remains regarding experiments of this nature, in which we attempt to paralyse marrow cells. In the long run we need to know about the susceptibility to paralysis of marrow-derived cells while they reside in peripheral lymphoid organs, after they have left the marrow. The obvious way of examining this matter is to attempt to induce paralysis among the peripheral cells of thymectomized, irradiated, marrow-recolonized mice. If we fail to induce paralysis, or induce a less impressive unresponsiveness than can be obtained in thymus-derived cells, will this be because these cells are per se less susceptible, or will it be because marrow-derived cells require thymus-derived cooperation in the induction of paralysis as well as in the induction of immunity?

The hypothesis that the thymus-derived cell population serves as a device for reaching other cells with low-affinity receptors (Fig. 26) has definite implications concerning the termination of tolerance by cross-immunization. Drastic tolerance-inducing schedules, of the type discussed by Dr. Benacerraf, should nibble into the marrow-derived population; however, regardless of how effectively the thymus-derived local concentrating mechanism might then operate, by means

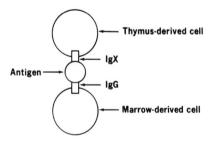

Fig. 26 Suggested interaction between thymus-derived and marrow-derived cells

of new determinants, few marrow-derived potential producers
would be available. Milder tolerance-inducing schedules,
on the other hand, would leave sensitive marrow cells that
could be reached via a local concentrating mechanism.

CHAIRMAN GOWANS: The two cell interactions that have been
introduced by Dr. Mitchison are (1) those between macrophages and lynphoid cells and (2) those between lymphoid
cells that are derived, respectively, from the thymus and
the bone-marrow.

It has been suggested that we should postpone the question of the complicity of the macrophages in the induction
of immunity until later when it will be taken up by Dr.
Humphrey. I think we should spend our time now discussing
interactions between thymus-derived cells and marrow cells.

Dr. Mitchison has put forward his own interpretation of
this marrow-thymus interaction in terms of an antigen-
concentrating mechanism but there are other possible explanations. Before we go on, I think it is important that we
have a few more facts at our disposal. The person who has
provided most of these is Dr. Miller, and I propose that
before discussing Dr. Mitchison's report, we hear from Dr.
Miller about his experiments.

DR. MILLER: I will first give you results obtained from
three very simple kinds of experiments and later on some
possible interpretations. We used three types of recipient
mice. The first was thymectomized at birth; as you know,
thymectomy at birth in mice interferes with the response,
not to all antigens, but to certain antigens such as sheep
or horse RBC. We determined the number of antibody-forming
cells per spleen in thymectomized mice challenged with sRBC
at 4 to 6 weeks of age. At the height of the response,
which was 5 days after antigenic challenge, we found about
2,000 PFC per spleen. This stands in contrast to the response of controls which produced about 30 to 40 thousand
PFC per spleen.

As shown in Fig. 27, the transfer into thymectomized recipients of either thymus or thoracic duct lymphocytes restored their responses. Ten million thymus cells gave rise
to about 20,000 PFC per spleen and 50 million thymus cells
restored the response to normal. Of particular interest was
that in this system thymus cells were as effective as

125

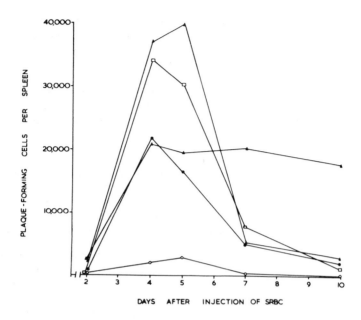

Fig. 27 PFC produced in the spleens of neonatally-thymectomized CBA mice at various times after injection of
sRBC and syngeneic thymus or thoracic duct cells.
Sham-operated controls given sRBC only (open boxes);
neonatally-thymectomized mice given sRBC only (open
circles); neonatally-thymectomized mice given 1 x
10^7 CBA thymus cells and sRBC (closed circles);
neonatally-thymectomized mice given 5 x 10^7 CBA
thymus cells and sRBC (open triangles); neonatally-
thymectomized mice given 1 x 10^7 thoracic duct
cells and sRBC (closed triangles).

(Data reproduced with permission of Journal of
Experimental Medicine)

thoracic duct lymphocytes, i.e., 10 million thymus cells
produced the same effect as 10 million thoracic duct cells.
Another interesting finding was that semi-allogeneic or
allogeneic lymphocytes also restored the response. In other
words, cells from C57Bl or (CBA x C57Bl) F_1 cells were as
effective as CBA cells, and this allowed us to determine
the identity of the antibody-forming cells by treating the
PFC with anti-H-2 isoantisera.

III. IMMUNOCOMPETENT CELL POPULATIONS

The results of such treatment showed that in this system the PFC were derived from the host rather than from the inoculated lymphocytes. This kind of experiment does not tell us which cellular system in the host provides the precursors of the PFC. In order to determine this, we had to use another type of host, namely, a heavily irradiated animal, given 800r total body-irradiation. We injected into such mice either bone-marrow cells alone or thoracic duct lymphocytes alone, or a mixture of the two cell types, and followed this by challenge with sRBC. The findings are illustrated in Fig. 28; the peak response occurred in these irradiated animals at about 7 to 8 days after challenge. With 1 million thoracic duct cells we got a peak response of about 100 PFC per spleen. With 10 million bone-marrow cells alone, we got a peak response also of the order of 100 PFC. But with a mixture of both cell types the response was one log higher, namely 1000 PFC per spleen, i.e., there was clearly a synergistic effect.

One would like to know which cell type provided the immediate precursor of the antibody-forming cells in this system. Unfortunately, however, no interaction took place between allogeneic cells in the acutely restored irradiated mice so that we could not use isoantisera to determine the identity of the PFC. This is in contrast to the situation in neonatally thymectomized mice. We therefore used syngeneic mice, namely, CBA and CBA/T6T6. Drs. Nossal and Cunningham examined individual antibody-forming cells, which were in metaphase, for the presence or absence of the T6 chromosome marker. They found that 75% of the antibody-forming cells in metaphase had the chromosome marker of the bone-marrow donor.

When we increased the dose of bone-marrow cells given to the irradiated animals, the number of PFC produced did not increase. When, however, we increased the dose of thoracic duct lymphocytes (given in the absence of bone-marrow) from 10 million to 30 million, the number of PFC rose from about 1000 to about 5000 and all the PFC were derived from cells in the donor inoculum. If, however, we added syngeneic bone-marrow to the thoracic duct cells, the number of PFC was increased by a factor of about one log above that produced by thoracic duct lymphocytes given alone. There is thus, again, a synergistic effect between bone-marrow and thoracic duct lymphocytes, and it is in this system that

127

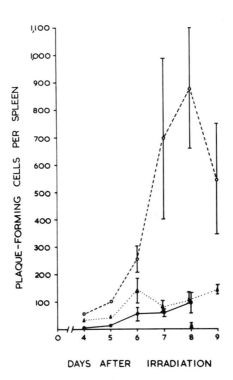

DAYS AFTER IRRADIATION

Fig. 28   PFC produced in the spleens of heavily irradiated CBA mice injected, after irradiation, with sRBC (open triangles); sRBC + 10^6 syngeneic thoracic duct cells (closed circles); sRBC + 10^6 syngeneic bone-marrow cells (closed triangles); sRBC + a mixed inoculum of 10^6 syngeneic thoracic duct cells + 10^6 syngeneic bone-marrow cells (open circles). The magnitude of twice the standard errors is shown by the vertical bars. Each point at 4,5 and 9 days represents the mean of determinations made on 2 to 5 mice and at 6,7,and 8 days on 6 to 13 mice.

(Data reproduced with permission of Journal of Experimental Medicine)

III. IMMUNOCOMPETENT CELL POPULATIONS

Drs. Nossal and Cunningham scored 75% of the PFC as having been derived from the bone-marrow and not from the thoracic duct lymphocytes.

Now let us consider the next host. This was a CBA animal which was thymectomized in adult life, given a lethal dose of irradiation (800r) and then protected with CBA bone-marrow. It was then allowed to rest for 2 weeks and challenged with sRBC. The findings illustrated in Fig. 29 show that the peak response was not more than about 300 PFC. If, however, we injected 10 million thoracic duct lymphocytes together with the antigen, the response was very markedly increased, namely, about 70,000 PFC per spleen. If we injected 10 million thymus cells instead of thoracic duct lymphocytes, strangely enough, the response was increased only to about 6,000 PFC per spleen. Thus, there is a discrepancy between the results obtained in irradiated hosts and in non-irradiated neonatally-thymectomized hosts, with respect to the activity of thymus cells.

It was important to determine whether the antibody-forming cells produced in the thymectomized, irradiated hosts were derived from the inoculated thoracic duct cells or from the bone-marrow cells used to protect against irradiation. We did get a synergistic effect with allogeneic cells in this system. By exposing the PFC to specific anti-H-2 antisera, we could determine their identity, and it turned out that 90 to 100% of the PFC produced were derived not from the thoracic duct lymphocyte donor but from the bone-marrow donor.

We next used mice made tolerant to sRBC by the cyclophosphamide method that was already mentioned by Dr. Schwartz. These mice were specifically tolerant in the sense that they could produce only about 1000 plaques to sRBC but a normal number of plaques to horse red blood cells (hRBC). We tried to break tolerance by injecting various cell populations into these mice. We did not succeed with 20 million normal thoracic duct cells nor with 20 million bone-marrow cells. But when we injected a mixture of both cell types, namely, thoracic duct lymphocytes together with bone-marrow, then we got a response that was at least one log higher than that in tolerant mice given either bone-marrow cells alone or thoracic duct cells alone (Table 21).

The fact that we could increase the response of tolerant mice by using a mixture of the two cell types raises the

129

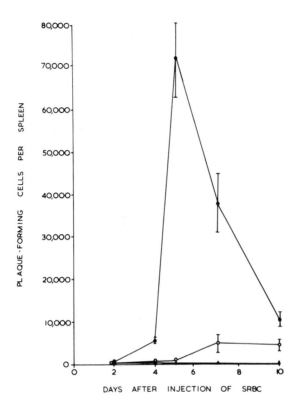

Fig. 29   PFC produced in the spleens of adult thymectomized
CBA mice, heavily irradiated and protected with syngeneic bone-marrow cells 2 weeks previously, and
injected with sRBC alone (solid triangles); sRBC +
1×10^6 syngeneic thymus cells (open circles) and
sRBC and 1×10^6 syngeneic thoracic duct cells
(closed circles). The magnitude of twice the standard errors is shown by the vertical bars.   Each
point represents the mean of determination made on
3 to 10 mice.

(Data reproduced with permission of Journal of
Experimental Medicine)

III. IMMUNOCOMPETENT CELL POPULATIONS

TABLE 21

Attempts to break tolerance by transfer of lymphoid cells

Cells Inoculated	No. of mice tolerant of sRBC	PFC per spleen $\pm$ SE
sRBC only	22	1,858 $\pm$ 255
2×10^7 BM + sRBC	6	1,987 $\pm$ 540
2×10^7 TDL + sRBC	13	2,947 $\pm$ 605
2×10^7 TDL + 2×10^7 BM + sRBC simultaneously	6	10,017 $\pm$ 2,300

question as to whether target cells for tolerance induction might not be present in both populations of cells, i.e., in populations of lymphocytes from thoracic duct (which we think are thymus-derived) and from bone-marrow.

We next took thoracic duct lymphocytes from sRBC-tolerant animals and injected them into neonatally thymectomized hosts. These thoracic duct lymphocytes failed to restore the response of their thymectomized hosts to sRBC, but they did reconstitute the response to hRBC. This suggests that there are tolerant populations of thymus-derived cells. If the neonatally thymectomized recipients were challenged not just with sRBC but with hRBC, also, the response to sRBC did increase, though not to normal levels. These findings are summarized in Table 22.

To recapitulate, lymphocytes from sRBC-tolerant donors given to thymectomized mice together with sRBC did not cause an appreciable response. But when such lymphocytes were given together with both sRBC and hRBC then the response to sRBC was increased to a certain extent, e.g., from about 10,000 to about 20,000, and whether this is due to cross-reactivity between sRBC and hRBC, we do not know.

131

TABLE 22

Reactivity of normal and tolerant lymphoid cells in neonatally thymectomized mice

Inoculum	Antigen challenge	No. of thymectomized mice	PFC per spleen ± SE	
			Anti-sRBC	Anti-hRBC
No cells	sRBC	16	2,356 ± 537	—
	hRBC	6	—	2,812 ± 1,480
10^7 control TDL	sRBC	7	52,543 ± 12,186	—
	hRBC	4	—	36,020 ± 7,246
	Both	7	64,457 ± 17,188	37,830 ± 12,420
10^7 sRBC tolerant TDL	sRBC	7	10,214 ± 2,677	—
	hRBC	5	—	32,715 ± 10,682
	Both	13	22,408 ± 5,494	32,338 ± 7,979

III. IMMUNOCOMPETENT CELL POPULATIONS

In conclusion, it may be said that bone marrow-derived cells are the precursors of the 19S antibody-forming cells in this system. What, then, is the role of the thymus-derived cells?

CHAIRMAN GOWANS: Aren't you going to tell us? We would like to know what you think.

DR. MILLER: One can suggest non-specific or specific functions. Among the non-specific functions, the one that comes to mind immediately is trephocytic. There are many data that suggest that trephocytic functions may not be responsible; for instance, the fact that specifically tolerant lymphocytes were able to restore the response to hRBC but not to sRBC.

DR. CINADER: What do you mean by trephocytic?

DR. MILLER: Providing nucleotides or their precursors as building blocks to dividing or differentiating cell populations.

Another possible explanation of the results is that as thymus-derived cells react with antigens and transform to blasts, they might release some pharmacologically-active agents which non-specifically induce the recruitment of bone marrow-derived cells into activity.

Another possibility has already been mentioned by Dr. Mitchison, namely, that thymus-derived cells recognize certain antigenic determinants on sRBC and bone marrow-derived cells recognize other determinants, and that the two cell types somehow have to come together so that the antigenic determinants can be anchored between the two cells in order to trigger off an efficient antibody response in the bone-marrow cell line (cf. Fig. 26).

Yet another possibility is that there is information transfer from thymus-derived to bone marrow-derived cells. I think there is no evidence for or against this and I am not convinced that we can, at this stage, devise experiments that would unequivocally prove or disprove this.

CHAIRMAIN GOWANS: The main points that strike me in these experiments are: 1) the neonatally thymectomized mouse, which is slowly but spontaneously recovering its capacity

133

to respond to sRBC, can be restored rapidly to full responsiveness with either peripheral lymphocytes or thymus cells.
These two cell-types are equivalent functionally. This is
a strange finding, because in other systems they are clearly
not equivalent. For example, irradiated rats and mice can
be restored to respond to sRBC by a simultaneous injection
of peripheral lymphocytes but thymus cells are completely
ineffective.

2) The second point is the relative inefficiency of
immediate restoration of the irradiated animal with mixtures
of syngeneic lymphocytes and bone-marrow. If the number of
injected cells is increased considerably, more or less normal numbers of PFC can be obtained, but with the sort of
doses used in the neonatally thymectomized animal, you get
relatively poor restoration in the irradiated animal. Another difference from the thymectomized animals is the
failure of allogeneic mixtures of lymphocytes and marrow
cells to restore irradiated mice.

3) In the more complex experiment, thymectomized mice
were given bone-marrow which promoted hemopoietic recovery,
but in the absence of the thymus, no immunological recovery.
Nevertheless, an injection of thoracic duct lymphocytes two
weeks later restored the response to sRBC. Again, thymus
cells were much less effective. Animals in experimental
models 1) and 3), rather than in 2), had a bone-marrow that
had been in residence for a period of time and had presumably
seeded the lymphoid tissue with lymphocytes.

In all these experiments, when we speak of "bone-marrow
cells" we are, in fact, speaking of lymphoid cells of some
kind which have passed from the bone-marrow into lymphoid
tissue where the interactions for antibody formation occurred.

In model 3) it was possible to use F_1 hybrid cells for
restoration, and to establish the key point that the specific antibody and the antibody-forming cells were both of
bone-marrow origin. On the other hand, lymphocytes from
immunologically-tolerant animals failed to restore antibody
formation in the neonatally-thymectomized animals, so lymphocytes or their precursors clearly have the ability to
react in a specific manner with antigen.

So much for the experimental data. As for the interpretation, Dr. Miller has given his list of possibilities, ex-
panding on those given by Dr. Mitchison. He included the

rather vague trephocytic function, the idea that nutrients
of some kind are provided by lymphocytes which thus promote,
in a non-specific way, differentiation or cell division;
there was also the antigen-concentrating mechanisms that
Dr. Mitchison discussed, and finally, and most controver-
sially, the possibility of an information transfer from one
cell type to another.

I wonder if we can now try to illuminate some of these
complicated matters.

DR. AUERBACH: We must carefully distinguish between thymus-
derived lymphocytes, thymus-dependent lymphocytes, and thoracic duct lymphocytes, all of which have been referred to
as T.D.L.'s. Only the thoracic duct cells are a definite
entity and even they represent a heterogenous population of
cells.

Concerning thymus-marrow interactions, one must bear in
mind that many interactions of this kind have been described
previously (e.g. by Metcalf, Globerson and Auerbach, Davies)
and it is unlikely that a single explanation of such interactions will suffice. Furthermore, the interpretation of
quantitative differences becomes possible only when the role
of cell division has been more amply determined.

DR. SILVERSTEIN: I think one would like to hear more from
Dr. Miller or from others about the situations involving
other antigens or the use of different animal species in
which the thymus-dependent system does not seem to operate.

DR. NOSSAL: Dr. Lind in my laboratory has shown that in the
rat, whose tolerance properties to flagellin we have discussed so extensively, the response to flagellin is markedly
thymus-dependent. It is, in fact, somewhat more depressed
by neonatal thymectomy than the sRBC response in the mouse,
at least as judged by serological reactions rather than
plaque techniques. It is reduced by a factor of 20 or more
below control animals, whereas as Dr. Miller said, the response to flagellin is not at all depressed by neonatal
thymectomy in the mouse.

When the response of the mouse and rat to sRBC, bacteriophage, and flagellin are compared, we have a rather puzzling
situation; in the mouse the sRBC response is thymus-dependent,
whereas the response to flagellin is not depressed at all.

135

In the rat, response to sRBC is not depressed at all by neonatal thymectomy, whereas the response to flagellin is considerably depressed and the response to phage is intermediate.

I would be very happy if Dr. Mitchison or anyone else can
make some sense out of this. Incidentally, Dr. Mitchison's
depiction of a hierarchy of antigens intrigued me a great
deal. Indeed, life would have been made much more simple
if we could have adopted the idea of "stickiness" as being
equivalent to an absence of the thymectomy effects.

DR. GOOD: I would like to address myself to some of the
questions that Dr. Silverstein raised and that I think must
be taken into consideration in the discussion of Dr. Miller's
work. First of all, I am very much concerned about separating thymus-derived from marrow-derived cells. It is very
clear from the work of Dr. Ford and others that the thymus-
derived cells are, in fact, marrow-derived cells. I would
much rather hear us talk about thymus-independent and thymus-
dependent cell populations. The thymus probably operates to
direct the differentiation of marrow-derived cells so that
the cells are immune, competent, and capable of exercising
their thymus-dependent functions. These functions include
the production of antibodies to certain types of antigens,
but not to others, the primary control of cell-mediated responses, including the classical delayed-type hypersensitivity and homograft rejection. Thymus-independent cells
probably have a micro-chemical environment that induces
their differentiation, and in the chicken this environment
is known to reside in the bursa of Fabricius. In many
mammals its location is unknown, but we have evidence that
in the rabbit it resides in the ilial lymphoid tissue and
in the lymphoid tissue of the appendix. Differential responsiveness to antigens is extremely important, and what
Dr. Nossal said about the fact that it may be different in
different species argues in favor of thinking that some sort
of indirect influence, and not a direct influence, is important for antibody synthesis. This indirect influence
could be what we call a trephocytic function. I also was
very much intrigued with Dr. Mitchison's view that it might
have something to do with the way in which antigen is presented to the antibody-producing system.

I think it is extremely important in this context to
recognize that in humans there must be influences other than
those involving thymic cells. Patients who have third and

III. IMMUNOCOMPETENT CELL POPULATIONS

fourth pharingeal pulse syndromes, and lack both thymus and parathyroid glands, have now been studied immunologically and they have perfectly normal levels of all of the A, M, and G immunoglobulins. They respond normally with antibody production to a wide variety of antigens and have normal levels of isohemagglutinins. They may have some indirect thymic influence via their mother, but they have no direct thymic influence. I don't know anyone who has studied responses of these patients to sRBC, but this may be interesting.

DR. WEIGLE: Do they reject grafts?

DR. GOOD: They do reject allografts, and proper stimulation results in perfectly adequate development of delayed-type hypersensitivity.

What I am trying to say is that we should keep this discussion focused on indirect influences restricted to a few antigens. We know that there are separate lines of differentiation of lymphoid cells responsible for separate types of immunological processes.

CHAIRMAN GOWANS: I wonder if Dr. Good could tell us what he thinks the link is between the intestinally derived cells that mediate antibody formation and the bone-marrow. Do cells pass from the bone-marrow into the lymphoid tissue and do these intestinal lymphocytes of marrow origin later populate the remainder of the lymph nodes and the spleen, providing antigen-sensitive cells and precursors for antibody formation?

DR. GOOD: There is no question that in the case of the chicken, where we have defined the site of differentiation of the thymus-independent population, we can manipulate the system separately; for example, we have been able to remove the bursa of Fabricius in 15-day old embryos. When this is done, one can readily produce complete agammaglobulinemia. Such animals can't respond with antibody production even to repeated antigenic stimulation.

Chickens prepared at a later stage of their development by fetal irradiation and bursectomy are also agammaglobulinemic. They can be completely restored by bursal lymphocytes. Thus it is clear that in chickens, it is the bursa of Fabricius that controls differentiation of the thymus-independent

137

immunoglobulin and antibody-producing lymphoid cells. The corresponding site in man remains unknown. However, the evidence of Perez et al. is that the thymus-independent line of cells in the rabbit is the Peyers patch type of tissue.

Dr. Perez and colleagues have given fatal irradiation to rabbits which one month previously had had their thymus removed or had been subjected to removal of the ileal type of lymphoid tissue. We remove the appendix, the sacculus rotunda and each and every Peyers patch. We wait a month and then give fatal irradiation (1250r) and then fetal bone-marrow from a 19-20 day old rabbit fetus (rabbit fetal cells cannot respond to antigenic stimulation). The animals that had their thymus removed redevelop a population of cells from this stem cell source and are capable of exhibiting a primary response to Brucella antigens just as well as do intact animals following recovery from the same amount of irradiation. The animals that have had their ileal lympho-epithelial tissue removed develop absolutely no ability to make antibody to Brucella.

Many antigens are difficult to study in this model because one suspects prior natural exposure to these antigens. Our experiments with Brucella show clearly that differentiation of antibody-producing cells occurs in the gut, specifically in epithelial lymphoid tissue. They also show that absence of thymus does not interfere with the development of thymus-derived cells.

Since cells to be seeded are stem cells, one would not expect preferential seeding as far as sites are concerned. One would expect, however, that differentiation of the cells is site-specific. Cells from the marrow go to the thymus, bone-marrow, spleen and Peyers patch-type lymphoid tissues. At each of these sites they encounter a microchemical environment that directs their differentiation.

DR. BENACERRAF: Dr. Miller, as I understand your data and comments, there is nothing that militates against the concept of information transfer. You stated that you cannot think of an experiment that might prove it.

In your last experiment you transferred cells from the thoracic duct into a thymectomized irradiated animal. If, instead of taking thoracic duct cells from a normal animal, you were to take them from a hyperimmunized animal where

III. IMMUNOCOMPETENT CELL POPULATIONS

you have a lot of memory cells, you might find that the production was a bone-marrow response in the recipient with characteristics of a secondary response. Under these circumstances would you be convinced that this is information transfer?

DR. MILLER: Actually we are doing this very experiment, but the results are not yet available. If the results are positive, we will seriously have to entertain the possibility that information transfer does occur since in the secondary response the affinity of the antibody produced is so much better.

I would like to make another point here. Dr. Good questioned the validity of the distinction between thymus-derived and bone marrow-derived cells. We are all aware that bone marrow-derived stem cells can repopulate the entire hematopoetic and lymphoid system. Stem-cells that migrate to the thymus do, however, differentiate to a stage where they can no longer act as stem cells. Accordingly, I think that it is logical to speak of cells derived from the thymus as "thymus-derived" in contradistinction to those cells that have not migrated through the thymus which one can for convenience refer to as "bone marrow-derived."

We know that in the chicken both bursa lymphocytes and thymus lymphocytes are derived from the same stem cell pool; nobody would argue against the concept of a distinction between bursa-derived cells and thymus-derived cells.

CHAIRMAN GOWANS: I think Dr. Benacerraf's point is very interesting. If you took memory cells from an immune animal and injected them together with normal bone-marrow into an irradiated animal and obtained a good secondary response with antibody of bone-marrow type, this would be very difficult to explain on any grounds other than information transfer, because the selective pressures of antigen to create antibody of high affinity could not possibly have been impinging on the bone-marrow cells that came from a naive animal.

DR. UHR: I don't believe that there is any good evidence against a trephocytic function of thymus-derived lymphocytes. Dr. Miller argued against this mechanism because of the failure of tolerant cells to restore specific responsiveness

139

although they could restore responsiveness to other antigens. In this situation, however, specific interaction berween antigen injected into the recipient and antibody on donor cells may be necessary to release non-specific agents or nutrients that may then magnify the immune response.

CHAIRMAN GOWANS: I think that this theory was, in fact, implicit in the idea that blast transformation might carry over some factor favoring differentiation or division in the other cells. This would be your specific element; the interaction of the specific cells with antigen causing the release of something.

DR. UHR: The specific interaction may or may not be associated with blast transformation. For example, it could also be the interaction of antigen with serum antibody which then fixes complement, forming a biologically active complex.

DR. LESKOWITZ: A short question to Dr. Miller: we all have a laudable desire to generalize a concept of tolerance, but what I would like to know is, are the data that you presented on these cellular interactions applicable only to 19S antibody-producing cells or do these same situations apply in respect to 7S PFC?

DR. MILLER: I did mention that our data on 7S PFC were rather meager but that they pointed exactly the same way as our data for 19S PFC, namely, that the 7S PFC are not derived from the inoculated lymphoid cells but from either the host in neonatally-thymectomized mice or from the bone-marrow in the thymectomized, irradiated marrow-protected mice. This has been supported by the experiments of Dr. Warner in which he looked at the allotypic specificity of the γG 2A antibody produced. The specificity was always that of the host or of the bone-marrow donor.

DR. COHN: I think we are using "information transfer" in a rather casual way. You can transfer information, meaning you are transferring structural information. However, the experiments indicate that you are not transferring structural information since the allotype of the recipient of the bone-marrow is the one that is expressed. Now, the transfer of information, such as regulatory information, is trivial here because you may be dealing with hormones, etc.

III. IMMUNOCOMPETENT CELL POPULATIONS

DR. BENACERRAF: Dr. Cohn, you are right when you ask what we mean about information transfer, but in mice the allotype marker is on the constant portion, so there is nothing that says that you could not have information transfer concerning the variable portion.

DR. COHN: That is a very good point.

DR. BENACERRAF: And I would further answer Dr. Uhr, that in the experiment that I proposed, on the transfer of hyper-immune cells, if the results show that the antibody produced is of a high affinity and of the bone-marrow type, it would prove that there was indeed information transfer.

DR. CINADER: Dr. Miller has mentioned as one of the three possible modes of interaction that both the thymus-derived cells and the bone marrow-derived cells may carry receptors, both having different ranges of restriction, but both being able to respond to an antigen directly. If this were the case, we could explain differences in the responsiveness of different species of animals and different antigens. These differences would be due to variations in the different responsiveness of the same species to distribution of re-sponsiveness in the thymus- and marrow-derived cells.

I find this general picture the least romantic, but the most convincing of the envisioned mechanisms of interaction. It presupposes that both types of cells can generate anti-body and hence allotypic specificity.

In this context it is worth stating that one can, in fact, transfer allotypic specificity of the light chain of rabbit immunoglobulins by injecting into newborn animals the thymic or lymph node cells (Chou, Cinader, Dubiski, J. Exp. Med.).

DR. GOOD: A brief point on Dr. Cinader's very interesting observation. It is extremely important to recognize that within the thymus there are many kinds of cells. Those that are not fully differentiated may function as stem cells and be subject to further differentiation. Also, there are mature thymus-dependent cells. But the thymus is a compo-site organ including fully differentiated cells of the thymus-independent system. Now in the experiments in chick-ens, where you can get things focused in very clear

141

perspective, an irradiated bursectomized chicken does not possess plasma cells. Such a composite population of cells makes Dr. Cinader's experiments most difficult to interpret.

DR. CEPPELLINI: I wish to present some information on the functional behavior of the lymph node during a so-called "primary" response. The findings, representing work done in my laboratory together with Drs. Luzzati, Tosi, and Carbonera, are pertinent to the question introduced by Drs. Mitchison and Miller whether interaction between different cell types is required for antibody production.

Our experimental model corresponds to a limiting dilution analysis which is based on the Poisson probability distribution. In fact, our working hypothesis was that the draining lymph node during a primary antigenic stimulation might be regarded as consisting of a number of functional units that are able to initiate antibody production. These units could consist of a single cell or a number of interacting cells. In either case, they should have a discontinuous distribution in the geography of the lymph node and it would therefore be possible to isolate them from one another by dividing the lymph node into minute fragments. As lucidly discussed by Dr. Groves and co-workers (Nature, 1968, in press) while considering the theory of limiting dilution analysis applied to antibody synthesis, an all-or-none type of phenomenon should be operative (active or inactive fragments), while the strength of the antibody response produced by the individual active fragments could be independent of their frequency.

The experimental model used was the following: rabbits were injected with 1 μg of Salmonella enteritides LPS. The highly purified preparation, kindly supplied by Dr. Landy, was known to be strongly immunogenic and the dose of 1 μg employed by us was 3 to 4 orders of magnitude greater than the dose shown by Dr. Landy to evoke a maximal PFC response in the draining lymph node. On the 5th day post-immunization the lymph nodes were excised and cut into tiny fragments, each corresponding to 0.5 mg net weight (approximately 2×10^5 cells). Each fragment was individually incubated in 0.3 ml of NCTC 109 supplemented with 20% fetal calf serum, plus C_{14} phenylalanine and C_{14} lysine (2 μC/ml each). Incubation was carried out at $37^\circ C$ for 24 hours in an atmosphere of 95% O_2 and 5% CO_2. The individual supernatants were

142

assayed for specific antibody activity either by agglutination of sRBC coated with LPS or by counting radioactivity
fixed on intact Salmonella. The two methods gave excellent
correlation, thus proving that what was being measured was
indeed antibody synthesized <u>de novo</u>. The percentage of
fragments showing detectable antibody activity varied in the
individual experiments, but fragments that did not produce
any specific antibody were encountered rather often. Thus,
evidence was obtained for a discontinuous distribution of
the active areas. Immunoelectrophoresis and chromatography
on Sephedex G-200 of the individual supernatants (after
addition of normal rabbit serum as cold carrier) proved
that radioactive products corresponding to IgM prevailed,
some IgG was also present; no evidence of small molecules
corresponding to free chains was found. High voltage
electrophoresis in agar (Wieme method) of the individual
supernatants, followed by autoradiography of the dried
slides, allowed localization of radioactive products. Although pooled supernatants from cultures of many fragments
showed a diffuse radioactivity over the entire Ig region of
the electropherogram, individual supernatants showed consistently the patterns depicted in Fig. 30, i.e., sharp,
discrete bands of radioactivity, each one with its own peculiar mobility. The bands were interpreted as corresponding to discrete and relatively homogeneous populations of
antibody molecules. These bands disappeared upon absorption
of the supernatants with a suspension of intact <u>S. enteritides</u>
that removed all specific antibody activity. The Ig nature
of the bands was also proved by their disappearance when the
supernatant was treated with an excess of precipitating
anti-IgG and anti-IgM sera. Similar removal of the bands
was obtained with precipitating anti-allotype sera, specific
for the b allotype of the rabbit used (Fig. 31). In those
instances where the animal was heterozygous, each band was
shown to carry only one of the two allelic L chains. However, in the majority of fragments from Ab4/Ab5 heterozygotes
both Ab4 and Ab5 molecules were found and their relative
amounts approached the 6:4 ratio usually found in the serum.
The number of discrete bands that could be detected by
electrophoresis and autoradiography in individual active
supernatants varied from a few to an almost diffuse mobility
of the radioactive fractions. The mode was 4-5 bands per
supernatant and this was observed even in experiments where
the majority (up to 90%) of fragments were inactive.

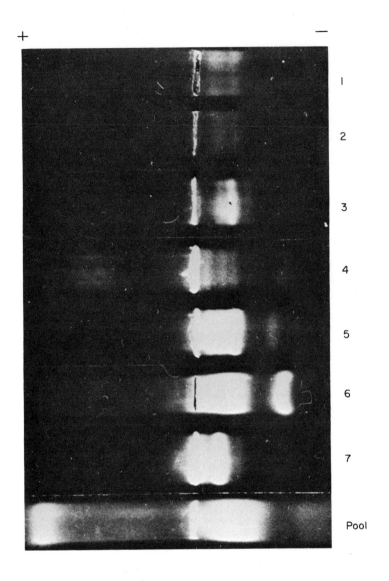

Fig. 30 Individual and pooled supernatants of cultures of
lymph node fragments analysed by autoradiography
following high-voltage electophoresis in agar

144

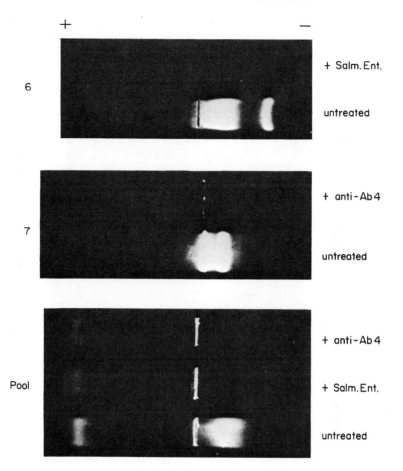

Fig. 31   Same as Fig. 30 except that supernatants were sub-
          jected to absorptions as indicated

According to the Poisson distribution, the few active
fragments (among a majority of inactive ones) should contain
one (or few) functional units. The antibody produced by
active fragments is still heterogeneous in regard to molecular structure (more than one band), but a significant restriction of variability is evident as compared with Ig of
the serum and even with the Ig secreted by the entire lymph
node itself (the diffuse radioactivity of "pool" in Fig. 30).

The residual variability has been shown to be due to differential activation of structural genes coding for the "constant" part of the Ig molecules (IgG and IgM, different L chains, allotypes), but it is likely that discrete banding is also produced by individuality of the "variable" (NH_2-terminal) part of the chains.

With reference to the issue originally posed, histological studies still in progress tend to exclude gross anatomical heterogeneity as the source of functional discontinuity. This is in harmony with the findings of Drs. Nakano and Braun who have previously shown an independent and non-random distribution of the antibody response in fragments of spleens derived from mice immunized with two different antigens.

Since a relatively high dose of LPS was used in our experiments the antigen may be assumed to have flooded the entire lymph node, hence antigen distribution is not likely to be a limiting factor. However, the possibility should be kept in mind that the non-responding areas may correspond to induction of local tolerance.

The simplest explanation for the functional heterogeneity of the lymph node would be that it contains a limited number of cells sensitive to a given antigen. These cells serve as originators of clones of antibody-producing cells. If each active area should indeed correspond to a clone derived from one progenitor cell, then the molecular heterogeneity of the antibody synthesized by individual fragments could only be explained by assuming that during the expansion of the clone, "differentiation" can still occur. This possibility has not been disproved directly. It encounters, however, many conceptual difficulties. Thus our data could be explained better by assuming that the discrete active areas correspond to complex functional units and that the limiting factor is represented not by the cells directly involved in clonal multiplication, but rather by a different and rarer type of cell(s), whose collaboration is necessary (although not sufficient) for initiating antibody responses.

The core of the active unit, on this hypothesis, should interact with and recruit a number of progenitor cells, each of which will give rise to a clone synthesizing a homogeneous population of Ig molecules, corresponding to a band. This would be in line with what has already been proposed and discussed at this symposium.

146

III. IMMUNOCOMPETENT CELL POPULATIONS

Since we are working with an open system, we cannot be entirely sure that the active fragments correspond to biologically meaningful units. However, the experimental conditions can be easily improved, for instance, by using cultures of dispersed cells, which would permit a better control over limiting dilution experiments. In any case, this or similar models which link together the anatomy of the organ, its function and the molecular structure of the specific product, are likely to produce important information.

DR. UHR: I want to ask Dr. Ceppellini whether this could be explained by a non-Poisson distribution of antigen in the lymphoid organ?

DR. CEPPELLINI: Of course. The next thing to do would be to repeat the experiment in irradiated animals and to use this technique with node fragments that are active in the Kennedy-type assay.

DR. BRAUN: The experiment about which Dr. Uhr inquires has been done, in a way. You may recall that 3 or 4 years ago, Dr. Nakano and I showed a non-random distribution of antibody-forming cells by analyzing fragments of spleens of immunized mice. More recently Dr. Nakano collaborated with Dr. Jaraslow at the Argonne laboratory and compared the distribution of the micropopulation of cells responding to a given antigen with the distribution of radioactively labeled antigen. There was no correlation between the distribution of the two.

DR. NOSSAL: This may be an appropriate place to mention that Dr. Marchalonis and I are now able to radio-iodinate antibody from a single cell active in a microdroplet. It seems to me the ultimate answer to Dr. Ceppellini's question may be obtained by doing a cloning experiment of the Kennedy type and then an analysis on the one or two hundred progeny that could be harvested from such a clone. One could iodinate all of the cell-products individually and perform Dr. Ceppellini's type of analysis.

The methodology for doing immunochemistry at the level of a single cell is not yet perfected. We still have considerable problems of denaturation, but I hope that further work will resolve this. I would like to emphasize that one can get quite good, heavy autoradiographs by iodinating single cells in microdroplets and I believe that this is one of the ways along which Dr. Ceppellini's methodology should move. We find that, in general, each normal antibody-forming cell produces as sharp an electrophoretic band as one obtains with a myeloma cell.

CHAIRMAN GOWANS: I wonder if we could turn the direction of the discussion back to the possible explanations for thymus and bone-marrow interactions. A number of people have expressed concern about what exactly is implied in this idea of antigen concentration and what the evidence is for it. I wonder if we could have this clarified. I know Dr. Rajewsky has an experiment that illuminates this point.

DR. RAJEWSKY: Our studies have been concerned for some time with the problem of two antigen-specific receptor sites being involved in the induction of antibodies, as has been coming into focus so clearly by what Drs. Mitchison and Miller have presented.

I will not go into any details regarding our published work on the immune response to the hybrid molecule of lactic dehydrogenase (J. Exp. Med. 126, 581, 1967; Cold Spring Harbor Symp. Quant. Bio. 32, 547, 1967). In short, two types of subunits are present in this enzyme molecule, only one of which was shown to possess carrier property; the other type of subunit had haptenic character and was unable to induce antibody formation by itself. The main argument for carrier-specific and hapten-specific receptor sites (probably some kind of immunoglobulins) being necessary for the induction of antibodies to the haptenic subunit was the finding that induction of tolerance to the carrier moiety of the enzyme resulted in a depression to the same extent of both anti-carrier and anti-hapten antibody production.

Together with Dr. Jerne we have recently done a further experiment using a conventional hapten-carrier system. The idea of the experiment was the following one: if two anti-gen-specific receptor sites are required for immune induction, one should be able to build them up independently of each other, and subsequently use them together for the induction of a secondary immune response. To speak in terms of an experiment: an animal is primed with hapten on carrier A plus carrier B, and then given a booster injection of hapten

148

on carrier B. The results presented in Fig. 32 show that a
strong secondary response is indeed obtained in this situation; the response equals that of the control animals
boosted with the hapten on its original carrier. In our
hands priming with carrier B could not be substituted by
passive infusion of either early or late anti-carrier B
antibody (or both) prior to secondary stimulation. The same
negative result had already been obtained in a similar experimental situation in the lactic dehydrogenase system.
Thus the initial antigen receptor could not be detected in
the population of circulating antibodies.

DR. MITCHISON: Dr. Rajewsky's experiment strongly suggests
that anti-carrier antibody and anti-hapten antibody are made
by separate populations of cells. But the point still requires formal proof. I have performed an experiment on the
adoptive secondary response designed to test this point.
Mice were primed by immunization with NIP-OA and their
spleen cells transferred to irradiated syngeneic recipients
which were then stimulated. Excellent stimulation, measured
by the yield of NIP-binding antibody, was obtained with NIP-
OA, but NIP on another carrier, NIP-BSA, proved far less
potent. If, however, spleen cells from other BSA-primed
mice were transferred along with the NIP-sensitive cells,
the potency of the NIP-BSA in eliciting NIP-binding antibody
increased 10- to 100-fold. Controls indicated that this
antibody was produced not by the BSA-sensitive cells, but
rather by cooperation of this cell population in the stimulation of the NIP-sensitive cells.

The BSA-primed cells also produced BSA-binding antibody
in this experiment. Their activity as cooperators and as
producers could, therefore, be compared by plotting the
yield of NIP-binding antibody against the yield of BSA-binding antibodies, in the manner of Dr. Rajewsky for anti-
carrier and anti-hapten antibody. Over part of the range
of antigen dose or cell number these two functions, cooperation and production, are proportional, provided that a
single population of BSA-primed cells is used. If, however,
comparisons are made between cell populations, certain interesting features emerge (these are preliminary results, subject particularly to the qualification that antibody has so
far been assayed only by a narrow-range binding test):   (1)
cells collected soon after immunization with BSA, in comparison with cells collected late, are disproportionally

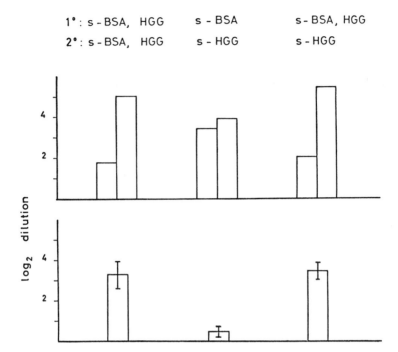

Fig. 32 Carrier specificity in the secondary response.
Groups of 7-8 rabbits were primed with sulfanilic
acid coupled to BSA (1 mg) and DNP coupled to BSA
(1mg) together with or without HGG (1 mg), in
Freund's complete adjuvant. Intravenous secondary
injections consisted of the haptens, coupled either
to BSA or HGG (1 mg of each hapten-protein preparation). Coupled HGGs were identical with native HGG
in double diffusion. For passive hemagglutination,
the haptens were directly coupled to sheep erythrocytes. The results for anti-sulfanilic acid antibodies are shown (the results for anti-DNP were
similar). Upper part: mean hemagglutination titres
before and 8 days after secondary stimulation.
Lower part: mean difference between primary and
secondary titers with standard errors.

good at cooperation in comparison to their activity in production; (2) cells collected from mice which had received in succession lethal irradiation, transfer of thymocytes, and BSA-immunization are disproportionally active in cooperation; (3) cells collected from ALS-treated donors are poor at cooperation; (4) elimination of cells active in production (by the allogeneic-transfer method of Dr. Davies and his colleagues--this experiment was performed in collaboration with Dr. Gershon, who was working with Dr. Davies at the time) did not prevent cooperation. These observations, which as I have said need to be treated with reserve, suggest that cooperation is mediated by the thymus-derived population.

DR. LESKOWITZ: I would like to make a comment about Dr. Rajewsky's data. When you prime an animal with a carrier in Freund's adjuvant, you presumably get delayed sensitivity to that carrier. We have done in the past a similar experiment in which we just reversed the system and produced delayed sensitivity to the hapten and then challenged the animals with the same hapten on a carrier that they had never encountered before. In this circumstance we got an enhanced response to the carrier.

Now, for explanation of this we relied on the proposition that had been advanced by Dr. Humphrey a number of years ago, that what was actually happening was that as a result of the delayed reaction we were getting an accumulation of phagocytic mononuclear cells around the site of the antigen, and that this was in some way capable of handling the antigen more efficiently. Whether this constitutes a real antigen trapping mechanism or is a rather trivial event, I really can't say.

DR. BRAUN: Dr. Mitchison, we have demonstrated that oligonucleotides can serve as non-specific stimulators of antibody responses. We have also demonstrated that these stimulators can be released in vitro and in vivo by an interaction between antigen and antibody-producing cells. My question is, if you prime an animal to a carrier and you introduce the carrier again--or when you reintroduce a hapten into a hapten-primed animal, you also release these non-specific stimulators. To what extent may these effects contribute to your results?

DR. MITCHISON: I can answer that very briefly by saying that there were adequate specificity controls and I am not going to go into them now.

DR. GELL: I would like to make two points. The first one is on the question of antigen trapping. It is known that antigen disappears from the site of a skin test reaction at exactly the same rate in a sensitized animal as in a normal animal; it does not seem to localize particularly well.

Another general point I want to make, is that delayed sensitivity is by no means always correlated with antibody production. It does not appear to be a normal predecessor of antibody production to a number of antigens. You can get, e.g., in the case of orthanilic acid hapten on guinea pig albumin in guinea pigs, good delayed sensitivity and no subsequent antibody production, regardless how hard you push the immunization. Therefore, I am inclined to think that delayed sensitivity may be a red herring when one considers the processes that must precede antibody formation.

CHAIRMAN GOWANS: I was wondering about the relation, if any, between the antigen trapping mechanism which is mediated by cells of thymic origin, presumably within lymph nodes where these collaborative events occur, and the possibility that the same system of cells mediates delayed hypersensitivity.

In the discussion on Drs. Rajewsky's and Mitchison's presentations the words "delayed hypersensitivity" were not mentioned. Dr. Gell has now told us that he is not too enamoured with the notion of delayed hypersensitivity as a mechanism of antigen concentration, becasue it is rather inefficient. That presumably alludes to the concentrating antigen in the test site where animals are challenged. Is that right?

DR. GELL: Yes.

CHAIRMAN GOWANS: Drs. Mitchison and Rajewsky are thinking in terms of antigen trapping by lymphoid cells within lymphoid tissue. I wonder whether each of you could tell us what in your own mind is the relationship between this antigen trapping mechanism and delayed hypersensitivity. Is Dr. Mitchison thinking about delayed hypersensitivity at all with his system, and does Dr. Gell regard antigen trapping in a skin site as being relevant to this issue.

DR. MITCHISON: I don't.

CHAIRMAN GOWANS: You don't think in terms of delayed hypersensitivity, but that does not mean it is not related.

DR. MITCHISON: Not at all.

DR. GELL: I think your point is a fair one, that it is the central trapping which is probably important. Still it is surprising that one can really detect no difference in the disappearance locally, although responsive cells, of course, are accumulating all during that period.

DR. BENACERRAF: I am inclined to agree with some of the things that Dr. Gell said and I disagree with some others. As far as delayed sensitivity is concerned I think he is right. We would be making a mistake if we equated it with the necessity for the first of two cell systems, because it is quite obvious that there are immune responses where there is no delayed sensitivity detectable.

DR. SILVERSTEIN: Since delayed sensitivity has once again been invoked, I feel called upon to make a comment. I don't think that at this point it's worth getting into the question of the relationship of delayed sensitivity to antibody formation per se, although I do think there is some intimate connection therein. But I do feel called upon to make the point that we have been concerned here primarily with antibody formation as the sole end product of antigenic stimulation. I don't think that I am wrong in suggesting that far fewer of the cells engaged in a response to antigenic stimulus end up in active immunoglobulin formation than undergo the proliferative events that we associate with the preliminaries to antibody formation, and with delayed hypersensitivity. I would suggest that perhaps one ought to consider delayed sensitivity in this sense as involving those cells that do not end up as producers of immunoglobulin. The reason I mention this is that one is straining, to a certain extent, to look for a role for "IgX" as a trapper of antigen, or as a concentrator of antigen to fit it into the scheme of eventual antibody formation.

153

I would suggest that the forces of evolution argue for just the opposite situation: that immunoglobulin X on the lymphoid cell is not the antigen trapper, but rather that (mediated by immunoglobulin X) it is the lymphoid cell trapper and concentrator, and indirectly the macrophage trapper. This is probably the more significant of the biological phenomena involved.

CHAIRMAN GOWANS: Very interesting.

Now Dr. Cinader has some comments about the way in which one should go about identifying IgX.

DR. CINADER: Obviously, it is rather difficult to prove the presence of IgX directly with antigen because of the tremendous heterogeneity of IgX. There are probably two ways in which one could get information which is based not on the combining effect of antigen, but so to speak, on the tail that wags the allotypic specificity present on immunoglobulins.

There are two lines of evidence, one obtained in studies with Dr. Gell and the other based on the observations made first by Dr. Dray, namely, that you can express allotypic specificity by injecting antigen into newborn rabbits at a stage when the animal is not capable of making antibody but can be made tolerant. This can also be shown to occur in mice injected with antibody to MUA2, which is on the heavy chain. Allotypic specificity was suppressed for about 105 days in such mice. Under these circumstances there is no effect of this on the suppression of other allotypic specificities on the heavy chain. There is no effect on the MUA 1 because the MUA 2 has been injected. The easiest way of thinking about suppression is to assume that it is due to an antibody-like receptor on the cell.

DR. HASEK: I would like to speak about the possible role of collaboration of IgX with lymphocytes in the efferent path of transplantation immunity, in considering a model in which the destruction of the graft is produced by passive transfer of serum isoantibodies. For the destruction of tolerated skin homografts in ducks we must transfer serum in amounts approaching 20% of body weight of the recipient. After such an intraperitoneal transfer, the skin graft is rejected and tolerance is abolished. The destructive reaction is complex; in some cases vasculo-necrotic reactions kill the graft

154

itself within 10 hours. But in most cases we observe, after transfer of sera, a dilatation of vessels and some small infiltration occurs within 6 hours. By 12 hours, there is an enormous lymphocytic infiltration into the graft and by 24 hours the graft is completely destroyed. Tolerance is abolished, because when the animal is again grafted 1, 4 or 8 weeks later the new graft is never accepted.

The question is what do the lymphocytes do in such a graft? When the recipient is X-irradiated or treated with ALS, no abolition of tolerance by serum occurs. This shows that lymphocytes cooperate with transferred antibodies and what is most important, they are lymphocytes from fully tolerant animals.

CHAIRMAN GOWANS: These experiments show that immune iso-antisera can destroy a graft in a tolerant animal as long as the lymphocytes in the tolerant animal are still here; if they are destroyed, the antiserum does not abolish tolerance. This is a very interesting observation. The antibody acts in concert with lymphocytes from tolerant animals. I wonder if this illuminates the concept of IgX in the other system.

DR. SCHWARTZ: I have a question for Dr. Mitchison: do you envision that antigen trapping by the hypothetical IgX is actually occurring within the body of the thymus, or is this occurring on thymic cells that have left this organ.

DR. MITCHISON: The latter.

DR. SCHWARTZ: So one would not expect to find physical evidence of antigen trapping in the thymus itself.

DR. MITCHISON: Correct.

DR. GELL: A comment regarding a point that Dr. Cinader raised about IgX, the hypothetical receptor. You remember the work that Dr. Sell and I did on the stimulation of the peripheral blood cells by anti-allotypic antibody; quantitatively we found you needed a great deal of antibody to produce blast formation optimally, something like 10^8 molecules of antibody to fire a cell into optimal proliferation. This may be a maximum figure for the number of the receptors,

as judged by antibody to them, and even if it is an over-
estimate by 1 or 2 orders of magnitude it is still very
large.

We do know, incidentally, by supernatant analysis that
about 80% of the antibody we add is removed by the cells.
If one tries to "count" the receptors on sensitized cells by
the amount of antigen you need to effect blast transformation optimally, I admit we are not on such strong ground,
because antigen may not be working so efficiently as antibody. We found that you needed something of the order of
100 μg for optimally producing blast transformation of the
lymph node cells of guinea pigs. Again, that works out to
the figure of something like 10^7-10^8 molecules per trans-
forming cell; about 10% or less of the cells transformed.

You really have to have an awful lot of both antibody in
the one system, and antigen in the other for blast formation.
Whether this represents a "count" of receptors or not, it
seems to me it is important to bear in mind the possibility
that actually the number of receptors which one has to think
of per cell may be of the order of millions! So, if a
relatively large number of receptors per cell have to be
attached to antigen for the cell to go into proliferation,
the cell could be "tolerized" simply by sub-threshold doses
of antigen, given over a period of time.

DR. WAKSMAN: I think we ought not to lose sight of the fact
that we may be talking about at least 3 different kinds of
cells, not 2. There was a question of a processing cell,
which might be comparable to or identical with a macrophage.
Then there was a lymphocytic cell, thymus-derived, which we
have been talking about as an antigen-concentrator, and then
a question of some unidentified cell, derived directly from
marrow but not by way of the thymus.

I would like to make a remark that has to do with delayed
sensitivity in relation to these. At the present time we
don't have concrete evidence to show whether a macrophage
type of processing cell participates in the primary immunization that is responsible for delayed hypersensitivity.
On the other hand, when we come to the elicitation of delayed reactions at a peripheral site, there is quite good
evidence to suggest that there may be a processing step.
Both Drs. Leskowitz and Schlossman have immunochemical

evidence in favor of this. Only antigens that are immunogenic have the property of being able to elicit a delayed
reaction. Dr. Mitchison said earlier that there are apparent exceptions to the macrophage processing step. He picked
at random, as one example, the direct cytotoxicity of
immunized lymphocytes on target cells in a transplant situation, where the lymphocytes had supposedly been purified.
There is nothing to suggest that processing of antigen had
to occur in order for this to be demonstrated. I submit
that this is not a convincing observation, since so-called
"pure" lymphocyte populations really are not very pure. It
has recently been recognized that monocytic cells, coming
from the bone-marrow may have the morphology of small lymphocytes and many of their properties; for example, they don't
stick to glass and can't really be purified by the common
techniques for separating macrophages from lymphocytes.
Therefore, so-called "pure lymphocyte populations" may include some processing cells. This comment also applied to
Drs. Bloom and Bennett's observation with the migration inhibition system; they supposedly have used pure lymphocytes,
allowing them to react with antigen and getting a response.
Indded, in the blast-transformation system it has recently
been shown that as you get macrophages out of your preparation, you reduce progressively the ability of the lymphocytic cells to give a specific response. It would certainly
be premature to set off delayed sensitivity as something
that does not involve any processing step, either in the
lymph node or the elicitation site.

This leads me to comment that there is one possible rather
straightforward interpretation of Dr. Hasek's strange observation that tolerance is broken when one puts isoantibody
into a tolerated graft and gets a lymphocytic infiltrate.
Perhaps this infiltrate is not lymphocytic but resembles a
delayed reaction, containing principally monocytic cells.
This then would constitute a local accumulation of processing cells with strong adjuvant activity. There are scattered
data in the literature which show that the site of a delayed
reaction is an adjuvant site for antibody formation to any
antigen that you put into that site. In this case, a small
number of non-tolerant lymphocytes may be stimulated to proliferate, resulting in termination of tolerance.

CHAIRMAN GOWANS: Should one not distinguish rather sharply
between the efferent and the afferent responses? The idea

that macrophages are involved in delayed sensitivity is strong now. However, I think that the arguments you made are not very compelling in regard to the idea that macrophages are essential to the inductive part of this response. For example, one can cite the experiments on GVH reactions in rats, where the suspect small lymphocyte populations were employed with very great efficienty (slaughtering 100 hybrid animals): these populations did not contain macrophage precursors by any of the tests that we performed. The evidence in mice suggests that under very special conditions there is something in the thoracic duct which, as Dr. Howard showed, can develop after an interval of 11 days or so into phagocytic cells.

There are no phagocytic cells in the rat thoracic duct lymph, nor have we obtained any evidence for the existence in it of macrophage precursors. That is not to say that cells of the morphology of small lymphocytes in blood may not be macrophage precursors. This is quite another matter because cells enter the blood from many sources.

DR. WAKSMAN: How do you rule out the possibility that the host himself may not provide the macrophages?

CHAIRMAN GOWANS: This is possible but this would also imply that the animal's own transplantation antigens are being processed all the time by its own macrophages. I agree that this cannot be formally excluded.

DR. GOOD. I think one of the things that is very difficult to deal with is the question that Dr. Mitchison has placed before us in regard to IgX. Unfortunately, we do not have an isolated IgX with which to work. I think knowledge on this point would be extremely helpful in working with the model that Dr. Hasek has introduced. The key element in Dr. Hasek's experiment was the very large amount of serum required to transfer adoptive homograft immunity. We have carried out some experiments that have helped us to look at these issues. We think these experiments are bringing IgX into focus. They will make it possible, we believe, to identify IgX so that this enigmatic protein can be studied in terms of its biological and chemical characteristics. The basic experiments were done by Scott Clark and John Foker at Minnesota. They took three dogs A, B, and C: a kidney from dog A was put into dog B for 3-4 days. After

the dog A kidney was removed from dog B, fatal irradiation
was given to dog B in order to reduce the number of circulating cells prior to the next step of the experiment. The
second kidney from dog A was then transplanted into dog B
and after a period of 4 to 12 hours that kidney was removed.
The kidney was biopsied and no lymphocytes, no granulocytes,
or cellular infiltrates could be demonstrated. The second
kidney was returned to dog A and it was subsequently rejected
by dog A within 4 to 12 hours just as though it were a het-
erograft. This rejection is specific and reveals sensitization of the second kidney. It was possible to take a
kidney from dog C, put it into dog B which is sensitized to
dog A, and one could do this at the same time as dog B prepares a kidney from dog A for rejection. Dog C will retain
this kidney, which has temporarily been resident in dog B,
and it will function normally in dog C. The sensitized kidney is functional at the time it is removed, but in dog A,
A's original kidney loses its function.

The rejection process involves platelets, granulocytes,
and also mononuclear cells. If the platelets and granulocytes are suppressed, as one can by certain procedures, the
lymphocyte involvement in the rejection process becomes
apparent.

There is then in the circulation of the immunized dog B
a specific antibody that is sensitizing homografts and
capable of inducing rejection of dog A's kidney. Drs. Perry
and Dupuy in my laboratory have applied this model to skin
graft rejection in inbred strains of mice and have shown
specific rejection with circulating antibody that they now
have in a test tube. The antibody appears to go specifically
on to the surface of indifferent lymphocytes which then can
transfer graft rejection. You can also transfer by the same
procedure delayed hypersensitivity to tuberculin. We thus
feel we have IgX in a discrete state and we shall now proceed to identify it.

DR. STERZL: My remark is directed to the issue that macrophages are obligatory for the induction of the immune response and to the statement that in transferring adoptive
immunity by a purified suspension of lymphocytes the function
of the host's macrophages is not excluded.

We used purified suspensions of thoracic duct lymphocytes
which were mixed with _Brucella_ _suis_ endotoxin, known to

adhere firmly to the surface of cells. After incubation, the lymphocytes were washed several times and transferred in diffusion chambers to recipients. This procedure excludes the release of antigen from the cells to the recipient and also prevents contact of host macrophages with transferred lymphocytes. On the 5th day after transfer, antibody-producing cells were detected in the chambers, which signifies that lymphocytes can change into antibody-forming cells by direct surface contact with antigen.

DR. NOSSAL: Mr. Chairman, the time is moving on and I have a burning desire to get a clarification of 3 issues identified by 3 short questions.

First of all, I would like you to talk about work going back 8 or 9 years that demonstrated circumstances under which thoracic duct lymphocytes alone can do quite a bit in adoptive immunity experimentation. I would like you to tell us whether you now believe that these populations in themselves are mixtures of thymus- and bone marrow-derived lymphocytes, or if they are predominantly thymus-derived; if so, what are your feelings about this whole cell-interaction work.

Burning question No. 2 is this: Dr. Mitchison has presented the idea that Dr. Weigle's work on breakdown of tolerance with cross-reacting antigens could be explained by means of some thymus-bone-marrow interaction mechanism. Does Weigle accept this as a reasonable explanation of his data?

My third question is directed to Dr. Humphrey. He, Dr. Benacerraf, and I represent the only hard core "antigen trappers" in this group; the people who in a simplistic way want to see evidence of antigen focusing, want to see little black grains that represent the antigen molecules on thymus-derived cells. I will go on record as saying that in 5 years or so of attempting to understand how antigen works by means of antigen fate experiments in vivo, I have never seen anything to suggest a thymus-derived "ferry" or "schlepper" carrying antigen around. I want to know whether Dr. Humphrey, who has done so much of this work, and perhaps Dr. Benacerraf, have at any time seen in autoradiographs of antigen in vivo anything that can substantiate Dr. Mitchison's idea of an antigen-focusing thymus-derived cell heavily labelled with antigen on its surface.

160

III. IMMUNOCOMPETENT CELL POPULATIONS

CHAIRMAN GOWANS: Taking the 3 burning questions in reverse order: have any of you seen with your own eyes labelled antigen trapped in areas where lymphocyte-lymphocyte inter- actions might be occurring?

DR. HUMPHREY: I propose to discuss later some aspects of antigen trapping. In the meantime, Dr. Nossal has wheedled out of me the necessity to talk about some experiments that I would prefer not to review, principally because they are so extremely difficult to interpret. These experiments are related to attempts seeking to establish whether lymphocytes from normal, or tolerant, or boosted animals, can under cir- cumstances where metabolic uptake is either not possible or unlikely, take up antigen that will withstand the necessary subsequent 6 or more washes before these cells can be sub- jected to autoradiography and subsequent scanning for anti- gen. I have started some experiments (in fact, I am on the fourth attempt to repeat them cleanly) in which we have used as antigen fully iodinated TGAL (about 2,000 $\mu C/\mu g$, one mole- cule yielding between 20 and 50 grains in the autoradiography according to length of time). We also used iodinated hemo- cyanin attaining even greater specific activity. All of this is fine conceptually. The difficulty is with what you actually see. The positive information is that it is very rare to find a cell in the thymus which takes up grains and looks like a hedgehog in autoradiography. I usually get tired of counting more than 6,000 cells under the high power microscope and a good many times I have not found more than one labelled cell; usually if I scan briefly, I can find no labelled cells at all. So I will say that the thymus does not seem to pick up antigen even when a primed animal is boosted.

A second positive statement is that in an animal that has recently been boosted one can find quite a lot of cells that pick up the antigen, but these are mostly macrophages. In other words, when you have cytophilic antibody around, as is likely in a boosted animal, you are likely to find macrophages that pick up antigen. I would like to add that in a primed animal there were also lymphocytes that pick up the label and in a normal animal there were more lymphocytes that pick up the label specifically than in a tolerant ani- mal. But whether there are cells that have receptors on their surface, I am quite unwilling to say at this stage. I think that various people who have been involved in this

161

agree that all of this represents an interesting phenomenon, but we are unwilling to say what it really means.

CHAIRMAN GOWANS: Is there any more direct evidence?

DR. BENACERRAF: I have some negative evidence, if you wish. There are 3 points regarding this. One, if you consider the cell by what it looks like rather than what it does, then you have excellent evidence that cells that look like lymphocytes may bind antigens.

If you are concerned with what the cell does, then it is indeed a considerable embarrassment that people who work on delayed sensitivity in animals without demonstrable antibody have found that cells from lymph nodes or from the blood do not form rosettes, i.e., could not be shown to bind antigen. There is no reliable way to detect the receptors on their surface, and in an experiment carried out long ago, when we immunized guinea pigs with ferritin, we could not find lymphocytes with ferritin grains but then we examined only about 100 cells.

The other point that is embarrassing when one deals with delayed sensitive cells, which must have specific receptors, is made by referring to experiments in which Dr. Kantor tried to desensitize such cells in vitro with specific antigen. Desensitization could not be achieved unless the antigen was of such type that it stuck non-specifically to the cells. Apparently, unless the antigen was bound non-specifically, there were not enough receptors on the surface of the cell, after exposure of 1 hour in vitro, to bind the antigen to these cells.

DR. WAKSMAN: This is to modify or at least to add something to Dr. Benacerraf's last point. Here again we are both quoting somebody else's work. I am referring to Dr. Kantor's studies and the matter of desensitization of sensitized lymphocytes. He could only achieve desensitization with an aggregated material. Your interpretation is that this is something that will stick to cells and that is it. But it could also be interpreted as being something that is readily taken up by processing cells.

CHAIRMAN GOWANS: Shall we move on to burning question number two? Dr. Weigle, I wonder if you would like to be provoked to tell us about the tolerance and cross-reacting antigens?

DR. WEIGLE: I would like to comment on Dr. Nossal's query about the possible role of thymus-derived cells in the termination of tolerance by cross-reacting antigens. I believe that competent cells derived from the thymus are probably responsible for the spontaneous termination of tolerance. But I very much doubt that such cells are involved in the termination of tolerance by the cross-reacting antigens in any other manner than if they were involved in an ordinary antibody response. Following the termination of tolerance to BSA in rabbits by injecting HSA, the rabbits will respond for a limited period of time to the previously tolerated antigen (BSA). However, the injections of BSA do not result in a further breakdown of tolerance. All the antibody that is made following the injections of BSA is specific for the determinants on the terminating antigen (HSA).

DR. HUMPHREY: A question to Dr. Weigle: When you terminate tolerance by means of cross-reacting antigens and you simultaneously administer small amounts of non cross-reacting antigen, could the result be explicable on the notion that you needed cell-cell cooperation, and that the use of the tolerated antigen might prevent a concentrating mechanism? In the absence of any further injections of either the tolerated or the cross-reacting antigen, the animals will return to an unresponsive state. I would not expect a return to the unresponsive state if the termination resulted from newly derived cells.

DR. WEIGLE: I believe the inhibition of the termination of tolerance in this manner has a great deal of biological significance. We talked about this earlier when it was suggested that such inhibition may be a general phenomenon used by the body to present massive autoimmune diseases.

DR. HUMPHREY: I agree.

DR. MITCHISON: If one searches for a type of termination of tolerance where this mechanism is most likely to be detectable, I would not choose termination of tolerance of one protein by immunization with another protein or with the

163

same protein to which hapten had been added. I would rather examine situations in which you have tolerance to one hapten on a carrier, and then you immunize with the same hapten on a second carrier, so that you see termination of tolerance to the hapten. The response to the hapten should develop with the time kinetics that could be predicted by the mechanism that we have been discussing.

CHAIRMAN GOWANS: If we have two cell lines which are collaborating and one of them is concentrating antigen by virtue of antibody sites on its surface, and the other is an antigen-sensitive cell giving rise eventually to antibody-forming cells, then we have specificity residing in two cell lines, one thymus-derived and the other marrow-derived. The problem then is to bring these two specific cell lines together. Does this necessity for the two cells to find one another raise problems? It seems an inefficient mechanism if it rests only on chance contacts.

Is one forced to make any additional assumptions about the thymus cells: that they have, for example, a much wider range of specificities than the marrow cells, in order to increase the chances of an appropriate coupling? Do you have any thoughts about this?

DR. MITCHISON: That is two questions, isn't it? One, how the cells meet and the other is their ranges of specificity. For the question of how they meet, a great deal hinges on whether IgX is, as Dr. Good suggests, diffusible: the problem disappears if that is so.

DR. GOOD: Diffusible only in the absence of lymphocytes.

DR. MITCHISON: But if the material is diffusible, getting across from one lymphocyte to another could occur without contact. Unfortunately, I am not convinced by the claim when I see the data: other people have made the same sort of claims and it has not stood up. On the question of the range of specificities, I believe there is only one G.O.D. (generator of diversity).

DR. ARGYRIS: I would like to bring the discussion back to the possible interaction between thymus and bone-marrow, specifically between tolerant thymus and non-tolerant bone-marrow. The experiments I am now referring to are quite

164

similar to the ones described by Dr. Mitchison as carried
out by Dr. Roger Taylor and also reported by Dr. Waksman
and collaborators with protein antigens. We have induced
specific homograft tolerance in C3H mice with the neonatal
injection of CBA strain spleen cells and used these adult
tolerant mice, as donors for "tolerant" bone-marrow cells
and "tolerant" thymus grafts. In our control series we
thymectomized and X-irradiated adult C3H, and transferred
"tolerant" thymus grafts subcutaneously and "tolerant"
bone-marrow cells intravenously. We were able to find a
specific homograft tolerance to CBA skin grafts in these
irradiated recipients. We, as well as others, have referred
to this as "adoptive" tolerance. In our experimental series
we transferred "tolerant" thymus grafts with non-tolerant
C3H strain bone-marrow cells to irradiated adult thymectomized mice and were able to transfer specific homograft
tolerance to CBA skin grafts, in other words, obtain "adoptive" tolerance.

There are two possible interpretations of these results.
The "tolerant" thymus cells may be imposing a "tolerant"
message on the non-tolerant C3H bone-marrow cells as was
suggested by Dr. Mitchison. On the other hand, it is possible, since we know that the transplanted "tolerant" thymus
grafts do contain a small number of the original donor CBA
strain cells, that we are dealing with the induction of
immunological tolerance in an adult population of non-
tolerant C3H bone-marrow cells, with the small amount of
CBA transplantation antigens which are contained in the
"tolerant" thymus graft.

CHAIRMAN GOWANS: It may now be appropriate to describe
briefly the experiments we have been doing over the past
few years on the ability of thoracic duct lymphocytes to
restore or transfer immunological responsiveness in irradiated rats. I would like to play off these experiments
against those of Dr. Miller and cite them as a contribution
to the debate as to whether antibody formation always involves a bone-marrow-thymus interaction.

We have performed two sorts of experiments employing
heavily irradiated rats as recipients of thoracic duct
lymphocytes. In the first, we have shown that small lymphocytes from the thoracic duct of normal (non-immunized) rats
will restore to lethally irradiated rats the ability to

respond to an injection of sRBC, as assayed either by serum
hemolysin titers or by the number of PFC in the spleen.
Inocula of about 2.4×10^8 lymphocytes restore a response in
irradiated recipients which is normal in magnitude and tempo
with the single exception that the peak of the response is
reached 24-36 hours after that of the normal animal. We
are confident that it is the small and not the large lymphocytes in lymph that are responsible for the restoration;
and we feel that the small lymphocytes provide the antigen-
sensitive cells because lymphocytes from specifically tolerant animals will not restore responsiveness (McGregor, D.D.,
McCullagh, P.J. and Gowans, J.L., 1967, Proc. Roy. Soc. B.
168, 229) (Ellis, S.T., Gowans, J.L. and Howard, J.C., 1967,
Cold Spring Harb. Symp. Quant. Biol., 32, 395). The question
remains, are the antibody-forming cells derived from the injected lymphocytes? The ability of lymphocytes to restore
antibody formation in lethally irradiated rats makes the
possibility of host cell collaboration extremely unlikely.
Jonathan Howard in our laboratory has now shown formally
that the PFC in the restored rats are indeed formed from the
injected small lymphocytes (Ellis, S.T., Gowans, J.L., and
Howard, J.C., 1968, Antibiotica Chemother., 15, in press).
He restored the response of lethally irradiated, parental
strain rats with an intravenous injection of F_1 hybrid
lymphocytes and showed that the PFC that developed in the
spleens of the recipients were virtually all destroyed during
incubation for one hour with an isoantiserum directed against
the donor. These tests with isoantiserum are not entirely
satisfactory since we found, as did Dr. Miller, that a size-
able proportion of the PFC were destroyed by incubation even
in normal serum; in our experiments up to 40% of PFC might
be lost in this way, in Dr. Miller's up to 25%. I do not
think that this vitiates the experiments and I am confident
that the PFC in our studies were donor in origin, but I mention this technical matter simply to point out that neither
of us is able to determined the origin of all the PFC.

The second experiment concerns the transfer of immunological memory by small lymphocytes. Dr. Uhr and I showed
that small lymphocytes from rats immunized with bacteriophage ØX 174 conferred on irradiated rats the ability to
respond in a secondary manner to a first dose of antigen
(Gowans, J.L. and Uhr, J.W., 1966, J. Exp. Med., 124, 1017);
but we did not determine the origin of the antibody-forming
cells. Susan Ellis and I have shown that a similar transfer

of responsiveness can be achieved in the case of tetanus
toxoid in rats (Ellis, S.T., Gowans, J.L. and Howard, J.C.,
1967, Cold Spring Harb. Symp. Quant. Bio., 32, 395). An
inoculum of about 2×10^8 small lymphocytes from rats immunized with a single intraperitoneal dose of alum-precipitated
toxoid will enable lethally irradiated recipients to respond
in a secondary manner to a challenge with 20 Lf of fluid
toxoid. As in the ØX system, no antibody appears in the recipients unless they are challenged. In other words, the
lymphocytes are not making antibody at the time of transfer,
and antibody only appears if the recipients are challenged.
On the basis of manoeuvres similar to those employed in the
experiments with ØX we are confident that the transfer of
responsiveness can be attributed to the small lymphocytes
in the donor inoculum.

We have since shown that equally good responses can be
obtained in irradiated recipients if the lymphocytes from
the immune donors are simply incubated with antigen in vitro,
washed 5 times and then injected intravenously (Ellis, S.T.,
Gowans, J.L. and Howard, J.C., 1968, Antibiotica Chemother.,
15, in press). Incubation for 1 hour at 37°C with fluid
toxoid at a concentration of 0.02 Lf/ml yields responses in
irradiated recipients which can rival those in normal immune
animals challenged with antigen in vivo. Although it is
quite likely that minute traces of antigen are carried over
into the host, despite the thorough washing of the cells, we
feel that this experiment suggests that macrophages are not
essential for the inductive stages of this secondary response.

We have followed the evolution of the response in the
irradiated recipients by means of immunofluorescence. By
5 days after cell transfer, large numbers of specifically
fluorescent cells have appeared in the splenic red pulp and
by means of the scheme outlined in Fig. 33 we have been able
to show that the antibody-forming cells are derived from the
injected small lymphocytes (Ellis, S.T., Gowans, J.L. and
Howard, J.C., 1968, Antibiotica Chemother. 15, in press).
Spleens from the lethally irradiated recipients were teased
into a cell suspension which was incubated for 1 hour at
37°C with either normal serum or with an isoantiserum directed against the donor. After incubation the cells were
smeared and examined by immunofluorescence. The fluorescent
cells that had been incubated in normal serum possessed a
sharp cell outline and a uniform fluorescence while those

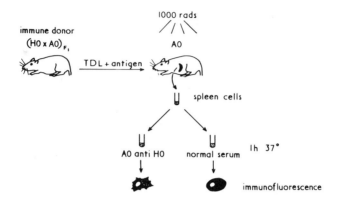

	% all cells surviving		% intact fluorescent +ve cells	
	i	ii	i	ii
AO anti HO	27	15	0	0·5
normal serum	91	94	99	92

Fig. 33   Antibody-forming cells from small lymphocytes.
Outline of experiment discussed in text. The lower
part shows the results of assays on spleen cells,
indicating their origin.

incubated in the antidonor serum were all severely damaged.
The damaged cells showed all stages from an irregular, hazy
cell outline with a granular fluorescence to fluorescent
cell fragments of various sizes.   Figure 33 records an analysis of two 5-day spleens in which virtually all the fluorescent cells are damaged by the antidonor serum.   The percentage of all cells surviving after incubation with serum
as determined by means of trypan blue exclusion is given in
Fig. 33.   It can be seen that the spleen cells survived
well in normal serum but that at least three-quarters of
them were destroyed by the antidonor serum; not all of them
were destroyed since, naturally, some host cells survived
the irradiation.

III. IMMUNOCOMPETENT CELL POPULATIONS

So in this secondary response we are certain that the antibody-forming cells were derived from the injected small lymphocytes and it seems likely that the small lymphocytes were also providing the antigen-sensitive cells because of the ease with which they could be stimulated in vitro with antigen. These conclusions are thus identical to those arrived at from the experiments with sRBC in rats.

Had it not been for Dr. Miller's experiments I would have assumed that a single variety of small lymphocyte was involved in each of our experiments, and that in each the antigen-sensitive cell and the precursor of the antibody-forming cells were one and the same. Now we must consider the possibility that our results are to be explained by a collaboration between two cell lines. We have not examined this possibility, but if there is such collaboration in our experiments then it is between two sorts of cells, both of which look like small lymphocytes and are present in thoracic duct lymph. My own view is that the antigen-sensitive cell is also the precursor of the antibody-forming cells and that if collaboration occurs then the second cell line exerts its influence by means not involving the transfer of the specific information for synthesizing antibody. We have already discussed possible mechanisms of collaboration. A final point, with which I know Dr. Miller agrees, is that antibody formation may not always depend upon the interaction of cells of marrow and thymus origin. It appears to do so in the response of mice to sRBC, but as we heard earlier, not in the response of mice to flagellin. Clearly, we cannot generalize at the moment.

IV

ANTIGEN HANDLING BY MACROPHAGES

Distribution of antigen in tissues and cells — The macrophage as a morphologic unit and as a functional unit — Heterogeneity of macrophage populations — Biochemical aspects of antigen "processing" by macrophages — The RNA-antigen complex derived from macrophages and its possible function — Non-responsiveness as a consequence of by-passing of intial antigen-handling cells — Precocious induction of antibody formation in newborn animals — Conversion of specific into non-specific responses — Multiplicity of antigen-dependent reactions in antibody formation — Antibody formation by "macrophage"-like cells — Lack of significant information transfer from macrophages to lymphocytes — Carrier function and "adjuvanticity" — Effects of adjuvants — Recognition of specificity by macrophages.

DR. HUMPHREY: I want to make clear that in much of what I have to say I shall be speaking about work done by others in our group, Drs. Askonas, Unanue, Balfour, and Mr. Kelly, and by colleagues who are not in the group at all, Drs. Parrott and Allison.

I propose to discuss factors concerned with immunogenicity rather than tolerance. My justification for this is that I entirely accept Dr. Mitchison's thesis that the main factor that determines whether or not administration of an antigen results in tolerance is whether or not it avoids concomitant immunization. I think that we now want to consider what happens when antigen is injected into animals and should not regard in vitro systems as necessarily representing what will happen in vivo.

Let me make some general points. First, in practice we are concerned with a variety of different immunogens injected by a variety of different routes. The immunogens range from whole cells, through complex proteins, to relatively simple hapten-carrier conjugates. After administration to the intact animal some remain in the circulation for relatively long periods, but most of those mentioned thus far disappear from the circulation quite rapidly.

A second point is that there is good evidence that the antibody response to a complex antigen can involve its tertiary or even its quaternary structure. This means that if the interaction occurs between receptors on immunologically competent cells and the immunogen, then that interaction must be taking place at a surface; relevant interactions could not take place after extensive intracellular digestion of the antigen.

A third general point is that we are dealing with large populations of cells despite the fact that interactions of the antigen with the competent cell, resulting in stimulating that cell to make antibody, or to divide, or to paralyze it, are very rapid events. When one is concerned with antigens that disappear rather rapidly from the circulation, we have to be able to explain how the whole population of cells can be affected by these antigens. As Dr. Nossal pointed out

173

earlier, although some antigens certainly persist for a long time in the body fluids, any valid generalization must be able to account for the behavior of those which do not so persist.

Anyone who looks at lymphoid tissues is, I think, bound to be struck by the obvious anatomical separation into distinct compartments; if he follows the fate of labelled antigens he will also be impressed by the very uneven distribution of the antigens within those compartments. I do not propose to review the studies on the distribution and fate of antigens made by Nossal and Ada et al., by Benacerraf et al., and by our own group, but I do want to underline some of the findings which are common to all of them.

After injection of a labelled antigen, whether of a kind that disappears rapidly or slowly from the circulation, it will reach the various tissues in a different manner according to the route by which it has been injected. Most antigens which reach lymph nodes arrive mainly by the afferent lymphatics, because they were injected subcutaneously. They enter along the afferent lymphatics into the marginal sinus and travel into the medulla via interlobular lymphatics and to a very small extent, either by minute channels or by percolation between cells, across the intermediate zone. When antigens reach the spleen they invariably arrive via the blood stream. This is quite an important consideration in determining their distribution there, since the arterial blood supply corresponds not only to the blood supply of a lymph node but also to its afferent lymphatics, and the venous blood serves the function of efferent lymphatics. Labelled antigens are first rapidly taken up by macrophages which line the marginal sinus and in the medullary sinuses of the lymph node; relatively little is seen to be concentrated, and virtually none persists in the intermediate zone; that is, the thymus-dependent area where multiplication of thymus-dependent lymphocytes is observed during stimulation of cell-mediated specific immunity.

In the spleen, again, the antigens are first taken up rapidly by macrophages in the red pulp and then rather later they appear in the marginal zone at the periphery of the white pulp, which may correspond to the marginal sinus of lymph nodes. Somewhat later, both in lymph nodes and spleen, antigens appear to be concentrated in germinal centers of primary follicles, more specifically on the dendritic macrophages with which you are all familiar. The speed and extent to which they are concentrated on the dendritic macro-phages, as Dr. Nossal has said earlier, appears to depend upon the presence either of natural opsonins or of specifi-cally stimulated antibodies, which were already present be-forehand or were made during the course of the immune re-sponse. There is good evidence that antigens are actually held at this site by combination with antibody.

Labelled antigens, as judged by the persistence of the label, rapidly disappear from the macrophages in the medul-lary areas; whereas, they persist for a very long time in or on the dendritic reticular cells in the germinal centers, though even from there they disappear gradually. It seems that the antigen-antibody complexes are attached in some peculiarly firm manner at these latter sites. When I state that antigens rapidly disappear from the medullary areas, this represents the state of affairs as judged by super-ficial inspection of autoradiographs. More careful inspec-tion under high power shows that significant amounts of labelled material remain in the medullary macrophages for quite a long time. Nevertheless, by comparison with the initial uptake, it seems that the great bulk of digestable antigens is rapidly broken down. Only if they are of a type that is not digestible, such as D-amino acid polypep-tides, do they remain in medullary macrophages in undimin-ished amounts for a very long time.

Except insofar as retention in the germinal centers is concerned, this description of what happens to labelled anti-gens applies whether or not an immune response is elicited. Uptake by the sinus-lining macrophages does not appear to depend upon preexisting antibody, although the speed and extent of uptake may be much increased in its presence.

When there is an accompanying immune response, changes occur with which many of you are familiar. One is develop-ment and enlargement of germinal centers, both in lymph nodes and spleen. This occurs rapidly, but it does not necessarily precede the formation of antibody or the ap-pearance of antibody-forming cells in the medulla, nor is there an absolute correlation between the enlargement of germinal centers and the production of antibody-forming cells in a primary response.

A separate series of changes follows an immunogenic stim-ulus which elicits a specific cell-mediated immunity, namely, extensive differentiation of lymphocytes and proliferation

175

of blast cells in the thymus-dependent areas; the products of these changes are an increased population of specifically reactive lymphocytes. It is by no means clear at present where anatomically the specific stimulation occurs. As I have already mentioned, the "thymus-dependent" areas are notably lacking in concentrations of antigen.

Following many immunogenic stimuli both types of change occur. However, the actual antibody-forming cells in a primary response, in my own, and I think in most other people's experience, always appear in the medulla of lymph nodes. In a late secondary or a tertiary response they can also appear in the germinal centers; this is not the general rule. In the spleen, antibody-containing plasma cells appear first in the medulla, at the margin with the white pulp. In chickens they appear remarkably soon, within 36 to 48 hours of a single first intravenous injection of an antigen such as diptheria toxoid or HSA. There is a rapid proliferation of antibody-forming cells in the medulla, which gradually dies away and only later do such cells make their appearance in germinal centers.

This brings us back to the three questions: what is the origin of the cells which interact with the antigen; where does the effective interaction take place; and how did the cells get there? I do not propose to go deeply into these since my main purpose is to start the discussion in this section of the program.

Dr. Gowans and his colleagues demonstrated very clearly the circulation of small lymphocytes (most of which appear to be of the thymus-dependent kind) from the blood through the post-capillary venules into the intermediate zone of lymph nodes, whence presumably they enter the medulla, and leave via the efferent lymphatics to join the main lymph trunks, or could possibly reenter the blood in the medullary sinuses. In the spleen similar lymphocytes arrive via the arterial blood and travel along to ancillary arteries to enter the periarteriolar sheath of the white pulp, whence they eventually return to the venous blood stream.

This circulation is reasonably clear and well demonstrated. It is not at all so clear what happens in the germinal centers. In the course of experiments carried out with Drs. Balfour and Parrott involving intravenous administration to isogenic mice of lymphocytes labelled with H_3-thymidine, they found singularly little evidence of entry of the

labelled lymphocytes from the blood stream into germinal
centers of the lymph nodes. Although occasional cells pene-
trated, there was certainly not the striking traffic that
Gowans could show from the post-capillary venules into the
intermediate zone. I understand that Dr. Nossal's colleague,
Dr. Austin, has evidence that lymphocytes may enter from the
blood stream into primary follicles, though not into germinal
centers, but that even there the traffic is not impressive.
Whence then do cells reach germinal centers, and how do they
leave?

A chance observation made by Drs. Parrott and Balfour suggested that the principle route of entry of lymphocytes into
germinal centers of lymph nodes is not via the blood stream
but by the afferent lymphatics. This is being checked at
Mill Hill by Mr. Kelly, who has been canulating the afferent
lymphatic duct of rabbit nodes, collecting the cells in the
lymph, labelling them in vitro, and reinfusing them via the
same afferent lymphatic. Preliminary results indicate that
quite a proportion of the cells find their way into the
mantle zone around the germinal center, although most go
to the intermediate zone and to the medulla. If these findings are confirmed we shall know one possible route of entry
of lymphocytes into germinal centers.

What happens to the cells that get there? All that is
known for certain is that rapid cell division occurs, and
it is presumed from the presence of "tingible bodies" in
macrophages that an undefined proportion of the cells die
there. It is tempting to suppose that some of the newly-
formed cells migrate to the medulla and turn into immuno-
globulin-synthesizing mature plasma cells. There is no direct evidence that this happens, but it is not difficult
to discover histological sections which seem to show a continuous procession of cells from the germinal center where
they do not contain immunoglobulin to the medulla where they
do. The static picture seen by the histologist can certainly
not be taken as indicating the true dynamic flow of cells,
and more convincing evidence is needed before its reality
can be accepted.

I have discussed this aspect because Drs. Nossal and Ada
and others have suggested that the immunological function
of the antigen trapped for long periods of time on the dendritic cells in the germinal center may be to interact with
virgin "X" cells and turn them into "Y" cells or even "Z"

cells or to interact with "memory" (Y) cells and turn them into proliferating cells or under certain circumstances to make "X" cells tolerant. It is difficult to evaluate any of these suggestions without knowing more about the traffic of cells through the germinal centers. I feel fairly confident, as Dr. Nossal said earlier, that the primary stimulation of immunologically competent cells does not necessarily occur in or require the participation of germinal centers. The hypothesis that such centers may be sites for continued production or stimulation of memory cells is quite tenable, though unproven on existing evidence.

There is general agreement that the first cells that can be shown to make antibody are found in the medulla, among the medullary macrophages, and that it is in the latter that antigens seem to be concentrated. As I have already remarked, antigens are not found to be concentrated in the "thymus-dependent" intermediate zone. In the days before interactions between thymus-dependent and bone marrow-derived, thymus-independent cells were recognized as important, various workers, including our own group, have considered that antigen held in the macrophages might well be the stimulus which "turned on" immunologically competent cells without prejudice as to the origin of the latter.

Naturally, a great stimulus for this came from the challenging experiments of Drs. Fishman and Adler. Dr. Askonas and her colleagues using mouse peritoneal macrophages and spider crab hemocyanin could show that a fraction of the hemocyanin that had been taken up by the macrophages was retained undigested for several days and probably longer, and that this material was markedly more immunogenic than the native hemocyanin. They also showed that a phenol extract of macrophages that had ingested hemocyanin contained a small amount of apparently undegraded hemocyanin, which seemed to be complexed with RNA, and that this material was more immunogenic than the original hemocyanin. They are, however, very cautious about attributing any necessary biological significance to this material which may be no more than an interesting artifact of the extraction procedure. Nevertheless, the fact remains that for many antigens uptake and some sort of processing by the macrophages seems to be an important step in making them immunogenic. This could, of course, as Dr. Mitchison pointed out, be partly accounted for if antigen in macrophages avoids immunological paralysis, but it probably is not the whole explanation. Saying more

178

about this, it should be made clear that most experiments with antigen in macrophages have been made for experimental convenience with peritoneal macrophages rather than the sinus-lining macrophages of lymph nodes or spleen. It is an assumption that they behave in the same way. Dr. Howard has produced good evidence that at least the Kupffer cells and lung macrophages have a common origin from monocytes which circulate via the blood stream. Drs. Volkman and Gowans showed that these, in turn, arise from the bone-marrow and can also become macrophages in the peritoneal cavity so there is a fair probability that the origin of all the macrophages is the same, even though they end up in different situations. This provides some justification for extrapolating from peritoneal to other macrophages.

It is important to point out that the requirements for a macrophage pathway certainly does not apply with equal force to all immunogens. A striking example is provided by the studies of Drs. Unanue and Askonas on keyhole limpet hemocyanin (KLH), which in its native form is a good immunogen, and elicits a good primary (mainly 19S) response in mice. If equivalent amounts of KLH are injected after ingestion by macrophages the immunogenicity is found to be strikingly decreased. Macrophage-associated KLH no longer produces a good primary 19S antibody response, although it still primes quite well for a secondary response. In this respect it now behaves like the much smaller spider crab hemocyanin which I mentioned earlier. The probability is that KLH can interact with immunologically competent cells directly (and rather effectively) to stimulate a primary response, as well as via macrophages to stimulate a much less effective primary response, but to prime quite well for a subsequent secondary response.

What is special when the antigen is in macrophages? I do not propose to recapitulate the evidence provided by various groups, showing that many soluble antigens in macrophages prime better than the native antigens, nor to review the evidence that after uptake by macrophages of, say BSA or hemocyanin, ninety percent or more of what is taken up is rapidly degraded. However, it is worth emphasizing that a small fraction persists undegraded for a relatively long time (of the order of at least one week and probably more) and that the presence of this material is correlated with the enhanced immunogenicity of antigens in macrophages. Dr. Unanue has evidence that at least part of this retained antigen is on the surface of the macrophage and is accessible to antibody and susceptible to digestion by trypsin. Thus, it would appear that macrophages can retain antigen at or near their surface in a configuration which resembles that of the original molecule, and presumably capable of interaction with a specifically competent cell.

It could be that this is all that macrophages do, though I suspect that some of you present hold the view that they do, in fact, process or alter antigens in such a way that they acquire new properties beyond what is implied by retention in a situation peculiarly accessible to lymphocytes, which is all that Drs. Askonas and Unanue could claim to have demonstrated. There are indeed some other findings which suggest that macrophages do more than this, and could be used to support the suggestion already mentioned in this symposium, that macrophages activated by the ingestion of certain materials can release some factor which influences lymphocytes in their vicinity to be stimulated rather than paralyzed by the antigen. These relate to the effect of adjuvants. One of the remarkable things about some adjuvants, as Drs. Dresser and Allison have shown using vitamin A, beryllium or B. pertussis, is that their adjuvant action is of surprisingly short duration, a few hours only. For example, if one examined the ability of 1 µg of spider crab hemocyanin to prime mice for a secondary response, simultaneous administration of 3 ug of beryllium sulphate i.p. increases the subsequent secondary antibody response (without beryllium) some 40-fold above control levels. If the beryllium is given one day before or after the priming dose of hemocyanin the increase is 10-fold, whereas there is no adjuvant effect when the interval is plus or minus 3 days. Thus, the period during which beryllium sulfate acts is quite short compared with the total period in which it is retained in the body. Similar, but even shorter time optima and an even more impressive adjuvant effect can be found using vitamin A or B. pertussis (Unanue, Askonas and Allison, 1968, to be published).

Drs. Unanue, Askonas and Allison have done experiments which I shall not discuss at length, indicating that the effect of the adjuvants is on macrophages rather than on lymphocytes, and that macrophages which have recently ingested adjuvant can enhance the immune response to hemocyanin even when these macrophages do not themselves contain the antigen.   This again is a temporary phenomenon.

Drs. Spitznagel and Allison have demonstrated that a number of adjuvants cause striking activation of lysosomes in the macrophages which take them up and believe that there is a causal connection between the two effects.   One could certainly envisage that uptake of antigens which possess "adjuvanticity," to use Dr. Dresser's term, could have some temporary non-specific stimulating effect on neighboring lymphocytes exerted through something released from macrophages, in addition to any more lasting effects due to retention of antigen which I have already mentioned.   I understand that Dr. Claman has already put forward a suggestion along these lines.

I find the idea that macrophages can have some non-specific stimulating effect on lymphocytes, which starts them off on the path of differentiation towards immunoglobulin synthesis (and presumably diminishes the likelihood of their being specifically paralyzed by antigens) interesting for another reason.   This is that everybody who looks carefully at the results of their immunization procedures finds that not only is synthesis of specific antibodies stimulated, but also that of "nonspecific" immunoglobulins.   This last may, of course, be antibody of such low affinity that its specific antibody function is undetectable, but I am inclined to think that this is not so.   It would be a simple explanation if something from macrophages could non-specifically activate potential immunoglobulin-producing cells irrespective of what immunoglobulin they were able to make.

To return to my main thesis that we cannot afford to neglect the detailed architecture and spatial relationships within lymphoid tissues, whether we consider tolerance induction or immunization, I leave you with these points for your further consideration: (1) antigen, in most cases, appears to be concentrated in well-defined anatomical situations and (2) the micro-environment in which immunologically competent cells may find themselves not only differs from place to place but may actually be altered by the antigen itself.   If we want to manipulate tolerance we need to know more about these events.

CHAIRMAN CINADER: There are a number of distinct problems that Dr. Humphrey has considered and I propose that we should identify them and discuss them separately.

He has started to come to grips with certain processes that were mentioned but not discussed in the prior proceedings. Let us, therefore, consider now the role of macrophages, the role of nucleic acid-containing complexes, and finally let us look at non-specific modifiers of the immune system. Let us then see if we can operationally distinguish non-specific modifiers ("adjuvanticity") from carrier functions as they were defined in prior discussions, i.e. as distinct from the conversion of a hapten into an immunogenic determinant. Let us see whether we can distinguish operationally between adjuvanticity that depends on the macrophage, and adjuvanticity that depends on non-specific "dispersal" factors of one kind or another.

The first area to be discussed is whether antigen is intact when it interacts with the surface of antigen-sensitive cells. You recall that Dr. Humphrey suggested that it was intact and that Dr. Sela came to the same conclusion on the basis of a different set of facts. Dr. Gottlieb has some information that has a bearing on this view and that may challenge it. I would like to have him expose his evidence and his conclusions.

DR. GOTTLIEB: In seeking to answer some of the questions that Dr. Humphrey has raised, I would like to move the discussion from the biologic aspects of immunity to the level of molecular biology of the macrophage. First off, let me make clear two personal points of view: (1) I do not believe that there is convincing evidence that any messenger, i.e. any RNA capable of specifying the amino acid sequence of gamma globulin, is resident within macrophages; the RNA or the ribonucleic-acid containing complex that I am going to describe is not a messenger RNA. (2) Regardless of whether processing is optional or obligatory for some or all antigens, I think that the required facts are not all in and we, therefore, have to reserve judgment.

Having exposed my prejudices, I will proceed to give my data and leave the interpretation to others. I will be referring to antigen-RNA-complex contrasted with another RNA which has been described by Drs. Adler and Fishman and which is currently regarded as having the ability to transfer allotypic specificity. The reason I mention this is to emphasize that I shall have nothing to say about allotypic transfer. I don't really know at this point whether the RNA that can transfer allotypic specificity comes from the macrophage, but I rather doubt it.

In the RNA of macrophages, antigens appear in a complex that has been localized in a particular fraction of the RNA, characterized by the unique property of banding at a light density in cesium sulfate density gradient by virtue of a relatively high content of protein. Cesium sulfate has the property of being able to distinguish by differential density between RNA, DNA, protein and combinations of all three.

If you take macrophages from animals that have been exposed to I_{125}-labelled T_2 phage, and extract the RNA, and put this RNA into a cesium sulfate gradient, and then plot the profile of radioactivity, two peaks are obtained. They are the major fraction of RNA and the minor light density fraction of RNA, which I will refer to as the RNP – an abbreviation for ribonucleoprotein complex. This is the immunologically interesting fraction. The iodine label is concentrated in the region of the light density band, but it is very important to note that there is a substantial amount of iodine label in the background along the gradient and, in contrast, there is no iodine label (no T_2 fragments) at the very right of the profile at the place where you would expect to find ungraded T_2 bacteriophage protein.

This profile says several things about the way the macrophages handle T_2 phage. It turns out that the handling of soluble antigens by macrophages is quite different. It indicates that the antigenic fragments that are immunologically active, both in vitro and in vivo, cannot be greater than 15 amino acids as part of the immunologically active RNP fraction. This is shown by the fact that the minor band in the RNP complex has a distinct density, a molecular weight of 6,000, and 25% of it represents protein.

There is no way in which physical constraints allow you to get around this conclusion. We have to accept the validity of this observation because it has now been made in several laboratories and this is the type of RNA that Dr. Fishman originally looked at.

A similar type of experiment was carried out by Dr. Bishop who, quite independently, using sRBC as the labeled antigen, observed localization of antigen in a light density peak, and a background of radioactivity along the gradient, but no radioactivity in undegraded protein.

Now, if you purify the ribonucleic acid complex of the light density band, iodinate it with I_{125}, and reband it in

cesium sulfate, you obtain the curve indicated in Fig. 34.
You can see that this material has a principal band at the
density of the ribonucleic acid-protein peak, and in addition there is a large amount of radioactivity on the right,
which indicates that a certain amount of radioactivity has
been stripped off by the high salt concentration of the
gradients which are equivalent to over two molar NaCl.

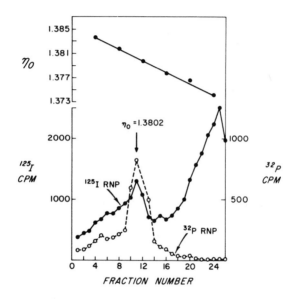

Fig. 34   Density gradient profiles if I_{125} labelled and P_{32}
labelled RNP

This tells us that a good deal of the protein on that band
exists in macrophages of non-immunized rats and is salt-
sensitive.   The interesting question is: What do these proteins represent in "normal" macrophages?

If one exposes macrophages to I_{125}-labeled GAT, a synthetic copolymer that the donor animals are not likely to
have encountered previously, one obtains a profile shown in
Fig. 35.   Again you see very much the same thing as in normal macrophages, a protein fraction which, in cesium sulfate
represents salt-releasable iodinated protein.   This is a

184

distinction between the way the macrophage deals with soluble proteins as opposed to particulate antigens, such as T_2 bacteriophage or sRBC.

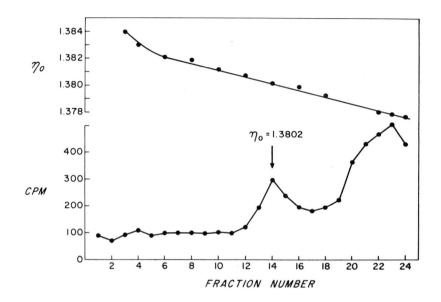

Fig. 35 Banding profile of RNA derived from macrophages exposed to I_{125} GAT copolymer

The last experiment I would like to describe attempts to show just what the nature of the label is in RNA derived from cells that have been exposed to the I_{125}-labeled GAT copolymer (Fig. 36).

RNA was subjected to electrophoresis on polyacrylamide gels, and the Rf measured against a standard I_{125} marker. All of the label in the total RNA extracted from macrophages bands in polyacrylamide gels; the precise location of the isolated ribo-nucleo-protein peak itself is shown in the upper part of Fig. 36 where I have indicated, for the sake of convenience, an sRNA marker as well as an I_{125} iodide marker. This is in contrast to the lower part of Fig. 36 in which the profile of the I_{125} GAT polymer itself is shown. Obviously, at physiological ionic strength, and indeed at

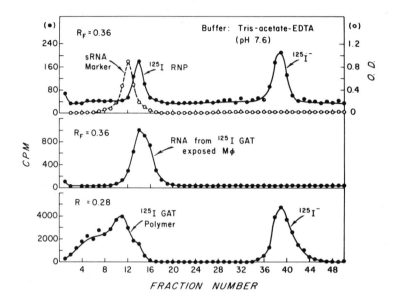

Fig. 36 Polyacrylamide gel electrophoresis of I_{125} RNP, I_{125} GAT and I_{125} RNA derived from macrophages exposed to I_{125} GAT

considerably higher ionic strengths, all of the GAT label migrates with the RNP complex. Since the amount of GAT polymer that gets into the RNP is very small, this does not affect the migration of the RNP seen in the polyacrylamide profile, but it does say that some of this antigen is salt-releasable. This may be a way in which the integrity of the tertiary structure is preserved in vivo provided you assume that the antigen determinants have been bound in ionic linkage to the ribonucleo-protein complex.

The characteristics of the so-called minor band of RNP that are of interest include the protein composition of 25% of the material, the molecular weight of 6,000, the sedimentation co-efficient of 1.8, and the attachment of the RNP to 28S RNA in vivo. It may very well be that in the intact cell, fragments of antigen preserving the tertiary structure are sandwiched between these RNP molecules on the surface of the ribosome.

IV. ANTIGEN HANDLING BY MACROPHAGES

In summary, I believe that there exists, in macrophages, an interesting ribonucleo-protein (RNP) which has a capacity to trap antigens to which these cells are exposed, and which may have an important role in the initiation of the primary response.

DR. SELA: When you say that the radioactive material within the particle with M.W. of 6,000 is the antigen, I assume that you infer this from its capacity to evoke immune response. However, do you have any direct information that it still carries antigenic determinants, that it is able to react with antibodies, and that you can isolate the antigenic determinant? In short, do you have immunological evidence that this particle does in fact contain the antigen?

My second question is: You mentioned a molecular weight of 6,000 for the T_2 phage particle. Do you have also information that the particle containing the synthetic polymer is around 6,000, and does it mean that this polymer, which probably is much bigger, is also chopped into something smaller?

DR. GOTTLIEB: With respect to your first question, the statement that immunological potential resides in the RNP complex, comes from two sources: one, the localization of I_{125} radioactivity, and secondly, the ability to remove the material present in this band and show that all of the immunological activity of the RNA from which it was prepared, is located in the light density RNP fraction.

You further asked whether if one injected the RNP, do the fragments still react with neutralizing antibody to T_2? We have not done this experiment.

With regard to the molecular weight measurements of the synthetic GAT polymer, the actual determination by sedimentation equilibrium has not been done yet. However, all the physical parameters show that, regardless of the antigen to which the cells have been exposed, the density of RNP in cesium sulfate, the Rf in polyacrylamide gels and the elution from DEAE cellulose are identical.

CHAIRMAN CINADER: I wonder whether Dr. Braun would now like to discuss the role he sees for the RNA trigger.

DR. BRAUN: To begin with, I want to emphasize that what I shall have to say in regard to the possible function of the macrophage should not be regarded as an alternative to the lymphocytic interactions that were discussed earlier. Rather, it should be regarded as an additional mechanism.

Most of you have seen the scheme shown in Fig. 37, and have heard me discuss, some three years ago, the suggestion that what the macrophage may be doing is to combine a processed antigen with a non-specific activator or derepressor.

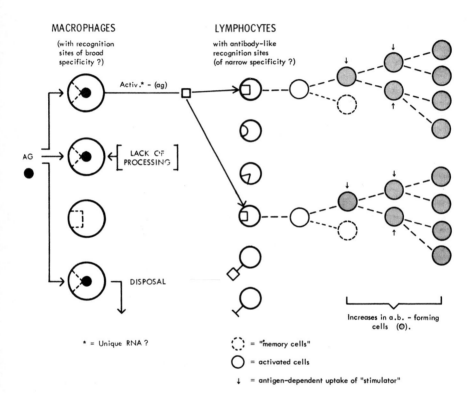

Fig. 37 Possible interactions between macrophages and lymphocytes leading to antibody-forming and memory cells

This activator may or may not be RNA in nature and is assumed to have the capacity of turning on all of those stem cells into which it can gain entry. The function of the antigen, in this concept, is merely that of guiding, like a pilot boat, the non-specific activator into the appropriate pre-existing lymphocytic stem cell.

This concept was proposed before Dr. Gottlieb found his minor band, and it is now, of course, tempting to suggest that Dr. Gottlieb's RNA may be the proposed activator or derepressor derived from macrophages. Whatever the actual nature of the activator, it is regarded as the factor that, with the help of the processed antigen, can get into the appropriate stem cell, but not into others, via an interaction between the antigen and a cell-associated antibody-like recognition site of the sort that has been mentioned by others in the preceding discussions.

I would like now to summarize some evidence that supports this concept.

First, as already inherent in prior speculations by others, by-passing of the processing step in the macrophages will permit "naked" antigen, devoid of the necessary activator, to go directly to available recognition sites on lymphocytes, where it will remain as a block, preventing the subsequent uptake of the activator. Thus, any overloading of the system, e.g., in immune paralysis will bring about reactions between recognition site and "naked" antigen devoid of activator.

This scheme can explain the old Feldman results in which specific non-responsiveness was induced when antigen was presented at the time of irradiation (the radiation employed was eventually demonstrated to damage the processing step). Again, an antigen provided at a time of non-functioning processing proceeds directly to the lymphocytic stem cells and will occupy the recognition sites, thus blocking subsequent uptake of the activator. If this is a proper explanation, we should be able to achieve the same result by merely "constipating" the processing cell system. Accordingly, we gave antigen at time of RES blockade by thorotrast and got essentially the same results that were obtained by Dr. Feldman with irradiation. Dr. Friedman has conducted similar studies using colloidal carbon.

The scheme shown in Fig. 37 could easily explain the development of natural non-responsiveness to self antigens. All we would have to assume is that the processing capacities mature later in development than the stem cell system. Consequently, any self antigen would, as naked antigen, in the absence of processing, occupy available recognition sites on lymphocytes and either block subsequent entrance of the activator or, possibly, eliminate the stem cell.

This was difficult to prove directly, but it led to the prediction that if stem cells are indeed already present in newborn animals (which are unable to respond to a number of antigens) then, if we were to provide the necessary mature processing cells, we should be able to turn on all antibody-responses in newborn animals. We were indeed able to do this with the help of adult macrophages which were injected into newborns together with an antigen (sRBC) to which the animals (mice) normally did not respond. We have suggestive evidence that the antibodies are produced by cells of the recipients. If you irradiate the recipient, the response is ruined. If the effect were due to donor cells, you would not expect this to happen. Dr. Argyris subsequently confirmed these data and extended them.

In addition, we have recently been able to achieve the same result by presenting an antigen (sRBC, to which the newborn animal normally does not respond) together with endotoxin. Since endotoxin is known to be capable of en-hancing the metabolic activities of macrophages, the result might be regarded as representing a "forced" maturation of these cells in newborns. In other words, a newborn mouse which cannot make antibody to sRBC until it is at least 10 days old, if given endotoxin plus sRBC at 2 days, will now produce spleen cells making antibody to sRBC (sRBC or LPS alone; 0; sRBC + LPS: 622 PFC/10^8 spleen cells). The con-sequence of such premature initiation of antibody formation, when tested in adult mice that had been exposed as newborns to sRBC + LPS is the exact opposite of tolerance, i.e., it results in an enhanced adult response.

Now, the next prediction that was possible if macrophages indeed contribute to the "hooking on" of a non-specific ac-tivator to a guiding antigen, was that the guidance system should be ruined under conditions that permit the entrance of the activator into all available stem cells. Under such conditions, instead of channeling activator into appropriate stem cells, it should be diluted into many stem cells, mak-ing much less available to the proper stem cells. This should lead to a reduction of the specific response while turning on, weakly, completely unrelated responses. And this is exactly what happened when an antigen was adminis-tered in conjunction with known modifiers of lymphocyte

permeability. If an antigen (sRBC, BGG, KLH) is injected
into mice together with ALS (certain lots) or epinephrine,
or chlorpromazine, or streptolysin, or endotoxin (in endo-
toxin-tolerant animals), unrelated antibody responses are
activated while the specific response declines.

DR. MÖLLER: I want to emphasize what Dr. Sela mentioned
during an earlier discussion. Facts show that the tertiary
structure of antigens is important in antibody formation
and hidden determinants are non-antigenic unless the molecules are split before immunization. I think those working
with RNA coupled to small pieces of antigen have to explain
these in vivo findings in terms of their concept. The
basic discrepancy between the two systems is very important.

DR BRAUN: A way out of this difficulty could be that we are
really dealing in activation with two important antigen-dependent steps. The first one involves antigen that has been
processed and may be as small a determinant as Dr. Gottlieb
has indicated, guiding an activator into the proper stem
cell, but there is also evidence, and time does not permit
me to cite it now, that this does not suffice to turn on production and proliferation.

There is probably an additional event which requires antigen that may not have been processed. In other words, what
I am trying to say is this: You have a dual function of
antigen, first in the step required for activating a stem
cell and then there seems to be a second step requiring antigen in order to bring a necessary stimulator for proliferation into the activated cell.

DR. HUMPHREY: I want to discuss one situation in which processing by macrophages seems to be unnecessary. This is the
primary response of the mouse to KLH. Five micrograms suffice to elicit good primary antibody formation, mainly 19S,
as well as allowing priming for a secondary response. The
primary antibody response is abolished when KLH is administered in peritoneal macrophages as shown by my colleague,
Dr. Unanue. However, priming for a secondary response is
not abolished by incorporation into macrophages.

A further observation is that there is a difference in
the specificity of the antibodies elicited by native KLH in
the first response and of antibodies elicited in the secondary response after the primary had been evoked with KLH

already in macrophages. Dr. Unanue found that the former were all directed against native (93S) KLH, whereas the latter were in part reactive only with dissociated KLH. When native KLH is injected into a mouse, much of it is rapidly taken up by macrophages, and a mixed situation results. My point is that native KLH appears to be able to stimulate a first 19S response, and that KLH ingested by macrophages fails (at the same dose level) to evoke a first response, and stimulates memory cells with a specificity directed towards the sub-units of KLH (such as can be obtained by simple pH-dependent dissociation).

How would Dr. Braun explain a stimulation of immunocompetent cells to make 19S antibody which bypasses macrophage "processing"?

DR. BRAUN: You may have the two steps which I have just mentioned. They may involve the same antigenic determinant group, but one is produced by a small part of the total antigen, and the other, which is required for productive performance, may be evoked by a much larger molecule.

CHAIRMAN CINADER: What you are saying is that processing by macrophages is not an obligatory step.

DR. BRAUN: It is a preparatory step. I think it is obligatory for the primary response, but it certainly is not obligatory for any secondary response, or for any antigen that may have been experienced previously.

CHAIRMAN CINADER: It does not appear obligatory for priming?

DR. BRAUN: I would say for true priming you require processing by macrophages.

CHAIRMAN CINADER: Where does Dr. Humphrey's data fit in with this?

DR. BRAUN: My answer to this would be very simple. I think that the macrophages that are really responsible for the events that I discussed, probably the dendritic macrophages, may differ in many properties from peritoneal macrophages, and we may be misled, as Dr. Humphrey himself suggested, by making comparisons between peritoneal macrophages and their

192

behavior and macrophages that I regard as critical for initiating events.

DR. HUMPHREY: All I tried to say is that under certain conditions there appears to be a direct stimulation of lymphocytes to become antibody producers which does not require the macrophage. It neither proves nor disproves the possibility that a macrophage pathway may not be required for eliciting memory cells.

DR. LESKOWITZ: I would like to contribute some information called to my attention by Dr. Kunkel some months ago on work that he and Dr. Mandy did. He pointed out that rabbits and humans make auto-antibody to their own papain-or pepsin-digested gamma globulins. Presumably this is antibody to previously hidden determinants exposed in the digested molecule. This sounds to me as though such individuals are normally tolerant to the antigenic determinants. However, once the gamma globulin molecule is digested in vitro, they are capable of responding to new determinants.

CHAIRMAN CINADER: Are you introducing this as a piece of evidence that there is processing?

DR. LESKOWITZ: That processing may be involved.

DR. SCHWARTZ: I think that Dr. Braun's suggestion that there might be two antigen "hits" is a very interesting one, and I would like to cite an experiment that lends some credence to this. We have been studying suppression of the response to sRBC in mice by anti-sRBC. We have evidence that the locus of action of the antibody is on macrophage-processed antigen. The response of mice to sRBC can be suppressed completely with antiserum, but these animals are primed because they have a classical secondary response when challenged at a later time. So it may be that there are two kinds of hits required.

DR. BRAUN: Let me cite another experiment of the same nature as Dr. Schwartz. I am referring to experiments recently made by Dr. Freedman, in which he has shown that a new derivative of chloramphenicol (=cetophenicol) can do exactly the same thing that Dr. Schwartz just described in the case of antiserum suppression of detectable primary responses. Like normal choramphenicol, cetophenicol suppresses a primary response, no evidence of productive response can be seen. When you reexpose animals to the antigen that had previously been given with chloramphenicol, the animal behaves as if it had never seen the antigen. However, the antigen given with the new derivative, cetophenicol, prepares an animal to behave as though it had been "super-primed."

CHAIRMAN CINADER: Now, we can go on to the macrophages. As you recall, Dr. Braun mentioned that when he passively transferred adult macrophages to newborn animals, they made an effective antibody response. Dr. Argyris has made some analogous experiments which she will now summarize for us.

DR. ARGYRIS: We also have found that peritoneal macrophages from thioglycollate-injected adult donors, transplanted into neonatal mice given sRBC 3 days later, results in an increase in the number of PFC in the spleen of the immature recipients. The effect of macrophage administration is dose-dependent, $0.5-1x10^7$ macrophages results in an approximately seven-fold increase in the number of PFC/10^6 spleen cells. Transplantation of 2×10^7 macrophages does not result in a further increase in the number of PFC in the spleen, which suggests to us that the PFC are of host origin. Heat-killed macrophages or Ehrlich ascites tumor cells are not effective in increasing the number of PFC. Macrophages from donors that are very young (less than one month of age) or very old (10 months or older), are not effective either. This suggests that the effect may be dependent on the physiological activity of the macrophages and for the moment we are suggesting that we are providing the newborn mouse with an antigen-handling system that at this stage of development normally is lacking.

CHAIRMAN CINADER: I would like to say briefly that about twelve years ago we thought of the same experiment that Drs. Braun and Argyris have just described. We used newborn rabbits, and got similar results with adult macrophages and could not get such results with macrophages of newborns. What interfered with our making the proper conclusions at that time was that we could get similar effects with a large number of cell types. We even succeeded eventually to evoke it with red cells to which we had coupled human gamma globulin with the help of bisdiazobenzidine.

IV. ANTIGEN HANDLING BY MACROPHAGES

DR. BRAUN: Since we can now produce premature antibody formation consistently with endotoxin, may I suggest that your
preparations were contaminated with endotoxin.

DR. BUSSARD: May I suggest that people speaking of macrophages should give a kind of operational definition of the
cells they are referring to.

DR. ARGYRIS: I agree with Dr. Bussard. Our peritoneal
cells were obtained from thioglycollate-injected mice;
these constitute 86% large macrophages, and 7% small lymphocytes. We did not purify our macrophage preparation but we
feel that our results were due to the effects of the large
macrophages in the peritoneal fluid. This belief is based
on the dosage effect, i.e. that high doses of peritoneal
cells failed to stimulate antibody production in the neonatal host. I certainly agree that when we discuss macrophages, we should be more careful and clearly define the
cells that we are talking about.

DR. LANDY: We should distinguish between "normal" peritoneal macrophages, which one obtains by simple washout of the
peritoneum, and "induced exudate" macrophages. The latter
are brought into the peritoneum in very large numbers by a
diverse array of natural products which are suspected of
being heavily contaminated with bacterial endotoxin. Oyster
glycogen, a favorite of early workers is known to be markedly contaminated with this potent microbial component as is
peptone, which is still employed extensively. It should be
noted that heat sterilization of these preparations diminishes the biologic activity of the endotoxin contaminants
only moderately. I would view this complication as being
of two kinds: (a) the probability that the cell populations
of induced exudates differ markedly from that normally present in the peritoneum, and (b) the phagocytic and enzymatic activities of the induced macrophages will have been
markedly enhanced upon exposure to endotoxin. The issue I
would therefore pose is - are these exudate cells in any
way representative of the macrophages we have been talking
about - the dendritic macrophages operative in lymphoid
tissue.

DR. STERZL: In connection with the experiments presented,
in which the onset of the immunological competence of new-

borns was accelerated by the transfer of peritoneal macrophages, I think it is pertinent to mention Dr. Holub's experiments in my laboratory. He detected, in peritoneal
exudate of immunized mice, cells that by all morphological
criteria are macrophages, but as judged by immunofluorescence and the hemolytic plaque technique are secreting antibodies. This shows that peritoneal exudates can contain
not only antigen-processing cells, but also cells that are
antigen-sensitive.

DR. UHR: In the context of the preceeding discussions I
would like to make two statements, one regarding RNA and
one regarding macrophages.

The postulation of RNA as an intermediate between antigen
and antibody receptor on the precursor cell is an unnecessary one. There is no problem, from the point of view of
information, of antigen meeting antibody, their interaction
resulting in some secondary effect that depresses a precursor cell. Hence it seems to me that a role for RNA
should not be seriously considered unless the evidence is
compelling. During the last decade of experimental studies,
the history of such a role for RNA has certainly been dis-
appointing. I think the experiments that Dr. Gottlieb presented show very elegant characterization of an RNA-protein
fraction in macrophages, but these studies do not yet establish any relationship of this fraction to the normal immune response. Moreover, I am not sure that with present
techniques a relationship can be established. For example,
the use of transfer techniques, whereby a fraction is injected into an additional recipient animal and an immune
response is subsequently measured, has proved to be complex,
since in such experiments antigenic material is in essence
processed twice. I think such experiments are very difficult to interpret.

In terms of macrophages, I do not think that there are
any studies that have been published or presented here, including our own, which really allow a unique explanation.
It appears that for every experiment in which the evidence
suggests that macrophages play an obligatory role, there is
a corresponding experiment in which they appear to be
unnecessary.

Here again one is confronted with a situation in which
we seek to determine whether in vivo experiments or the use

196

of the available models of immunologic response in vitro will
lead to a solution of this problem. Perhaps simpler and
better characterized in vitro models are necessary for this
purpose.

I think there are two hard facts in terms of the problem
of macrophage processing. One that has been discussed already is that the tertiary structure of the immunogen must
be retained. The second fact is that passive antibody can
interrupt an immune response by combining with persisting
antigen. It is possible that the passively administered
antibody can also enter a macrophage, find the relevant
antigenic determinants and by combination with antigen, block
its driving force. I think it is more likely, however, that
the immunogen is not within cells, but on the surface of
cells or reticulum and thus available to antibody in the
circulation.

I think, therefore, that the simplest explanation of antigenic stimulation, to use Dr. Braun's terminology, is that
the "naked antigen" penetrates the "virgin" lymphocyte and
stimulates it in an optimal fashion.

DR. BENACERRAF: I want to ask Dr. Uhr if his attack is directed against macrophages in general and to anything that
they may do, such as localizing the antigen in a manner
which has been ably described by Mitchison and Humphrey, or
if he is attacking only the processing step and the formation of some hypothetical fragment or unit which is postulated to be involved in immune responses. I would like a
clarification of this point, since as far as I am concerned,
he didn't make his position clear.

DR. UHR: I am not arguing against the possibility that
antigen is fixed on the surface of a macrophage, but rather
against the intracellular processing of antigen.

DR. ARGYRIS: My comment is directed to Dr. Uhr. We have
found, and I understand that Dr. Schwartz has also found,
that specific antibody injected passively with antigen acts
on the macrophage and makes for a more rapid degradation of
the intracellular antigen in vivo and in vitro. This can
be interpreted as evidence that the passive antibody actually
gets to the macrophage and also to the antigen that is inside.

DR. SCHWARTZ: We did not do the experiment that Dr. Argyris quoted us as doing. All we demonstrated was the following: If you inject a newborn mouse with anti-sRBC there is no more antibody serologically detectable in the animal 6 to 8 weeks later. At that time, peritoneal macrophages can be "fed" sRBC and can be transferred to normal "test" mice. Unlike peritoneal macrophages taken from normal animals, these macrophages will not provoke an immune response in the recipient mouse.

DR. GOTTLIEB: First, let me make a parenthetical note about the definition of macrophages as I used it. They are, in our studies, mineral oil - induced, mononuclear cells taken 5-6 days after injection; 95% of the cells harvested have the morphology of macrophages and the same percentage will adhere to glass. Next, let me say that Dr. Uhr is quite right in respect to his statement that the technology may not be available to make a truly definitive judgment at this point. I think what is required are some physical-chemical techniques of separations that would assure us of harvesting defined lymphocyte populations and macrophage populations, respectively.

I would like to ask one question, though, and that is that I have been intrigued, among other things, by the very profound increase in immunogenicity of antigens that are attached to our RNP complex. I wonder if there are any thoughts as to why nature should have invented the macrophage system in the first place, and why handling by macrophages may enhance immunogenicity by two to three orders of magnitude.

DR. SILVERSTEIN: The answer is that nature did not initially devise the macrophage solely to serve an immunologic function, but had somewhat more basic biologic functions for it to fulfill.

DR. SISKIND: With regard to Dr. Argyris' comment about passive antibody, it has been shown by a number of workers, including ourselves, that if you have two antigenic determinants on one antigen molecule, in our work two different haptens on a common carrier molecule, passive antibody against one determinant suppresses the immune response to that determinant without suppressing the immune response to the second determinant. If the major effect of passive antibody were to increase destruction of both determinants inside macrophages, one would expect to see depression of both in a parallel fashion, which does not occur.

DR. ARGYRIS: I think that is a very good point and we have tried to think of an explanation. The only one that I can offer at the moment is that the antiserum allows for digestion of that part of the antigen molecule to which the specificity is directed, and not to the whole molecule.

CHAIRMAN CINADER: Do you have any evidence for this?

DR. ARGYRIS: No.

DR. CINADER: But once it chews up a portion of the molecule you have the problem that has been mentioned repeatedly, namely, that the maintenance of the tertiary configuration is required.

DR. SCHWARTZ: Dr. Siskind mentioned an interesting experiment in which an antigen with two haptenic determinants on it was used. An antiserum to one of the determinants blocked the response only to its corresponding antigen. Doesn't this mean that the passive antibody does not act on unprocessed antigen, because if it acted on the antigen in the circulation before it came into contact with any cell, one would expect the whole antigenic molecule to be removed.

DR. SISKIND: I am perfectly in agreement with that comment. The one thing we can say is that passive antibody does not act by either causing destruction of the antigen molecule or by simply bringing about a rapid excretion of the antigen. It appears that circulating antibody acts to compete with potential antibody forming cells for available antigen.

DR. PLESCIA: Drs. Bernardini, Imperato and I carried out an experiment similar to the one Dr. Siskind has just described, the essential diffenence being that antibody was added directly to the antigen in vitro. We selected BGG-DNP as the antigen because it carries two distinct classes of determinants, those common to both BGG and BGG-DNP and those determinants that comprise the DNP hapten. We could therefore use DNP or BGG-specific rabbit antibodies (or univalent fragments of these) to block preferentially, through steric hinderance, one or the other of these two classes of determinants. Thus, rabbits were immunized with complexes of BGG-DNP-antibody, or with complexes of BGG-DNP-antibody fragments. The complexes were prepared at equivalence or in antibody excess. The resulting antisera were analyzed, by quantitative complement-fixation and precipitation, for antibodies specific for native determinants of BGG and for DNP. The results clearly showed that antibody to BGG suppressed the formation of antibody to native determinants of BGG-DNP, whereas they had relatively little effect on the synthesis of antibody to DNP. In contrast, antibody to DNP affected primarily the synthesis of antibody to native BGG determinants.

These data support our hypothesis that induction of antibody synthesis is a response to individual determinants and depends on the accessibility of determinants, in one form or another, to antibody-forming cells. The molecule (or the complex) of which a determinant is a part, serves only as a carrier for that determinant, enabling it to interact with appropriate immuno-competent cells.

DR. FRIEDMAN: I would like to bring the discussion back for a moment to specifically tolerant animals and to describe the effect of transfer of RNA-rich extracts from tolerant mice to normal recipients. Donor mice made tolerant at birth to sRBC or Shigella antigens do not form antibody following antigen stimulation. Phenolic extracts prepared from the spleen of such mice are rich in an RNA-antigen complex, as demonstrated by a variety of means. Such extracts induce a rapid and specific rise in the number of specific PFC in normal non-tolerant mice. Similarly, such RNA-antigen fractions induce specific antibody formation in cultures of normal spleen cells. The response of recipient mice or tissue cultures to the RNA extracts from tolerant donors was similar to that observed when similar RNA extracts from specifically immunized donor mice were used for antibody production. In addition, when the antibody-forming cells of recipient mice or of cultures treated with RNA from tolerant donors, were tested for allotype specificity, the allotype of the PFC was always that of the recipient type. No evidence for donor type allotype was noted in experiments in which donor and recipient mice were of different allotypes. These experiments indicate that no detectable transfer of information occurred in these situations. Controls

for these experiments with immunogenic extracts from
tolerant donors consisted of preparations inactivated with
RNAase or treated with specific antisera to the original
antigenic determinant.

Thus, it seems clear that donor mice tolerant to a
specific antigen, and not forming detectable antibodies, can
be the source of RNA-rich materials capable of inducing a
specific immune response in other animals. It seems plausible that this effect is mediated mainly by a "super-antigen" associated closely with the RNA. However, such RNA-
antigen complexes were unable to stimulate an immune response in the tolerant donor.

DR. BUSSARD: I would like to mention an experiment we
have done in collaboration with Dr. Speirs. We have taken
peritoneal washings of normal mice or of B. pertussis-
treated mice and studied the appearance of hemolytic plaques.
We compared the activity of the total peritoneal cell suspension with that of cells remaining free after removal of
cells that had attached to glass in the presence of serum
within 2 hours at 37°C.

In the right column of Table 23, you see the number of
PFC appearing after 3, 24 and 45 hours in our carboxy-methyl-
cellulose system. The unfractionated population of cells,
incubated in siliconized glass, usually has lower activity
than the cell population that had been freed of macrophages.
This is not invariably the case, sometimes there is the reverse effect, but you can see that at least sometimes, the
macrophage is not necessary for plaque-formation in our
system; in many cases activity could be increased by the
absence of "macrophages."

In another experiment we looked at the activity of free
cells versus cells attached to glass. The latter procedure
is simple, since one can add carboxy-methyl-cellulose and
complement to cells that have attached to a microscopic
slide. As you can see from Table 24, the activity of free
cells is much higher in terms of PFC than the activity of
attached cells. But the interesting fact is that the cells
attached to glass are not totally devoid of immune activity.
What I want to emphasize is that macrophage-like cells can
produce antibody in carboxy-methyl-cellulose and that such
plaque formation is complement-dependent. The cells involved
look histiocytic morphologically, but they are difficult to
identify with one of the known cell types found in blood or

TABLE 23

Effect of the removal of cells attaching to glass
on the primary stimulation of peritoneal cells

Donor of cells	No x 10^6 of cells/ml	Incubation Conditions	Vessel	Cell recovery %	Activity (PFC/10^6) 3 hr.	20 hr.	45 hr. After
Normal CBA	1.8	2 hours 37°C	Silic.glass	40	0	7	92
	"	"	Glass	38	0	43	586
Pertussis treated C57Bl	6.5	2½ hours 0°C	Silic.glass	87		206	227
	"	" 37°C	Glass	5C		123	136
Pertussis treated C57Bl	6.4	2½ hours 0°C	Silic.glass	31		315	
	"	" 37°C	Glass	6		540	
Normal CBA	10	2 hours 0°C	Silic.glass	75	0	28	72
	"	" 37°C	Glass	75	0	15	72
	"	" "	"	42	0	27	109

202

TABLE 24

Plaque forming activity of cells attached to glass and of free cells from peritoneal exudate

Treatment of mice	Incubation		Cell recovery %	Activity	
	Conditions	Type of cells studied		PFC/10^6	Kinetics (T_{50})
None	$1\frac{1}{2}$ hours 37°C "	Free Attached	10 14	890 83	30 28
Pertussis Vaccine	$1\frac{1}{2}$ hours 37°C "	Free Attached	10 15	2300 78	<2 <2
Pertussis Vaccine	1 hour 37°C "	Free Attached	10 36	2600 60	<2 <2

lymphoid organs, as their morphology is presumably profoundly modified by the attachment to the glass. Nevertheless, it seems to me that the fact that peritoneal cells attached to glass are able to produce antibody is a significant one. This is not to say that these adhesive cells are really macrophages as it is well known that lymphoid cells can also--under certain conditions--attach to glass and because the only valid demonstration that the cells we are looking at are really macrophages, i.e., phagocytic activity, was not made.

The last column on the right of Table 24 shows the kinetics. I have used an index, T_{50} which is the time necessary for the total number of PFC to appear; usually in the case of peritoneal washings, T_{50} is about 30 hours, and is similar for free cells and for attached cells. However, if instead of normal mice we use mice pretreated by injection with B. pertussis vaccine, we find a very great change in the kinetics of antibody secretion. It is faster, and we can see that the free cell population is again much more active than the cells attached to glass. I should add that B. pertussis vaccine does not cross-react with sRBC and injection of the vaccine alone does not cause a rise in PFC above background.

So much for facts. Now, I would like to generalize my concept of the action of the macrophage. I think that we can propose a unifying concept, which is that macrophages can be divided functionally into three classes. The first would be the classical function of macrophages directed to the disposal of antigen. The second would be the processing of antigens, and the transfer of processed antigen, free of antibody, to lymphocytes. The third is the possibility that the macrophage itself can produce antibody. I believe that these properties depend on qualitative factors, e.g., the stage of maturation of the cell, the physico-chemical nature of the antigen and the ratio of lymphocytes to macrophages. Also, the amount of antigen and the number of macrophages must play a role because under conditions of excess antigen the purely disposal type of activity may be overwhelmed.

DR. BENACERRAF: There is no way to define macrophages other than (1) by their state of maturity, how close they are to those that come from bone-marrow precursors or (2) by their metabolic properties according to where they localized eventually. For example, alveolar macrophages are different

204

in their metabolic properties from those of the peritoneal cavity.

DR. HUMPHREY: I would like to mention the theoretical possibility that typical macrophages may have on their surface unique antigens of their own to which one can make antibodies. Experimental data in support of this have been published.

DR. BENACERRAF: Another point one should make about macrophages, besides what Dr. Humphrey has said, is that they are as different as individual human beings, as far as their functions and properties are concerned. This is a matter which has been emphasized by Drs. Cohn and Mackaness.

DR. BRAUN: I agree that one of the most important aspects of future study is that of the heterogeneity of macrophage populations.

Now, in terms of what Dr. Uhr said about the roles of macrophage and antibody, careful distinction should be made in regard to the various levels at which antibody may act. It may, as Dr. Uhr himself has shown, be critical in the handling of an antigen by macrophages. In addition, there are effects on antigenic determinants that seem to take place much later in the series of events leading to antibody formation (cf. Fig. 37). Consequently, one has to be careful about generalizing on the nature of antibody effects in the initiation of an immune response.

There has been a great deal of discussion in this session about the possible significance of RNA in events leading to antibody formation. I am sure that neither Dr. Gottlieb nor I are insistent that RNA must be a critical participant in these reactions. It is suspected of such, but certainly not proven to be so, and as far as I am concerned, I am willing to accept the possibility that other components in the RNA-rich complexes may play the role of the activator in the events that I discussed earlier.

DR. SELA: I would like to come back to the role of RNA. I think both Dr. Braun and Dr. Gottlieb are agreed on one thing, that this RNA does not transfer information. This is inevitable if you assume that the particle has a molecular weight of 6,000 and three-quarters of it is RNA, because this allows for the presence of less than 50 nucleotides, which would code for just a few amino acids. If at least the antigenic part would contain the antigen and could serve as a guided missile in the form of an antigenic determinant one could suggest that the RNA would be very helpful, when led into the right spot. When we come to the antigen or antigenic determinant, I think that it is premature to discuss it because we don't yet have any evidence that active antigenic determinants are present in the small RNA-peptide complex.

A comment concerning the role of conformation in antigenic specificity. In one antigen with which we are all familiar, the gamma globulin molecule, essentially 100% of its antigenic determinants are conformation-dependent, because if you open all the disulfide bridges in such a molecule, the product is not able to react any more with any of the antibodies prepared to intact gamma globulin. This situation holds for most proteins and the exceptions to the rule are rather few.

But I would like to bring a completely different argument that favors the likelihood that recognition of an antigenic determinant on an antigen occurs at a stage when the antigenic macromolecule is still intact. I am referring to some recent work of Dr. Rude in our laboratory (Rude et al., Biochemistry, in press) concerned with some earlier observations in which we found an inverse correlation between the net electrical charge of an antigenic molecule and the type of antibody that is being formed, as recognized by its position in chromatography on DEAE-Sephadex. Anti- "arsanil" antibodies, obtained by immunization with an arsanilated protein, are found mainly under the first anti-acidic peak. When we attach peptides of lysine to the same protein, so that the net charge is now very basic, and immunize with this material, we find that approximately 80% of the anti- "arsanil" antibodies are found under the second peak. Thus, the antibodies formed reflect the overall net charge of the molecule, rather than the charge within the limited area around the determinant in the immunogen. It is clear that the decision to make this antibody was made at the stage when the antigen was still intact. I think this is one more argument that a unique antigenic determinant in a big complex molecule is recognized, and the order to make antibody goes out while the molecule is still complete.

DR. GOTTLIEB: Could I add one additional fact which might

help the argument somewhat? Again, talking about the localization of I_{125}-labelled antigens in the RNP complex, if you
treat that complex with pronase from which ribonuclease has
been removed, you lose all of the label and you lose all
immunogenicity. It seems to me that you cannot have the
ability to stimulate neutralizing antibody against T_2 phage
without having an antigenic determinant for that particular
function, which may very well require a sequential determinant rather than a conformational one for induction.

There is one other point that I would like to make and
that is that in nearly all the Fishman-type experiments the
antigen used was T_2 phage. I think that T_2 is a bad antigen
to study in terms of the primary response, because one cannot be sure that the animal has never experienced E. coli
phages before. In fact, it is most likely that these responses are secondary, and I wonder: if conformation is required for priming, is it necessarily required for the secondary response?

DR. SELA: I think that if you destroy conformation, then
the fact that you may have determined the components (amino
acids or peptides) is meaningless. They cannot form a determinant whereas your concern is really for a determinant
for secondary responses.

DR. BENACERRAF: I think we can say that there is really no
major disagreement involved here. Dr. Gottlieb finds that
there is a small molecule that is attached to an RNA molecule and this is antigenic. There is nothing extraordinary
in this. Molecules with a molecular weight of 4 or 5 thousand can be antigenic especially when they are put on larger carriers. One should not be surprised about this. Such
molecules may induce antibodies which might cross-react to
some extent with the parent molecule from which they are
derived. However, this does not mean that the parent molecule needs to take this pathway in order to be immunogenic.
So as far as observations are concerned, there is no basic
contradiction. I don't see any, and I wonder if others
agree with me.

DR. PLESCIA: I don't disagree, but I think I might ask the
following question: is it meaningful to compare the immunogenicity of the intact antigen with a portion of that antigen associated with RNA? We know in fact that the immune

response to an antigen consisting of more than one determinant is a heterogeneous population of antibodies, each being specific for one or more of the other determinants. Therefore, I think it might be more meaningful to ask whether or not the fragment associated with the RNA leads to immune responses which will result in a population of molecules as heterogeneous in specificity as the population of molecules that results from immunization with the intact original molecule.

CHAIRMAN CINADER: Perhaps we can now attempt to define the borders of adjuvanticity and carrier function. Dr. Sela earlier made a very useful distinction. He said we should distinguish between the carrier function, which consists of "enlargement" of a hapten to a determinant, and the carrier function which is not connected with the determinant but appears to depend in some way on the whole antigen molecule.

DR. BENACERRAF: You are asking, in fact, three questions and not one.

(1) How much of the carrier is part of the determinant? The determinant is always larger than the hapten.

(2) The other question you are asking is why can certain carrier molecules act as inducers of the immune response for non-immunogenic haptens (for instance the pneumococcus for its polysaccharide, or BSA for DNP-PLL)? There is, thus, a basis of recognition of immunogenicity of some sort contributed by the carrier for which a variety of hypotheses have been proposed involving two cell types.

(3) The third point concerns adjuvanticity; that is a property which has been shown to be closely related to the activity of the macrophage and has no necessary relation with immunogenicity because adjuvanticity can be obtained with compounds that are not antigenic such as beryllium, and others that are immunogenic but whose crucial property is to cause proliferation of macrophages or of macrophage precursors.

DR. BRAUN: When we talk about adjuvant effects, we must again distinguish several levels at which such effects can occur. One has been clearly discussed here; it depends on the appetite of the initial cell for the particular molecule, and various factors can influence this step. The next one is the activity of that cell, and you have heard me talk in

the past quite frequently about stimulatory effects of oligonucleotides which now have been shown clearly to influence
not only the propagation of activated antibody-forming cells,
but also the metabolic activity of macrophages. The next
level at which non-specific modifications of events can occur
is at the level of lymphocytes, their activities, multiplication and interactions with other cell types. Again, oligonucleotides, and events releasing them naturally, contribute
to such effects, but I shall desist from citing specific
illustrations since many of them are familiar to most of you.

DR. LESKOWITZ: I would like to give some evidence that, I
think, inferentially bears on the problem of processing. In
the system I am dealing with, delayed hypersensitivity to a
rather simple determinant (arsanil-L-amino acids conjugated
to tyrosine), the molecule behaves as a complete determinant
in that it will immunize and will produce tolerance. On the
other hand, if one conjugates arsanilic acid to polymers of
D-amino acids, such materials will neither immunize nor
elicit tolerance. This indicates that tolerance does not
represent a passive interaction of these conjugates with an
antibody-like site on the cell but rather represents a necessity for a processing step that cannot occur with unnatural
amino acids.

DR. SELA: I have offered an alternative explanation earlier,
namely, that I believe in "processing," but only after recognition, as a necessary step to get rid of the antigen afterwards.

DR. SCHWARTZ: Does anybody have any knowledge that the
recognition of antigen by macrophages has any specificity
to it? The only experiment that I can recall at the moment
is one in which chicken RBC and sRBC were incubated with
macrophages and some macrophages ingested only the nucleated
chicken cells while others ingested only the non-nucleated
sheep cells. Are there any additional data on this? Is it
conceivable that there is a specific recognition system at
the level of macrophages which might help us out of this
dilemma?

DR. GOOD: With respect to this last point of Dr. Schwartz,
I think that the recognition system involved in the macrophage population probably goes back to the oldest recognition

system of the animal kingdom, the amoeba. You know amoeba never eat other amoeba. They will, instead, starve to death. They will eat tetrahymena, paramecia, bacteria and foreign proteins but not their own kind. There is a recognition process involved here which seems to be dependent on surface polysaccharides. There are surely recognition phenomena in human macrophage populations. Dr. Jeunet working in my laboratory carried out experiments with the isolated perfused rat liver. In this system, he has been able to show very clearly that the isolated rat liver macrophages will be able to recognize and consequently engulf many organisms, for example, Brucella melitensis, Salmonella, and so on, and will not at all touch or remove Brucella abortus prepared in the same way. But if you put antibody on the Brucella abortus, the complex will be taken out selectively by the liver macrophages. If you inject Brucella abortus intravenously into the intact rat, they are taken out of the circulation not by the liver macrophages but selectively by the spleen and other macrophages. We have been able to define, we believe, at least three separate systems of macrophages which operate in relationship to, but independent of, the immunological apparatus. This is only one example. There exists throughout nature a sensitive cell-surface recognition system which controls traffic patterns of cells, cell to cell interactions, and even molecule to cell interactions.

DR. WEIGLE: In regard to the problem of recognition, I would like to append some data of Dr. Golub and myself concerned with antigen handling in mice injected with ultra-centrifuged gamma globulin.

The basic system is that of Dr. Dresser. We injected mice with HGG that had been centrifuged at 20,000 xG for 30 minutes. When these mice were injected 7 days later with HGG in adjuvant, they proved unresponsive. There was a marked difference in the dose of centrifuged HGG needed to induce unresponsiveness in different strains of mice (Table 25). All C57Bl/6 mice injected with even small amounts of the centrifuged HGG (0.1 mg) became unresponsive. In contrast, even 10 mg of centrifuged HGG did not render BALB/c mice unresponsive. DBA mice appear to behave similar to C57Bl/6 mice and A/J mice require more HGG to make them unresponsive.

If one looks at centrifuged HGG in an analytical centrifuge small shoulders of aggregated material can be seen leading the main component. When the concentration is in-

210

TABLE 25

THE EFFECT OF HGG_{20} ON THE INDUCTION OF

UNRESPONSIVENESS IN VARIOUS STRAINS OF MICE

Strain	mg HGG_{20}				
	0.1	0.5	1.0	5.0	10
C57BL/6J	10/10	10/10	10/10	10/10	10/10
BALB/cJ	0/10	0/10	0/10	0/10	0/10
A/J	–	0/10	10/10	10/10	–
DBA/2J	–	10/10	10/10	10/10	–

creased to 40 mg per ml the presence of some aggregated
material is quite obvious. Gamma globulin can also be
disaggregated chemically with sodium sulfate; such chemically disaggregated HGG preparations are free of aggregated
material. When C57Bl/6 and BALB/c mice were injected with
the chemically disaggregated HGG, it took almost the same
amount to make both strains unresponsive.

We also utilized biological filtration as described by
Frei and Benacerraf as a means of removing aggregates and
obtained the same results as they did. Both BALB/c and
C57Bl/6 mice were able to filter out aggregated material;
their blood, in turn, rendered mice of either strain unresponsive to HGG.

Thus, it appears that the difference in the dose of centrifuged HGG required to render mice from different strains
unresponsive is due to strain differences in the capacity
for responding to small amounts of aggregated material. Apparently BALB/c mice handle aggregated material very efficiently, and make an antibody response rather than becoming
unresponsive, whereas the reverse applies to C57Bl/6 mice.
I am not suggesting that antigen processing is involved. I
would rather consider a handling mechanism whereby the aggregated antigen is presented intact to potential antibody-
producing cells in a manner quite different from that of
monomeric antigen.

DR. AUERBACH: What about the F_1 hybrids?

DR. GOLUB: The F_1 all behaved like C57 which is very exciting because at first approximation it looked like control
by one gene.

CHAIRMAN CINADER: And the backcross?

DR. GOLUB: The result of back-crossing was less exciting
because it indicated that we were dealing with more than one
gene. Regrettably, the number of mice required to determine
the actual number of genes involved becomes astronomical; we
are, therefore, not likely to pursue this further.

DR. HUMPHREY: I think these are very interesting observations. Dr. Dresser's early findings suggested that resistant
strains might be made to respond like other strains by admin-
istering an adjuvant at the same time as the tolerogenic dose
of HGG. Some strains of mice which had an inapparent chronic
infection with Eperythrozoon coccoides, were found by Dr.
Gledhill some years ago to behave as though they had a chronic stimulation of the RES and to make unusually high antibody
responses (I forget to which antigens). It would be worth determining whether strain differences of the sort that have
been discussed here might also involve obscure infections.

DR. BENACERRAF: It may be worth mentioning that in the original experiments with the biologically filtered BSA, carried out by Drs. Frei, Thorbecke and ourselves, animals that
had been given endotoxin at the same time could not be made
tolerant by filtered material and instead produced an immune
response. This suggests that adjuvant counteracts the relative lack of aggregated material and will render small remaining amounts effective; this is, in fact, the gist of
adjuvant action.

DR. BRAUN: This may, of course, fit into the story with newborns where endotoxin can also produce a response that or-
dinarily is not obtainable. Is anything known about the
capacity of cells from these animals to handle aggregated
and disaggregated materials in vitro?

DR. WEIGLE: We have not carried out any in vitro studies
with macrophages. There is some question whether we would
be able to detect subtle differences; such experiments are
nevertheless still worth doing.

DR. SMITH: There have been reports here on the ability of
endotoxin to prevent the induction of tolerance in newborns.
Paraf showed a number of years ago that when BSA and Freund's
adjuvant were injected at separate sites into newborn rabbits

induction of tolerance to this protein was prevented. In all likelihood this involved mechanisms similar to those in the experiments reported here by Argyris and Braun.

A related point is the question whether so-called processed antigen or RNA-antigen complexes, are less tolerogenic than antigen that has not been processed. This is pertinent since such modified antigens have been shown to have altered immunogenicity.

DR. WEIGLE: When we are talking about processed antigen, we are not inferring that it is broken down. We do not believe that antigen handling results in a marked change in the structure of the antigen. It may be that the aggregated material is merely stuck to a macrophage or to another cell type and is thus presented to a potential antibody-producing cell in a manner different from that applying to the monomers.

DR. BUSSARD: Dr. Smith mentioned the old experiments involving the injection of Freund's adjuvant into young animals, and it should be pointed out that what this does, in effect, is to raise the threshold of tolerance about two logs. You can still induce tolerance in such animals by injecting higher doses of BSA; this is why we postulated that it may be a question of the ratio between cells and number of available antigen molecules.

V

IMMUNE RESPONSES BY LYMPHOCYTES; THEIR
NATURE AND REGULATION

Role of antibody in homeostasis and suppression – Antibody-producing cells and antigen-sensitive cells ("memory cells") as separate entities – Antigenic competition – Intracellular regulation of antibody synthesis-19S vs. 7S antibody formation –Influence of antigen and antigen dosage on replication of antibody-forming cells – Histocompatibility antigens; their nature and their role in tolerance – Ontogeny of the immune response – Is immunological competence essential for tolerance induction? – Role of maternally transmitted antibodies and antigens.

V. REGULATION OF IMMUNE RESPONSES

DR. MÖLLER: I shall deal with factors regulating the immune response. Some of these factors act primarily at the population level, by interfering with interactions between antigen and antigen-sensitive cells, or by inactivating some other cells involved in immunity. I shall mention the role of immunological tolerance as a regulating phenomenon and also indicate, in this context, the importance of suppression of antibody formation by antibody. I shall also deal with some non-specific factors that are involved in the regulation of immunity.

I will start by analyzing the mechanism of antibody suppression and its importance as a regulating and selective phenomenon in the immune response. Antibody injected passively into antigen-treated animals, suppresses the immune response. This can be achieved even after the immune response has been initiated. Fig. 38 illustrates some basic facts that have been found to be true in most studies so far. If antigen (sRBC) is injected into mice, a typical immune response follows. This response can be supressed completely if antibody is injected at the same time. However, the immune response can also be suppressed if antibody is injected _after_ the antigen. Suppression is observed after a certain period, which is usually of the order of 60 to 72 hours. Different classes of antibodies vary in their suppressing efficiency.

In Fig. 39 the normal immune response in antigen-injected animals has been taken as equivalent to 100%. 7S antibodies efficiently suppress this response, even when given in low doses; the degree of suppression increases with the dose of antibody used. 19S antibodies may increase the immune response in low doses, but in higher doses they also cause suppression.

I will next deal with this phenomenon as a mechanism for quantitative suppression of the immune response, and thereafter I shall consider its function as a selective mechanism.

If antibody suppression operates in the normal immune response as a feedback mechanism, regulating the intensity

217

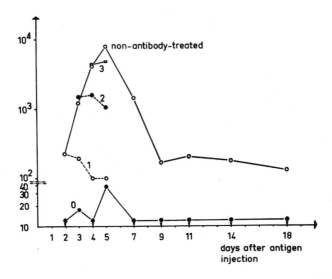

Fig. 38   Effect of passive antibody to sRBC on the 19S PFC
response in mice. The animals were immunized at
time 0 and given passive antibody at days 1, 2, or
3, as indicated.

(Data reproduced with permission of Journal of
Experimental Medicine)

of the immune response, it should be possible to obtain much
more pronounced antibody synthesis in the absence of any
serum antibodies. In other words, if antibody synthesis
could be achieved in an environment with little or no serum
antibodies present, one would expect a marked increase in
the number of antibody-producing cells. This situation can
be realized by adding antigen to pre-stimulated cells and
transferring this mixture into irradiated normal hosts. As
is shown in Fig. 40, an experiment of this type does result
in an increased number of antibody-forming cells in the
secondary host. The number increases from day 4 to day 7,
when a maximum is reached, the doubling time being 10 hours
and the maximum number at day 7 is generally more than 1 x
10^6 7S antibody-producing cells per spleen.

Generally, the number of 7S PFC varies between 5 x 10^4
and 2 x 10^6 in non-irradiated, hyperimmune animals. Since

218

V. REGULATION OF IMMUNE RESPONSES

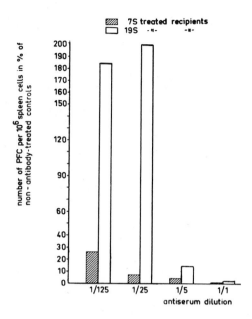

Fig. 39   Effect of various concentrations of 7S and 19S antibodies to sRBC on the number of 19S PFC developed. The number of 19S PFC was determined 4 days after administration of antibody + sRBC.

(Data reproduced with permission of Journal of Experimental Medicine)

in our tests the recipients were irradiated and thus had small spleens, the proportion of antibody-producing to non-involved cells was quite high, usually around 10%; it was always more than 1% and sometimes as high as 50% or even more. This is in contrast to the normal proportion of 7S PFC in a hyperimmune animal, which is usually in the range of 0.01-0.05%. Thus, by this simple maneuver, both the total number and the proportion of antibody-producing cells is increased far beyond that normally found.

Another question in this respect is whether this phenomenon operates in the primary immune response as a feedback mechanism, that is, if antibodies produced during a primary immune response regulate their own synthesis. To study this, Britton and I have used the endotoxin of E. coli as

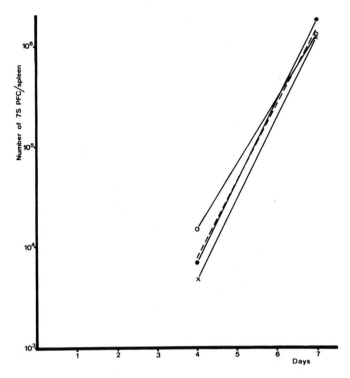

Fig. 40   Development of 7S PFC in irradiated (600 r) syngeneic recipients of sRBC + 10^7 spleen cells from
hyperimmunized animals.

(Data reproduced with permission of Journal of
Experimental Medicine)

antigen. This substance stimulates preferentially 19S antibody synthesis and 7S antibodies have not been detected even
after several months of immunization. In such a system,
where only one type of antibody occurs, a feedback suppression must be mediated by this antibody alone. The simplest
hypothesis would be that the antigen stimulates the appearance of antibody-producing cells. The product of these
cells would eventually be capable of interfering with antigen stimulation of the immunocompetent cells and the number
of antibody-forming cells would decline. At the same time
serum antibodies would decrease, and since cells and antibodies both have a short half-life (10 hours), antibody

suppression would disappear. If, at that point, antigen
were still intact and functional, it would be capable of
once again stimulating antibody synthesis.

It was found (Fig. 41) that after one injection of bacteria, a first peak of antibody stimulation occurs (measured

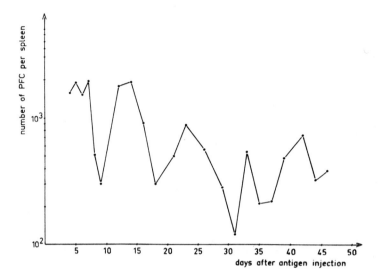

days after antigen injection

Fig. 41   Cyclical fluctuations of 19S PFC to E. coli somatic
antigen after a single intra-peritoneal dose of
heat-killed E. coli. Data show average response of
groups of five animals; sRBC coated with somatic
antigen were the indicator cells for enumeration of
PFC.

(Data reproduced with permission of Journal of
Immunology)

by the plaque technique) which rapidly disappears. Thereafter a second peak appears, which also declines and this
cyclical response continues for a long period of time. If
this finding is to be explained on the basis of feedback suppression, it would be necessary (1) to demonstrate that the
appearance of any new peak is due to an absence of suppressing antibody, and (2) to show that the antigen persists in an
immunologically active form during the entire period of time.

The demonstration that the first assumption is correct is given in Fig. 42. The supporting evidence was obtained in tests in which the experimental group received antibody at the time of the expected appearance of the second peak of PFC and this resulted in a suppression of the second peak.

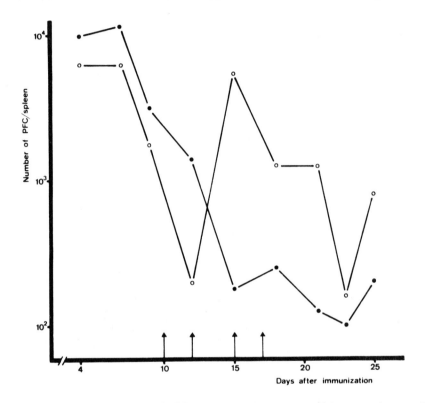

Fig. 42 Suppression of 19S PFC against E. coli somatic antigen by passive antibody. Mice were immunized with heat-killed E. coli at time 0; open circles indicate immunized controls; closed circles represent mice that received antibody passively 10, 12, 15 or 17 days after active immunization.

(Data reproduced with permission of Journal of Immunology)

V.   REGULATION OF IMMUNE RESPONSES

Another experiment illustrates a similar result. In this case, the antibody and the antigen were given together at the same time. In the controls that had not received antibody, a normal PFC peak appeared, but in the antibody-treated mice no such peak was seen. However, after a certain period these animals started to form antibody-producing cells spontaneously (Fig. 43). The time required corresponded to the disappearance of the passively transferred antibody.

The second question concerns the persistence of the antigen in an immunogenic form during the whole period of time of the cyclical antibody response. This has been shown in studies by Britton, Wepric and me, using a biological system. E. coli antigen was inoculated into animals and after various periods of time, the mice were given a lethal dose of X-irradiation. Thereafter the animals were repopulated with normal spleen cells. If the antigen had persisted in an immunogenic form, it should now manifest itself by stimulating an immune response in the adaptively transferred spleen cells. This test system was used with sRBC, HSA and endotoxin. The results obtained with endotoxin are the only ones presented. The animals were immunized at time zero, and, as indicated in the controls of Fig. 44 this resulted in the usual cyclic fluctuation of the response. The experimental group was injected at day 0 and was subjected to lethal X-irradiation 14 days later, followed by repopulation with normal spleen cells. In this group an initial decline in the amount of serum antibody occurred following irradiation, but then a normal immune response developed. Even when X-irradiation is postponed up to 50 days, the antigen resident in the host is still capable of immunizing the adaptively transferred spleen cells. This is not the case with HSA and sRBC, both of which have a much shorter biological life time.

These results seem to establish that the phenomenon of antigen retention may also function in the primary immune response to suppress that response quantitatively. Obviously the same mechanism may also act to select the quality of antibodies. This has been demonstrated by Siskind, who has shown that passive transfer of antibody causes an increase in the affinity of the actively produced antibody. Most likely, the antigens combine with antigen-sensitive cells having receptors of different affinities. Antibodies produced by cells having a high affinity will combine preferentially with the antigenic determinants and thus prevent

223

them from stimulating cells that have a lower receptor affinity.

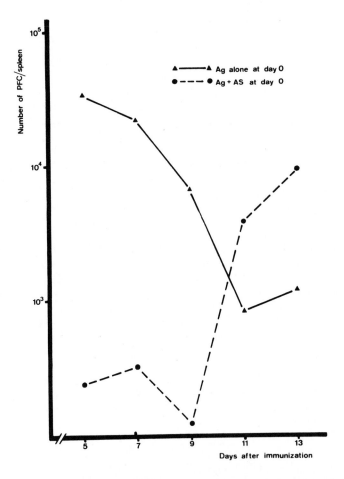

Fig. 43   Effect of antibody to E. coli given passively together with heat-killed E. coli; triangles indicate mice receiving bacteria only; circles represent mice given both bacteria and antiserum.

(Data reproduced with permission of Journal of Immunology)

V.   REGULATION OF IMMUNE RESPONSES

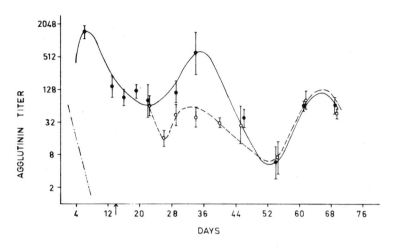

Fig. 44   Passive hemagglutinin titres (sRBC coated with
E. coli somatic antigen) for CBA mice immunized
with heat-killed bacteria (closed circles) and
for mice irradiated with 900 r at day 14 and then
repopulated with syngeneic bone-marrow and spleen
cells from nonsensitized animals (open circles).
Bars indicate standard error; dashed lines the
half-life of 19S antibodies.

(Data reproduced with permission of Immunology)

In tests with antibody-forming cells one would, accordingly, anticipate that if antibodies are injected passively
they would preferentially suppress the stimulation of those
antigen-sensitive cells that have a receptor of lower affinity than the passively injected antibody. We have performed
an experiment based on this thesis. If a high dose of antigen is injected, it is likely that it stimulates most of
the available antigen-sensitive cells, both those having a
low and a high receptor affinity, whereas a low antigen dose
would not be likely to be captured preferentially by high-
affinity cells. Consequently, it should be more difficult
to suppress the immune response by antibody when immunization was performed with a low dose as compared to a high
dose. sRBC in an amount of 10^8 was used as a high dose, and
10^5 as a low dose. When specific antibody was transferred
to animals immunized with a high dose, a 97.8% suppression

of 19S PFC was obtained (Table 26). With a low antigen dose, the degree of suppression of 19S PFC was only 53%. When 7S antibody-producing cells were studied, an analogous result was found; 99% suppression was obtained after a high dose, and only 25% after a low dose.

TABLE 26

Effect of passively transferred antibody on the number of PFC
in animals immunized with high vs. low dose of sRBC

sRBC dose	Antibody treatment	19S PFC	7S PFC	Suppression %
1×10^8	-	155,000		
"	+	3,400		97.8
1×10^5	-	9,800		
"	+	4,600		53.1
1×10^8	-		35,000	
"	+		270	99.2
1×10^5	-		2,700	
	+		2,000	25.5

I will now consider the level at which suppression by antibody occurs. As is shown in Fig. 38, suppression by antibody was observed after a latency period of 50 hours. This demonstrates two points: (1) the immune response is antigen-dependent during the exponential increase and (2) inactivation of the antigen functionally by antibody, results in termination of the immune response. This applies not only for the 19S response, but also for the 7S response even several months after immunization, since passively transferred antibody of high affinity will, as shown by Wigzell, suppress the 7S response.

It seems likely that interactions between passively transferred antibody and antigen occur immediately. If so, the latency period of 50-70 hours must be explained. During this latency period an exponential increase of the number of antibody-forming cells occurs. The simplest interpretation is that those cells that have been stimulated will

continue to divide 4 to 6 times in the absence of antigenic
stimulation. After that they disappear. If they disappear
after 50 hours, some recruitment (at an exponential rate)
of new antibody-forming cells must occur, in order to explain the exponential phase of the response. I will use
the term antigen-sensitive cells to designate the population
from which such recruitment occurs.

In terms of this concept, it would be expected that antibody suppression occurs rapidly by inactivation of the antigen that is required to stimulate antigen-sensitive cells.
However, those antigen-sensitive cells that have already
been initiated will continue, for a limited time, to divide
and to transform into antibody-producing cells in the absence of antigen; then they disappear.

I will now consider the possibility that antigen-sensitive cells and antibody-producing cells exist as different
entities. We have used a few biological approaches to distinguish between these two postulated cell types. We have
used animals that had been hyperimmunized with sRBC. These
animals then received repeated injections of anti-sRBC,
thereby decreasing the number of antibody-producing cells
to 1,800 as compared to 32,000 in the hyperimmunized controls.

We wanted to study whether the passively transferred
antibody affected only the antibody-producing cells or had
an effect also on the antigen-sensitive cells. This was
done by removing the spleens from the two groups of animals
and transferring the spleen cells, mixed with antigen, to
X-irradiated hosts. Seven days later the number of 7S antibody-producing cells in the hosts was assayed. It was
found (Table 27) that the same number of 7S antibody-producing cells developed in the secondary hosts, regardless
of whether or not the cell donors had been treated with
antibody.

Thus, passively transferred antibody did not affect the
number of antigen-sensitive cells although it depressed the
number of antibody-producing cells. This is in agreement
with the findings of Dr. Uhr that priming is more difficult
to suppress than actual antibody synthesis.

We have performed an analogous experiment in which we
treated hyperimmunized animals with ALS. This treatment
does not depress the number of antibody-producing cells.
However, when spleen cells from such animals were transferred,

TABLE 27

Effect of passively transferred antibody against sRBC on
antibody-producing and antigen-sensitive cells

Passive antibody at day 0	7S PFC/spleen in donors at day 18	7S PFC in irradiated recipients at day 25
-	32,000	403,000
+	1,800	375,000

(Data reproduced with permission of Journal of Experimental Medicine)

together with antigen, into irradiated recipients, the number of antibody-producing cells in the secondary hosts were
only 1,300, as compared to 467,000 in the recipients of
cells from donors that had not been treated with ALS.
(Table 28).

TABLE 28

Effect of ALS on antigen-sensitive cells

ALS treatment	7S PFC/spleen before transfer	$7S\ PFC/10^6$ cells after transfer into irradiated recipients
-	3,200	467,000
+	15,800	1,300

Thus, the antilymphocyte serum did not affect antibody-
producing cells, but had a pronounced effect on the antigen-
sensitive cells.

It is also possible to separate the two kinds of cells
physically by centrifugation in an HSA gradient. The antibody-producing cells go up in these discontinuous gradients
and no antibody-producing cells are found at the bottom.

However, the latter population is fully competent to give
rise to antibody production upon transfer, and therefore
contains antigen-sensitive cells.

The preceding experiments have indicated that regulation
by antibody occurs at the level of antigen-sensitive cells
and there appears to be sufficient data to suggest the existence of two different categories of cells, antigen-sensitive and antibody-producing cells, the latter having a short
life span.

Now I shall concern myself with tolerance as a regulating
mechanism. It is obvious that the tolerance phenomenon is
capable of regulating the immune response quantitatively,
but tolerance also affects the quality of antibody produced.
This has been demonstrated in partially tolerant animals by
Siskind. By employing the affinity argument developed previously, it is to be expected that antigen would preferentially interact and suppress (or kill) cells having a high
affinity receptor, simply because the antigen has the greatest likelihood to react with the most avid receptors. In
partial tolerance, therefore, one gets, as has been demonstrated, a preferential suppression of the high-affinity
cells. Thus with regard to the quality of antibody produced,
antibody suppression and immunological tolerance are reversed. They select for different affinity properties of
the antibodies. In a system where both feedback suppression
and partial tolerance operate, the outcome, with regard to
antibody affinity, is difficult to predict.

I also want to discuss the level at which tolerance operates with emphasis on antigen-sensitive and antibody-producing cells.

Britton, in some recent experiments, made use of the fact
that tolerance can be induced to detoxified endotoxin.
Eight to 10 mg of endotoxin will induce complete specific
tolerance in mice, whereas 1 mg leads to an immune response.
Britton was also able to induce tolerance in animals already sensitized. Animals were immunized with bacteria and
24 hours later they were given a tolerogenic dose of endotoxin. The number of 19S antibody-producing cells in the
control group and in the group injected with the tolerogenic dose increased in parallel for 70 hours and thereafter
there was a drastic fall in the number of antibody-producing
cells in the endotoxin-injected group (Fig. 45). In this
case it was possible to induce tolerance in animals where an

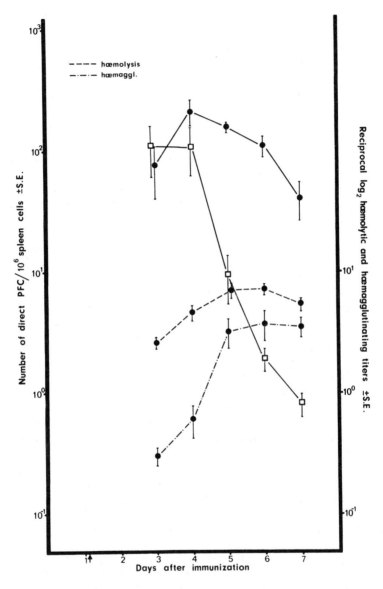

Fig. 45 Induction of paralysis to detoxified E. coli somatic antigen (endotoxin). Two groups of CBA mice were immunized with heat-killed bacteria at time 0; one group received in addition 10 mg endotoxin at day 1. (Fig. 45 legend continued on next page)

At indicated intervals 19S PFC were determined in animals given bacteria alone (circles) and those given bacteria followed by endotoxin (squares). Animals given bacteria alone developed hemagglutinating (alternating dashed lines) and hemolytic antibody (dotted line); those injected with endotoxin additionally produced no detectable antibodies.

immune response had already been initiated, but there was a lag phase of 70 hours before such tolerance was expressed. This latency period is remarkably similar to that in suppression by antibody.

In the same experiment, Britton studied the kinetics of suppression of the immune response by antibody to endotoxin and by a tolerogenic dose of endotoxin. Mice were immunized with bacteria and 20 hours later they were divided into 3 groups. One group remained untreated, the other two groups received either a passive transfer of antibodies to endotoxin or a tolerogenic dose of endotoxin. In both cases nothing happened. The number of antibody-producing cells increased as in the control group for 70 hours, but after that the number declined in parallel in both groups (Fig. 46). The similarity in the kinetics of suppression by antibody and antigen, respectively, is striking. The simplest explanation is that the lag period is caused by uninhibited proliferation of antibody-producing cells and that suppression involves an effect on the recruiting population, that is, and effect on antigen-sensitive cells. This suggest that antibody-producing cells are not amenable to tolerance induction. Therefore, tolerance must be an effect on the recruiting cell population, that is, on the antigen-sensitive cells. It is likely from the kinetics that induction of tolerance is rapid, or even instantaneous.

We know very little about the possible existence of intracellular regulation. To illustrate some possible mechanisms involved in such intracellular systems I turn to a model system, which may have nothing to do with tolerance or immunity. The system involves human lymphocytes and their acquisition of a cytotoxic potential for various human target cells.

Cytotoxicity must be initiated. Normally, human lymphocytes when added to targets do not attack the targets, but when the lymphocytes have been stimulated by any one of a

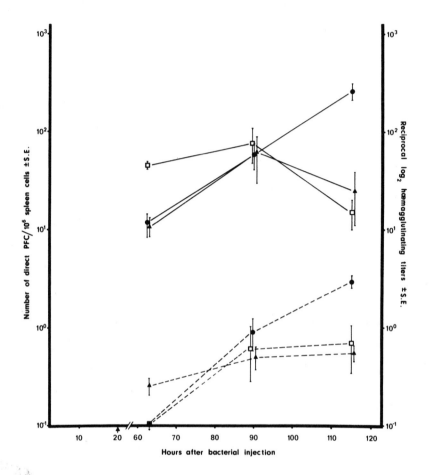

Fig. 46   Comparison between the kinetics of paralysis induction and suppression of antibody synthesis by passively administered antibody. CBA mice were immunized with bacteria at time 0. The group indicated
by solid circles received no further treatment;
other groups were given 10 mg detoxified endotoxin
(open squares) or antibody to E. coli 20 hours later
(solid triangles). 19S PFC production is shown by
solid lines and hemagglutinins by dashed lines.

(Data reproduced with permission of Immunology)

variety of substances, such as PHA, streptolysin, ALS (high
concentrations only), or by specific antigen added to sensitized cells, the lymphocytes acquire the ability to kill the
target cells. This is illustrated in Table 29.

TABLE 29

Cytotoxicity for allogeneic fibroblasts by human lymphocytes exposed to PHA
and ALS. Antagonism between ALS and PHA-induced cytotoxicity.

Lymphocytes	Substances added	Plaque-formation on allogeneic cells	
		day 1	day 6
A	-	-	-
"	PHA	++	+++
"	ALS 1/10	-	++
"	ALS 1/100	-	-
"	ALS 1/10 + PHA	-	++
"	ALS 1/100 + PHA	-	-

The interesting finding is that the various initiating
agents when given jointly can antagonize each other. For
example, PHA alone led to a marked cytotoxic activity,
whereas ALS, diluted 1/100, produced no effects. However,
the mixture of ALS and PHA failed to stimulate any cytotoxic activity by lymphocytes.

Human lymphocytes from individuals that have been sensitized to other humans by skin grafts, are competent to kill
various allogeneic targets directly without further activation. The degree of cytotoxicity varies with the target as
could have been expected from the partial crossreactivity of
histocompatibility antigens. When the sensitized lymphocytes are placed on various target cells in the presence of
PHA, an inverse relationship between the degree of cytotoxicity caused by the cells alone and in the presence of PHA
is observed. Whenever the lymphocytes are very toxic for
the target cells, they are weakly active in the presence of
PHA. If the lymphocytes by themselves do not induce a cytotoxic effect, they are very potent in the presence of PHA
(Table 30).

Various other experiments of this type show that there
exists an antagonism between different inducing processes.

TABLE 30

Cytotoxicity of lymphocytes, from patients immunized by allogeneic skin grafts, for allogeneic fibroblasts. The effect of PHA.

Lymphocyte donor	Substances added	Plaque-formation* on target fibroblasts		
		R	ST	LA
AE	-	++++	+++	+++
"	PHA	+	+	+
MD	-	+++	-	++
"	PHA	++	+	++
KA	-	+++	-	++
"	PHA	++	+++	+++
RK	-	++++	++++	++++
"	PHA	+++	+	+

*Plaque-formation in the presence of PHA was read at day 1; in the absence of PHA, read at day 7

It is unlikely that the inducing substances all act on the same receptor since they are so different, and also, include specific antigens. The simplest possibility, namely that the various inducers compete for the same receptor is, therefore, unlikely. If this is excluded, it follows that a cell activated by one substance may become blocked by another.

Analogous results have been obtained when induction of DNA synthesis has been studied using C_{14}-thymidine incorporation. Low doses of one substance usually act synergistically with a low dose of another substance, whereas, at higher doses antagonism can be observed. Thus, two inducing processes can either antagonize each other or stimulate each other. The mechanism must be at the cellular level. It seems possible, that a cell can distinguish how much of its surface has reacted with the stimulus.

Finally, I will deal with non-specific regulating mechanisms, in particular with antigenic competition. It has been shown by Liacopoulos that antigenic competition is an efficient mechanism for induction of non-specific tolerance. There are two other findings that I want to mention in this connection, namely the experiments by Simonsen and by Talmadge. Talmadge demonstrated that there can be antigenic competition between horse and sheep RBC, provided there is a sufficient interval between the injections of the two antigens. Talmadge drew the pertinent conclusion that this condition would not be expected if competition for space or for cells were involved and suggested that antigenic competition is not due to competition for anything.

Simonsen has studied antigenic competition in the case of GVH reactions. He injected X-irradiated (AxB) F_1 hybrids with parental strain A cells. These cells were either normal or preimmunized against sRBC. After the GVH reaction had occurred for 7 days, he immunized the F_1 hybrids with sRBC, and studied the immune response to this antigen later. In animals subjected to GVH reactions a marked suppression of the immune response to sRBC was observed. This was so even when the parental cells were pre-immunized against sRBC.

We have performed a slight variation of this experiment, getting identical results as shown in Table 31. We did not

TABLE 31

Suppression of the primary 19S immune response to sRBC in
animals subjected to GVH reaction for 7 days

Recipient	Donor of lymphoid cells	19S PFC/spleen	% suppression
A x 5M	A x 5M	138,300	-
A x 5M	A	40	99.9

irradiate the F_1 hybrid recipients, but left them untreated and subjected them to a GVH reaction. Seven days later the animals were injected with sRBC. Hybrids given hybrid lymphocytes produced 138,000 PFC, whereas, hybrids injected with parental cells yield only 40 PFC. This represents an extremely high degree of immunosuppression. Is it due to antigenic competition or not? Immunosuppression is obviously a consequence of the GVH reaction, but, as yet, we don't know the exact explanation. The most likely possibility seems to be a nonspecific suppression of immunocompetence in the recipients. The results are the same whether the recipients are pre-immunized to sRBC or whether the donor cells are pre-immunized. As long as the GVH reaction has been going on for 7 days, there is no immune response in the animals.

We have studied whether the antigen-sensitive cells persist in the host or in the donor cell populations by taking cells out and transferring them to a "neutral" environment together with sRBC. We found that antigen-sensitive cells are present both in the host cells and in the parental cell population. Thus, there has not been any change in the number of antigen-sensitive cells by the GVH reaction. However, expression of immunocompetence seems to have been blocked. I suggest, therefore, that antigenic competition can represent a non-specific effect. Presumably, some substances produced by GVH reactions have the capacity to prevent immunologically competent cells from expressing their competence without killing them. It seems likely that this effect is of short duration.

CHAIRMAN GOOD: Let us focus primarily on four major points that Dr. Möller raised:

   1) the nature of antigenic competition;
   2) the role of antibody in achieving a negative feedback operating through antigen-sensitive cells;
   3) the operation of the tolerance-inducing mechanism at the level of antigen-sensitive cells;
   4) intracellular regulation of antibody systhesis.

DR. SERCARZ: Byers and I performed some experiments involving the in vitro induction and escape from tolerance. The general conclusion from these experiments is that the antibody "response-clock" is turned off right at zero time by a high dose of antigen. The metaphor of a clock is particularly appropriate, I believe. Once the clock is wound, you no longer can have any control over its movement by trying to turn the winding handle (the receptor). Thus, high-dose antigen suppression of the immune response requires a certain kind of early interaction with the antibody receptor, and this interaction is no longer possible very shortly after optimal antigen stimulation. We can ask whether during the high-dose delay, the works of the clock are actually going. Thus, do the necessary biochemical preliminaries, characteristic of the early immune response, take place during this delay?

After the normal antigen triggering of a response, messenger RNA must be made. Ivanyi and I found that the sensitivity

236

of the early in vitro response to actinomycin D was delayed
by a high dose of human serum albumin, as was the response
as a whole. This suggests that the clock never really starts
after a high enough antigen dose.

Finally, it is interesting that passive antibody can
modulate the immune response, even after the time that it is
no longer sensitive to excess antigen. These relations are
represented in Fig. 47. The system used is the rabbit popliteal lymph node, primed 3 months earlier with 10 mg of BSA
and then placed in organ culture for secondary stimulation.
If you give an optimal antigenic stimulus for 2 hours, and
then look at the subsequent response, it starts at about 6
days and peaks several days later. If you have a high dose of
antigen present during the first 3 days of culture, right
from time zero, it will delay the response so that it starts
later and shows similar kinetics but with the displacement
of the whole reaction to a later time. However, if you first
add the optimal stimulating dose, and then follow this several hours thereafter with the high suppressing dose, you
do not delay the response. The clock already has been wound.
Finally, if instead of the suppressing antigen dose you add
passive antibody for 18 hours, the subsequent response can
still be turned off. Thus, at a time where there is no
further sensitivity to high-dose suppression, passive antibody can interfere with the induction. After the first day,
passive antibody no longer has an effect, but the response
is still actinomycin D-sensitive.

If high-dose antigen suppression of the immune response is
reversible in vitro, as in our experimental model, and this
is accepted as a model of tolerance, the clear conclusion
from this fact is that tolerance need not involve cell killing. As a matter of fact, tolerance of a large proportion of
the available X-cell pool may be a common feature of the immune response to a traditional antigen dose. This would be
observable as a displacement to the right of the cellular
kinetics curve of the response with increased doses of antigen. We have observed this in a very sensitive assay system and this is shown in Table 32. A suspension of mouse
spleen cells is prepared at various times after injection of
β-galactosidase and incubated at $37^{\circ}C$ with 15 ug, of β-galac-
tosidase for one hour, followed by overnight storage in the
cold, washed in an excess of Hank's solution, and then sus-
pended in buffer to detect the amount of antigen (enzyme)
that is bound to cells that have either produced antibody or

237

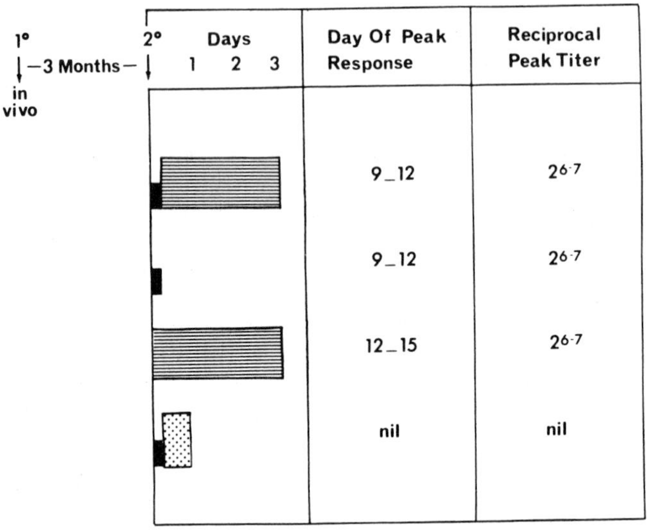

1° ↓ —3 Months— ↓ in vivo	2° Days 1 2 3	Day Of Peak Response	Reciprocal Peak Titer
		9_12	$2^{6\cdot7}$
		9_12	$2^{6\cdot7}$
		12_15	$2^{6\cdot7}$
		nil	nil

Fig. 47 The effects of BSA and anti-BSA on the secondary
response in vitro in lymph node cultures derived
from rabbits immunized with 10 mg BSA 3 months
earlier.

Solid bar = 2 hour treatment with inducing dose of
0.5 mg BSA/ml

Horizontal lines = 5 mg/ml BSA (tolerance-inducing
dose)

Dotted bar = Rabbit anti-BSA, reciprocal HA titer -
2^{14} (9-day post-2° serum)

Following incubation the culture fluids were removed,
the fragments washed repeatedly (6x) and incubation
was continued for 3 weeks. Fresh culture fluid
was replaced every 3 days and assayed for antibody
content.

have receptors on their surface. To detect this enzyme, one
adds a fluorogenic substrate and the fluorescent product is
measured microphotofluorometrically.

The table indicates the antigen-dose effect on the formation of anti-β-galactosidase on day 2 and day 5 after injection of 10, 100, and 1,000 µg of antigen. The values shown
are antibody units, which are related to the amount of

fluorescein produced per cell per hour. Notice that the peak of the response after 10 µg occurs quite early, at 2 days; actually, antigen-binding activity is detectable even at 12 hours after injection. When 1,000 µg is used, the peak of the response is only achieved on day 5 or 6; no antigen-binding activity is evident at 12 or 24 hours.

It appears that even within the normal dose range, the conventional antibody response may start out at the cellular level with tolerance followed by immunity.

TABLE 32

Effect of antigen dose on the formation of anti-β-galactosidase

Day after injection		µg β-Galactosidase		
		10	100	1000
2	TEST	569 ± 66	802 ± 118	424 ± 56
	INTRINSIC	63 ± 6	108 ± 21	115 ± 24
	NET	506	694	309
5	TEST	320 ± 79	580 ± 96	1400 ± 157
	INTRINSIC	165 ± 52	270 ± 57	128 ± 21
	NET	155	310	1272

DR. RAJEWSKY: I would like to cite some findings that have a direct bearing on Dr. Möller's discussion of the suppression of the immune response by bacterial antibody. We have been studying this problem with Dr. Lang and Miss Goddard in the Mishell-Dutton system and observed that passive antibody can suppress only the very early stages of cell recruitment, being ineffective later on.

DR. HASEK: Dr. Möller clearly demonstrated that during certain immune responses a phenomenon resembling antigenic competition can occur. We have some data bearing on this and I would like to cite them since they may indicate that this can be a fundamental point demonstrating there is one common pathway for both immune responses and tolerance.

What we have found is that when we induce tolerance to quite unrelated complex antigens, for example, to turkey tissue in chickens, the animal will accept not only heterografts from the donor, but also other heterografts with different isoantigens from other individuals, a situation that normally does not occur. I wonder whether in these instances we might not also be dealing with some non-specific substance capable of a general suppression of the immune response.

DR. SELA: I also would like to make a comment concerning antigenic competition in the tolerant state because recent work of Dr. Schechter showed another example of this. However, in doing so I must once again say something about semantics: to what extent are we using the same name for entirely different phenomena? Antigenic competition of the type that Dr. Möller discussed involving molecules that have nothing in common is a completely different kind of competition from that studied by Dr. Schechter, which concerns competition between defined, related antigenic determinants. Schechter analysed competition between polyphenylalanyl and polyalanyl determinants when these are attached to different molecules but of the same kind (e.g. ribonuclease or serum albumin). Each one of these, separately, leads to a good immune response (to polyalanyl or to polyphenylalanyl, respectively), but when you immunize with the mixture of poly-alanyl-ribonuclease and polyphenylalanyl-ribonuclease, you get almost exclusively antibodies to the polyphenylalanyl. This competition takes place only as long as the determinants are attached to identical or similar protein carriers. If both of them are on separate molecules of serum albumin there is competition, but if you put one of them on ribonuclease and the other on serum albumin and mix and immunize, you have no competition at all. This again raises the problem of the influence of the carrier.

Now, where the tolerance comes in is this: Dr. Schechter has made newborn rabbits tolerant to polyphenylalanyl serum albumin. These animals still make antibodies to the poly-alanyl determinant when immunized with polyalanyl serum albumin, but they make antibodies against neither determinant when they are immunized with a mixture of the two. Thus, the competition persists in the tolerant states.

DR. SMITH: If antigenic competition, in which one antigen inhibits the response of a closely related one, represents a general phenomenon in which timing is vitally important, it should be demonstrable that closely spaced or properly spaced tolerogenic doses of antigen should be likewise

V. REGULATION OF IMMUNE RESPONSES

competitive in respect to their capacity to induce tolerance. Does anyone know of such experiments?

My other comment refers to Dr. Möller's suggestion that there may be a refractory state, perhaps quite non-specific, in lymphoid cells after stimulation with PHA during which they can't respond to ALS stimulation in order to explain his results. Holtzer's data may be pertinent here, as he shows that during active mitosis, cells that normally are subject to contact inhibition and related effects, temporarily lose this capacity and perhaps other properties that are normally engendered by the cell surface.

DR. LANDY: Among the fine models Dr. Möller alluded to, I would be concerned about the possible relevance of the situations in which he utilized ALS and PHA. Unlike antigen-sensitive or antigen-reactive cells, where at any given time one is dealing with very limited numbers, virtually every lymphoid cell in the host environment is susceptible to these two reagents. Lymphoid cells normally have blood group-like receptors for PHA, while in the case of ALS, its very method of preparation assures its capacity to interact strongly with all lymphocytes.

DR. SISKIND: Dr. Benacerraf earlier referred to some of our recent studies and I would like to say something about some of the results that he and Dr. Möller already alluded to. We have been interested in the maturation phenomenon in the immune response, that is, in the progressive increase in antibody affinity with time after immunization. We first studied this phenomenon in Dr. Eisen's laboratory several years ago. We found that there is a progressive maturation (increase in affinity) with time and that this increase in affinity is influenced by antigen dose in a very predictable fashion. Using DNP-BGG in complete Freund's adjuvants, a large dose of antigen leads to a very slow maturation of the immune response and to the production of large amounts of antibody early in the immune response.

On the other hand, a lower dose of antigen leads to a more rapid increase in the affinity of the antibody being formed, and the increase in its amount occurs, at least initially, at a slower rate. Very high concentrations of antibody appear late in the immune response.

In addition, we have shown that the induction of partial tolerance lowers the affinity of antibody. This indicates

241

that high affinity cells are preferentially rendered tolerant. Furthermore, repeated doses of passive antibody will suppress antibody synthesis but lead to an increase in the affinity of the antibody present in the circulation, i.e. suppression under these conditions predominantly affects low-affinity cells.

We therefore seem to have a variety of interplaying factors that control the progressive increase in affinity. The increase is a simple selective process in which decreasing concentrations of antigen select cells of progressively higher affinity. Low-affinity cells fail to capture antigen at low antigen concentrations and therefore drop out of the immune response. The more antigen one starts with, the less the selective pressure and the less the pressure towards an increase in affinity. Furthermore, over a large range of antigen dosages, the average affinity of the initial antibody formed is approximately the same. It looks as though one starts off with a pool of cells of average affinity and then, as a result of antigen concentration, one gradually selects out cells of highest affinity.

Under conditions of high antigen concentration one tends to drive cells into a production phase early in the immune response, an event that presumably involves relatively little proliferation. This, I think, is consistent with the observations of Sterzl using sRBC. With a large dose of antigen, one apparently does not have a large proliferating pool of cells; the final amount of circulating antibody in the serum is reduced, and one fails to see an increase in affinity. Presumably tolerance induction also plays a role, in that with supra-optimal doses of antigen, one induces tolerance. Since tolerance induction seems to involve the highest affinity cells preferentially this results in a decrease in affinity.

Finally, circulating antibody should interplay with this system by competing with cells for available antigen and depressing cells making low-affinity antibody because under these circumstances they would fail to capture antigen. Thus, in the course of the immune response (i.e. with increased affinity of the antibody formed) one should get a progressive increase in the suppressive effect of circulating antibody, with higher affinity antibody suppressing the formation of low-affinity antibody. We have been able to show clearly that high-affinity antibody is indeed much more efficient in suppressing the immune response than is low-affinity antibody. Also, as the affinity of the cell population increases with time, the cells compete better for antigen and thus become more resistant to suppression.

One additional point I would like to make concerns the question of augmentation, by passive antibody, of the primary immune response. Möller mentioned that with 19S antibody there was an augmentation provided low doses of antibody are used. With 7S antibody one sees exactly the same thing. I think this type of augmentation is not specific in terms of the determinant, but probably involves the entire molecule. I suspect that some of the observations mentioned by Dr. Leskowitz earlier, dealing with two determinants on the same molecule, may be explainable by considerations such as the ones that I have just outlined.

DR. NOSSAL: I want to return to Dr. Möller's thoughtful series of experiments. Dr. Möller's main point was a biological dissection of antigen-sensitive cells and of antibody-forming cells. To me, there was a distinct echo here of the sort of work that Miller presented regarding a separation between the quality of "antigen reactivity" and the quality of "antibody formation." To this I want to add yet a third kind of evidence which also leads us to the conclusion that antibody-forming cell lines and antigen-sensitive cell lines (or memory lines if you want) are separate and distinct. The experiment I am referring to is conceptually very simple and was performed by my colleague Dr. Cunningham. Animals were immunized against sRBC and the question was asked: is the capacity of transferring an adoptive immune response with spleen cells from these animals attributable to antibody-forming cells or to some other types of cell?

What Cunningham did was to remove by micromanipulation, PFC from the pool of spleen cells. His plaque assay is a monolayer assay and from this layer he removed, physically, all PFC, a tedious but straightforward procedure. He ended up with (1) a suspension of PFC and (2) a PFC-free suspension of spleen cells.

First of all, Cunningham's results with these preparations killed, if it needed killing, once and for all, the old Jerne idea that background plaques are the target for antigenic action, because when you take a virgin animal and remove the background plaques and inject them into a recipient animal, subsequently exposed to sRBC, absolutely nothing happens. But when, instead, you use the plaque-deprived spleen population, you get a perfectly normal adoptive immune response. I don't think these results would have surprised any of us, since most of us have doubted for some time that the background plaques are the target for antigen action. What I think is a more interesting aspect of the experiment is this: at 2 or 3 days after antigen injection you have, of course, an increased number of PFC, most of which display blast morphology. You now ask the question whether these cells have the capacity to continue this line, to yield further antibody-forming cells. In other words: is the PFC the target for the antigens' further driving action, or is it not? Cunningham was able to show that the population of plaque-formers was unable to confer an adoptive immune response. However, PFC-deprived population was as effective as the total population in its capacity to confer an adoptive immune response. Though not conclusive, these results certainly fit in well with Dr. Möller's concept of antigen-sensitive cell lines being separate from antibody-forming cell lines.

DR. CINADER: I want enlightenment! I need to get one point clarified! What I heard Dr. Möller say indicated to me that he had two cells of which one was antigen-sensitive and might go on to antibody production after contact with the antigen. I heard nothing that made me think that there were two different cell lines which had different cellular origin. I am not sure that I heard in the factual statement of Dr. Nossal anything that would enable me to draw conclusions about separate cells of thymus or marrow-origin. What I want clarified is whether I have failed to hear some important evidence or whether we see the manifestation of a "fashion"; are these experiments suddenly evidence for two cell lines which have different cellular origin?

CHAIRMAN GOOD: I would like to ask Dr. Nossal whether he means that they are truly separate lines or separate stages. Could it be either/or?

DR. NOSSAL: There is of course no evidence in what Dr. Möller presented, and there is also no evidence in what I have just said of Cunningham's work, as to where these cells come from. If one attempts to put this kind of experimentation together with the data of quite separate origin presented by Miller earlier, then one reaches the tentative conclusion that two different cell lines may be involved. Of course, Cunningham has not yet shown us that one line comes from the thymus and the other from the bone-marrow.

CHAIRMAN GOOD: What is Dr. Möller's comment on this?

DR. MÖLLER: As I said before, we found that you could separate antigen-sensitive and antibody-producing cells by biological and physical methods. Our original interpretation was simple, namely that the two cells developed from the same cell line. The same facts are of course entirely compatible with an idea of two cell lines of different origin.

DR. BRAUN: I want to cite additional results that are in support of Dr. Möller's and Dr. Nossal's report on two cell populations. Mr. Jimenez in our laboratory assayed many fragments of individual spleens of mice that had been immunized with sRBC and had either been suppressed in their response by 6-mercaptopurine, or stimulated in their response by poly A plus poly U. Using the procedure of Nakano and Braun, he assayed the number of microcolonies (clones) forming antibody to sRBC and determined that the number of such clones remained the same regardless of whether the response of the spleen donor had been depressed or stimulated. The only thing that was altered was the size of each clone at the time of assay.

But when spleen cells from stimulated or depressed donors were tested in the Kennedy-type of experiment, by transferring them into an irradiated recipient which was then exposed to sRBC, it was found that there had been a significant alteration in the number of antigen-sensitive cells, even though the number of antibody-producing clones had not been altered by the pretreatment with 6-MP or poly A plus poly U. There were more antigen-sensitive cells in spleens obtained 48 hours after immunization from stimulated donors, compared to spleens from normal donors, and even less antigen-sensitive cells were recovered from 6-MP-treated donors.

So here again is evidence for two types of cells, performing cells and non-performing cells, which can behave entirely differently. Whether or not these represent separate cell populations or are derived from one common stem cell remains a question.

We already referred earlier to the possibility that there may be a process of activation that is antigen-dependent and that there may be a second antigen-dependent step, namely stimulation, in order to permit an increase of activated cell populations, either by division or recruitment. The second step apparently is also antigen-dependent because we demonstrated, quite some time ago, that in order to alter the rate with which antibody-forming populations increase, stimulators, such as those derived from poly A plus poly U are enabled to enter into the cell only if we have antigen present to permit such entrance.

Incidentally, in relation to some of the previous discussions, it should be noted that when we talk about inhibitory effects of antibody, we must clearly distinguish between effects of antibodies at this level of stimulation of activated cells and effects of antibodies at a much earlier level of the immune response (cf. Fig. 37). As soon as we do this, many of the available results become very much clearer.

DR. BENACERRAF: I want to propose that we can distinguish between the hypothesis that we are dealing with two cell stages, or in fact with two cell lines. If there are two cell lines, as proposed by Dr. Nossal, would we not be ready to postulate that the one that is proliferating, so-called Y cells, will never turn into Z cells? In that event, a decisive experiment should be easy. One could isolate the cells involved in a BSA gradient, tag or label them in some way in vitro, reinject them and determine whether or not they give rise to antibody-producing cells.

DR. NOSSAL: Obviously, the Cunningham experiment cannot be construed as definitive at this point. It can only lead in a certain direction. The biophysical separation of cell lines followed by appropriate in vitro stimulation or adoptive transfer is going to provide us with a real answer. Dr. Shortman in our laboratory is trying to achieve such separations and has done so with some success.

CHAIRMAN GOOD: I think that if the concept of separate cell lines is going to have any meaning, it has to have such meaning in a general context and not in the context of specific responses to a few antigens.

Let me just describe what I think are very critical experiments that have been done in our laboratory that indicate

246

that there may be indeed two separate antigen-sensitive cell
lines. Basically, if, after the 17th day of embryonation,
one removes the bursa of Fabricius of a chicken, as Drs. Cain,
Alten and Cooper have done in my laboratory, and introduces
no exogenous influences, such as drugs, or irradiation, one
can get complete elimination of 7S production. Germinal center formation is eliminated by this maneuver. However, 19S
gamma globulin and 19S antibody production remain intact.
On the other hand, 19S production is eliminated by removing
the Bursa prior to 17 days. Under these circumstances 19S
antibody is eliminated along with 7S production. Although
such animals do not have cell systems that can make immunoglobulins, they do have a perfectly adequate system of cells
that can be stimulated to form homograft rejection including
accelerated homograft rejection. Thus, the animals surely
have antigen-sensitive cells.

On the opposite side of the coin, one can completely eliminate the thymus-dependent population in which case these
chickens are still perfectly capable of forming antibody to
a variety of antigens. I suspect that one can look at some
of the issues that have been raised by Möller in terms of
whether one has several stages of differentiation or two
separate lines of cellular differentiation. I think that
it may be a real mistake to draw general conclusions based
on the thymus-dependent lines of cells that have been tested
only for their response to certain antigens such as sRBC.

DR. STERZL: I would like to present one of our experiments
dealing with the use of antiserum against sRBC in which our
objective was to test the intensity of the secondary response when we prevented the completion of the primary antibody response by removing the antigen by an injection of
antiserum 24-48 hours after immunization.

In the first set of experiments (Table 33), mice were injected with different doses of sRBC and antiserum. When
the dose of antiserum was high (dilution 1:10) and the dose
of antigen low (10^8 sRBC), both the primary and secondary
responses were completely eliminated and the results re-
sembled the negative response to a subminimal dose of antigen. When the ratio of antiserum to red cells was lowered
(dilution of antiserum 1:100 and 10^8 sRBC, or antiserum
1:10 and 10^9 sRBC), then the peak of antibody-forming cells
was postponed to the 15th day after immunization and the
majority of cells were of the 7S type. A second dose of

247

TABLE 33

The effect of antiserum given simultaneously with sRBC

Dose of sRBC	Dilution of antiserum	Antibodies detected						After revaccination with 10^8 sRBC	
		4th day	15th day		30th day			4th day	
			compl.	anti-IgG	compl.	anti-IgG		compl.	anti-IgG
1×10^{10}	1:10	403	-	-	-	-		-	-
	1:100	960	-	-	-	-		4,500	510,000
	1:1000	43,503	108	4,063	-	-		4,800	348,500
	0	61,353	58	3,803	-	-		16,675	175,000
1×10^{9}	1:10	5	943	3,436	5	173		41,500	460,000
	1:100	2,029	2,685	23,530	33	183		100,500	1,913,000
	1:1000	10,910	615	17,470	-	-		-	-
	0	48,000	1,130	6,000	-	-		30,400	1,120,000
1×10^{8}	1:10	21	46	-	-	-		8,650	7,000
	1:100	182	353	3,660	3	390		60,900	384,000
	1:1000	3,262	865	16,630	30	80		94,000	1,518,000
	0	42,480	1,224	19,748	106	52		835,000	2,533,000

sRBC evoked a typical secondary response.

An interesting observation was made when we examined the effect of injecting the antiserum at the same time as antigen, in contrast to giving the antiserum 24-48 hours after administration of antigen (Table 34).   When the antiserum (dil. 1:10) was injected at the same time as 10^8 sRBC, the immune response was found to be completely inhibited when the mice were assayed 4 or 15 days later in terms of secondary response.   However, when the same amounts of antiserum and antigen were used and the antiserum was given 24-48 hours after the antigen, a significant lowering, but not a complete inhibition of the immune response was observed at 4 days.   In addition the number of antibody-forming cells decreased to background levels by 15-30 days after immunization.   When the secondary response was evoked, a significant increase in the number of antibody-forming cells was detected, this increase involved only cells that formed antibodies of the 19S type; cells of the 7S type were not present at all. When the serum against sRBC was given later, 72 or 96 hours after antigen injection, the secondary response was normal even though there was a significant inhibition of the primary response.

These results indicate that the cell lines for 19 and 7S antibody formation are not different.   The quantity of antigen injected was large enough to allow the development of both 19 and 7S antibody-forming cells, but when the antigen was bound by antibodies 24-48 hours after immunization, only precursors for the 19S secondary response developed.   This leads to the conclusion that for the appearance of 7S precursors an intensive proliferation and selection process is needed involving the presence of antigen and that the shift to 7S precursors occurs during the interval of 48-72 hours after immunization.

DR. BUSSARD: I want to come back to the Cunningham experiment mentioned by Dr. Nossal.   I think that the results may be ambiguous because they do not tell us whether we are looking at two cell lines; it may well be that we are looking at two cell stages.

May I point out that Cunningham's method, just like Jerne's method, detects only the actual current performance of antibody-producing cells.

The cells in the Cunningham system, regarded as non-plaque

TABLE 34

The effect of antiserum (1:10) given at various time intervals following 10^8 sRBC

Time of serum administration with respect to injection of sRBC	Antibodies detected					After revaccination (10^8 sRBC) 4th day	
	4th day	15th day		30th day			
		comp.	anti-IgG	comp.	anti-IgG	comp.	anti-IgG
simultaneously	21	46	0	-	-	8,650	7.200
24 hrs. later	1,880	57	132	26	261	329,000	304,000
48 hrs. later	2,550	40	50	61	26	705,000	700,600
72 hrs later	10,350	180	60	48	6	327,000	1,360,000
96 hrs. later	88,000	733	1,098	21	7	680,000	1,460,000
none	42,480	1,224	19,748	106	52	835,000	2,533,000

producers, may be endowed with the capacity for antibody
production once they have been transferred to an irradiated
recipient animal. I don't think this kind of experiment
tells us anything, as I said, about whether we are dealing
with two cell types or two cell stages.

DR. UHR: I think the question should be left open as to
whether antigen-sensitive precursor cells recognize different degrees of antigen stimulation. Dr. Shinka in my
laboratory has obtained results which suggest that the dose
of antigen can regulate the extent of replication in the
secondary antibody response. He studied the biosynthetic
properties of individual cells from the popliteal lymph nodes
of rats undergoing a secondary antibody response to the flagella of S. paratyphi B. The cells were exposed to tritia-
ted leucine or thymidine, were identified by bacterial ad-
herence, and were then micromanipulated onto slides for
radioautograms. Dr. Shinka examined cells from animals
boosted with 100 µg or 2 µg of antigen that gave a rapid or
slow rise in serum antibody kinetics, respectively. He
showed that 3 and 4 days after the injection of a booster,
the antibody-producing cells from the group receiving the
larger dose had more grains after leucine labeling and a
higher percentage of the cells were labeled with H_3-thymidine
(with 100 µg, 29.5 and 24.5% of the cells on days 3 and 4
respectively; with 2 µg, 20 and 8.3% respectively). By days
5 and 6, there were few or no cells that labeled with thymidine, and leucine labeling was identical in the two groups.

These results indicate that the dose of antigen can indeed affect the extent of replication in the secondary response. The explanation that is most consistent with the
incorporation data is that antigen-sensitive precursor cells
or early differentiating antibody-forming cells recognize
the dose of antigen injected and replicate at an antigen-dependent rate. The other major possibility is that antigen
may affect the rate of recruitment of precursors which then
replicate and differentiate at fixed rates. This possibility
does not easily explain the thymidine incorporation data but
cannot be excluded.

DR. SISKIND: On the question of exponential recruitment, we
don't yet know what does the recruiting. If what does the
recruiting is growing exponentially, wouldn't you expect exponential recruitment and wouldn't that explain your data?

DR. UHR: Yes, certainly. But what can you suggest that would be growing exponentially?

DR. SISKIND: An antigen-sensitive cell.

DR. MÖLLER: My comment on Dr. Uhr's statement is that it is simple to understand an exponential recruitment of antibody-producing cells if the cell population from which recruitment occurs grows exponentially by, e.g., division, which is the simplest explanation.

There are many explanations for your finding that there is an effect of antigen both on the number of committed cells and on the amount of antibody produced per cell. It is a very intriguing finding, because it suggests that the differentiation from antigen-sensitive to antibody-producing is gradual and continues to be antigen-dependent in each of its various steps. A simple explanation, I think, was offered by Dr. Braun when he suggested that two antigen-dependent steps are needed for the differentiation process. A consequence of your findings would be that two are not sufficient. The cells may need to meet the antigen 3 or 4 times before they eventually develop into truly antibody-producing cells, and it would only be at that stage that they become antigen-independent. How such a scheme can be worked out at the population level remains obscure, but a hypothesis in these general terms would explain the facts.

DR. THORBECKE: I think that for the problem of tolerance it is of importance to determine whether it is possible, after the primary response has already been under way for a while, to interfere with the proliferation of the primed cells that will be able to give a secondary response. I think that it is evident that the major proliferation of primed cells occurs after the peak of the primary response is over, at least, in those systems where a single antigenic stimulus has been given. Histologically, it seems that the preparation for a secondary response is linked to the proliferation of germinal centers. At the time germinal centers are proliferating, it is possible to significantly depress the preparation for a secondary response by treating the animal with either immunosuppressants or passive antibodies. This can be detected most readily by challenge soon after such treatment; if one waits, there is a rapid recovery because of the persistence of antigen and the continued cell proliferation that permits a recovery of the memory cell

population. We have some published evidence - and there is
also evidence from Dr. Sterzl's and Dr. Good's laboratories
that one can affect the formation of immunological memory
preferentially.

I am convinced that antigen continues to drive the immune
response to sRBC. But I think it would be worth looking for
other circumstances where this may not be the case, for
example, in the pattern of stimulation that Gowans discussed
earlier. You will recall that under his conditions isolated
lymphocytes, stimulated in vitro and carefully washed, then
transferred to an irradiated recipient, gave rise to a pla-
teau of antibody production, with no hint of a decline of
the type that would be expected after a day or two on the
basis of the hypothesis that antigen is necessary for driving the system. There is, of course, a question about antigen carry-over in experiments of this type, and this question is not yet resolved.

DR. MÖLLER: I think the basic question in such experiments
concerns antigen uptake on the cells and subsequent transfer
of antigen into the recipient of the cells. Experiments performed to rule out antigen uptake may be very misleading, as
pointed out by Dr. Uhr and by the experiments of Dixon dealing with the very small amount of antigen actually involved
in stimulation. The major part of the antigen is involved
in phagocytosis and very little seems to be needed for immunization. Dixon could not even detect the relevant antigen
by an in vivo absorption with labeled antibody. The same
argument is probably good for the experiments with labeled
antigen, it is unlikely that you will detect the relevant
antigen because it is present in such small quantities.

CHAIRMAN GOOD: We have thus far discussed certain factors
controlling increase and maintenance of immune cells. An
entire conference could be focused on this point alone. However, we need also to move on and consider the ontogeny and
phylogeny of immune responsiveness.

In beginning this discussion, I would simply remind you
that the whole concept of immunological tolerance developed
in context to developmental biology and particularly to
ontogeny. Originally, it was thought, on the basis of
Owen's work, Burnet's interpretation, and the experiments
of Billingham, Brent, and Medawar, that tolerance was something quite peculiar to the developing embryo and could be

produced only in the embryo. In our own work we reasoned that translating tolerance into a useful clinical perspective might involve determining whether or not tolerance could be induced in adult life. We carried out many, many experiments, the results of which established that immunological unresponsiveness or tolerance can indeed be achieved in adult life. This view in a real sense was introduced by Simonsen's findings that argued for an exhaustive immunization.

One question that would be of particular interest for this conference would be whether there is anything truly different between embryo and adult with respect to tolerogenesis.

Another important question is that of the nature of tolerogenic antigens. This aspect is of particular importance for clinical manipulations. Much work has been done along these lines; and many interesting manipulations became possible once we knew enough about histocompatability antigens, such as H-2 in mice, to permit proper matching. It has now become possible to define similar major histocompatibility loci in dogs, monkeys and man, and it seems likely that just as in mice, all mammals will turn out to have a single major histocompatibility locus with multiple alleleles.

To begin this discussion, I would like to call on Dr. Ceppellini to deal briefly with the major histocompatibility locus of man.

DR. CEPPELLINI: Since one of the most important practical applications of induced tolerance relates to allotransplantation in clinical medicine, it would seem appropriate at this point to review some recent developments in our knowledge of histocompatibility in man. There are at the moment two main sources of information: the rate of clinical success of kidney transplantation under immunosuppressive therapy and the survival time of experimental skin grafts. In both situations it has been shown that blood group incompatibilities involving the ABO system, and possibly P as well, affect graft survival adversely. It is also clear that matching for the major red cell antigens is of itself no guarantee of graft acceptance.

Thus, following Medawar's early lead, attention was focused on leucocyte antigens as a better tool for tissue

typing. Progress toward this objective was greatly facilitated by an unusually effective international collaboration
achieved through a series of Workshops sponsored by the
National Institute of Allergy and Infectious Diseases and
the WHO, and held at Duke University, 1964, University of
Leiden, 1965, and the University of Turin, 1967. At these
meetings, techniques, results, and ideas were compared, and
the swift-paced impressive results of these Workshops have
been published in vols. I, II, and III of "Histocompatibility Testing" (Munksgaard, Copenhagen).

Briefly, the majority of serological specificities associated with the lymphocyte membrane belong to one genetic
system, now known as HLA. The HLA antigens are also expressed on the majority of tissues (in decreasing order of
strength: spleen, kidney, liver, skin, muscle, brain).
The equivalence between the factors as described by different laboratories is shown in Table 35; it should be noted
that equivalence does not mean identity but rather close
similarity as judged by significant positive correlation
coefficients.

The HLA specificities are inherited as linked traits in
given combinations or haplotypes (Table 36). Haplotypes
(haploid type) thus correspond to the products of complex
alleles which occupy the HLA region. The number of alleles
that have been shown to exist is very large indeed, they
would total at least 40 if we consider only the better defined factors. However, not all possible combinations of
factors are found in the haplotypes. Recent observations
suggest that different series of mutually exclusive or "segregant" specificities can be recognized. In our laboratory
two series have been identified: series a (or LA) consists
of TO 8, 9, 10, 12, 13 (while TO 14 is a cross-reacting
specificity shared by factors 9 and 12); series b consists
of TO 5, 11, 22 (related to 4a of van Rood) and TO 7, 20
(related to 4b). The members of each series are never inherited in coupling, as, e.g., TO 9 and TO 10, TO 5 and
TO 11 in the family of Table 36.

Family studies suggesting the occurrence of crossing-
overs between determinants belonging to different series have
been reported recently by Amos and Terasaki. However, in
our studies and those of Dausset, involving more than 200
offspring from backcross matings, no recombinants have thus
far been found, indicating that recombination frequencies

TABLE 35

Approximate equivalences between the HLA determinants described in different laboratories

HLA	Amos	Batchelor	Bodmer Payne	Dausset	Engelfriet v.d. Weerdt	Kissmeyer	v. Rood	Terasaki	Walford	Ceppellini TO	%
										2	90
	3			3		4A	4a	3		3	75
										4	65
5	45	25		5	7	MH		6		5*	24
	15			4		T12	4b	9		11*	23
				7				7		6	78
8	41	2	7d	8	1	7d	7d	11	Lc-7	7*	14
7	2		4d	10	3	7c	7c	5	Lc-8	20*	14
1	19	1	LA1	11	4	LA1	LA1	1	Lc-1	8**	21
2(MAC)	1	5	LA2	1(MAC)	2	LA2	8a	2	Lc-2	9**	44
3	4		LA3	12		LA3	LA3	8	Lc-3	10**	26
	3	3		16		LA4		4	Lc-10	12**	29
								12	Lc-20	13**	19
										14**	41
										21*	8
										22*	17

(1) Official designations decided by the WHO committee (New York, September 1968) for the determinants that have been considered to be sufficiently well characterized.

(2) Approximate frequency of the TO determinants in the population of Torino.

(3) TO 14 is recognized by a monospecific antibody and seems to be a crossreacting specificity shared by TO 9 and TO 12

* : Segregant alleles at series 4. Note that 5, 11, 22 are positively associated to TO 2(4a) while TO 7, 20 are positively associated to TO 6(4b)

**: Segregant alleles at series LA.

TABLE 36

Distribution of HLA specificities in family 044

Family No.		A	B	1	2	3	4	5	6	7	8	9	10	11	12	Chromosomes
044	1	+	+	+	+	+	+	+	+	-	-	+	+	+	-	a/b
	2	+	-	+	-	-	-	-	+	-	-	-	+	-	-	c/d
m	3	+	-	+	+	+	+	+	+	-	-	-	+	-	-	a/?
f	6	-	+	+	+	+	+	+	+	-	-	-	+	-	-	a/?
m	7	-	+	+	+	+	+	+	+	-	-	-	+	-	-	a/?
f	9	-	+	+	-	-	-	-	+	-	-	+	-	+	-	b/d
Paternal haplotypes	{			+	+	+	+						+			a: h3
									+					+		b: h27
Maternal haplotypes	{								+				+			c: h31
									+							d: h29

(from Vol. III Histocompatibility Testing; reproduced with permission of Munksgaard, Copenhagen)

within the HLA region must be lower than 1%. This close linkage is confirmed by the observed significant association at the population level of determinants belonging to the two series, and by the fact that combination in the haplotypes is not random even for factors belonging to the two different segregant series. In other words, a marked linkage imbalance still exists between different areas of the HLA region.

The real meaning of the segregant series of determinants will not be clearly understood until the data of formal genetics are integrated with information on the molecular nature of the antigenic product. It is possible, but by no means certain, that each segregant series corresponds to different but closely linked cistrons. The chemical characterization of HLA antigens will therefore be of great interest for a better understanding of the genetic situation. Of greater urgency is the testing of the assumption that specific tolerance can be achieved by appropriate administration, to transplant recipients, of chemically purified donor HLA antigens (together with small, non-toxic, doses of either chemical or biological immunosuppressive agents).

Evidence that HLA is an important (possibly the main) histocompatibility system in man has been accumulating gradually, the data becoming decisive only this past year. As shown in Table 37 the survival time of skin grafts exchanged between siblings who share the same HLA genotype

TABLE 37

Survival of skin grafts (days) and number of HLA incompatibilities

Genetic class of grafts	No.	x̄	HLA Incompatibilities					
			0	1	2	3	4	⩾5
Unrelated	78	12.1	13.6	13.0	12.8	12.9	12.8	11.8
Parent: Child	30	13.8	14.5	13.6	13.8	13.2	13.0	-
Sib : Sib ≠	25	12.8	12.9	13.0	13.1	12.0	12.0	10.0
Sib : Sib =	12		20.0					

≠ with different HLA genotype   = with same HLA genotype

(as ascertained from family analysis) is prolonged by more than one week, in comparison to HLA non-identical siblings. It should be noted that grafts from a donor to a sibling with different HLA genotype do not fare well even if compatible in the sense of blood transfusion (no known antigens are present in the graft that are absent in the recipient). This apparent contradiction is easily understood if one recognizes that HLA typing within families allows the identification of the four parental haplotypes that contribute to the genotype of the children, whereas in the case of unrelated subjects (and even of relatives differing by one or two HLA chromosomes) the few detected HLA specificities are combined with a variety of still unknown specificities that contribute to the overall configuration of the HLA molecules.

Because of the great number of different alleles with low frequency, actual identity of HLA structure is very difficult to achieve in other than members of the same progeny (who at worst have 25% probability of sharing identical genotype). Nontheless, survival of the graft is negatively correlated with the number (and nature) of the HLA factors for which donor and recipient are incompatible. This correlation is barely significant ($P \sim .05$ for the data of Table 37) in the case of experimental skin grafting, which is known to be a very exacting test, but reaches higher values in the case of kidney transplantation under immunosuppressive therapy. Clinical data indicate that identity is better than simple compatibility. In fact, van Rood and Eernisse,

when typing <u>a posteriori</u> recipients who had survived at
least 18 months after transplantation found a high proportion of survivors who had HLA identical to their sibling
donors, suggesting that only HLA-different recipients had
disappeared from the sample because of death (Table 38).

TABLE 38

Relation between kidney graft survival and leukocyte groups

| | | Sib to sib | | |
	random families A	random expected B	patients found C	patients expected D
Identical	174	10.4	10	4.7
Compatible	137	8.3	2	3.7
Incompatible	358	21.3	6	9.6
Total alive			18	
Total operated		40		
			P<0.01	

(from Advances in Transplantation; reproduced with permission of
Munksgaard, Copenhagen)

The majority of clinical data show that recipients matched
for HLA do well, while the fate of known mismatches is un-
predictable, i.e., some times they appear to survive as
well as matches.   This finding suggests that under immunosuppressive therapy even HLA does not behave as a strong
locus and some incompatibilities can be "tolerated."

It is thus evident that tissue typing and the induction
of immunological tolerance are complementary tools; the
less the histocompatibility differences (achieved through
typing), the easier the production of specific tolerance.

DR. SIMONSEN: In relation to Dr. Ceppellini's discussion
of the importance of the HLA locus in man, I think it probable that each species has a single strong locus of over-
riding importance for transplantation and tolerance to
grafts.   In this context I would like to mention some kidney transplantations in rats performed in our laboratory by
Dr. Sakai.   As mentioned already by Dr. Ceppellini, there
is a minimum of 25% identical siblings to be expected with
respect to one locus no matter how many alleles the latter

may comprise. If the result of kidney grafting is really determined by the one strong histocompatibility locus (in the rat called Ag-B) then there is a mininum of 25% of long-term survivors to be expected in grafting between siblings in an outbred colony of rats.

In the particular outbred colony we have studied, close to 50% of the sibling kidneys lasted for many months without any extraneous immunosuppression whatsoever, while the rest were rejected within 3 weeks, usually around the 12th day. The long-term survivors had normal serum creatinin and normal kidney histology after 3-4, even up to 9 months. Such findings do strongly suggest that, provided identity is arranged with respect to the strong locus, incompatibility caused by weaker loci may be overcome spontaneously by a mechanism which I suspect is that of high-dose tolerance.

CHAIRMAN GOOD: We think, Dr. Simonsen, that we have a clinical observation that goes along with this and with your early work on exhaustive immunization.

We have been concerned with the issue of reconstituting immunologically defective children whose thymus failed to develop in the normal manner and whose thymus-dependent system and thymus-independent system (plasma cells) failed to develop normally. In the past, we have been able to reconstitute such children only temporarily; they ultimately died of fulminating GVH reactions. Such GVH phenomena occurred in about nine such cases distributed around the world. For one child in which matching was made by HLA typing and by the mixed lymphocyte cultures (zero response with the donor cell from a sibling) we have been successful in effecting reconstitution. As would have been predicted from the studies in mice, the child has gone through a relatively mild GVH reaction including splenomegaly, hepatomegaly, skin rash, i.e., all the characteristics of the GVH reaction. This male child has now recovered and is immunologically competent, at least to a degree, and is chimeric for female lymphoid cells.

We think the successful treatment of this patient represents in a dramatic way the induction of high-zone tolerance, far beyond the neonatal period, still allowing this child to express immunological vigor, at least with respect to certain immunological responses. We have not had to use immunosuppression to achieve this tolerance to transferred immunogically competent cells when, by matching, major histoincompatibilities have been avoided.

One of the questions that has constantly stimulated those of us working with tolerance, is the possibility that we could eventually obtain the key antigens in purified form, and would know enough about them to induce, at will, tolerance across major or minor barriers. In our laboratory we have been able to achieve tolerance with sub-cellular material quite regularly across the non-H-2 barriers in newborn mice. In a few experiments we have even been able to bridge relatively weak H-2 barriers. Dr. Davies has made extensive studies of these transplantation antigens and I wonder if he would agree that what we need at the moment is not only a degree of matching, as suggested by Dr. Ceppellini, but also the appropriate purified soluble HLA transplantation antigens, such as those reported at the recent Transplantation Congress in New York.

DR. DAVIES: To understand transplantation systems, it is necessary to study simpler model systems. These reveal some properties of antigens that one feels are desirable and perhaps even necessary for tolerance induction. One of these is solubility; the transplantation antigens are cell-bound, rather firmly so in many cases, so that for some years there were only insoluble preparations available that limited the scope of experiments one could carry out.

About a year or two ago, methods for solubilizing the antigens were worked out and now we are in a very much better position to study the system. I will shortly give you some idea of how far we are at this point from attaining real prospects of tolerance for transplantation antigens.

I won't go into details of purification, as it has all been published. The first question I think we should ask is this: are the many antigens that are determined by different genetic loci, discrete separable molecules? It is not self-evident that this should be so. Take the ABO system in man, for example. This complex structure is built up by enzymes that attach different determinant groups. These enzymes are coded by loci that are not linked. But it turns out that by various methods one can isolate products from which it is possible to separate the antigens determined by different histocompatibility loci.

Figure 48 shows an example where five different mouse iso-antigens, H-2 (in which we are mainly interested), H-6, H-7, TL, and theta (a brain-thymus isoantigen) are shown to be separable. The separation starts with papain treatment of membrane preparations of lymphoid cells. One of three things may happen: some antigens may be destroyed (an example of that is H-7). Others may still be active on the

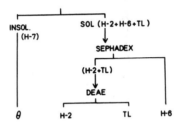

Fig. 48   Separation of products of different loci of mouse iso-antigens.

insoluble residue (an example is theta), and still others may appear in the soluble fraction. In the soluble fraction we have H-2, H-6 (as Lilly and Nathenson have shown), and TL. H-2 and H-6 can be resolved by gel filtration and the others can be resolved on DEAE columns.

The next question is whether H-2 in the mouse and HLA in man are single molecules with many different antigenic determinants, or whether they are a family of closely similar molecules each carrying one kind of determinant. Enzyme-solubilized H-2 antigens from a single individual of an inbred strain of mice permit the separation of different antigenic components.

Figure 49 shows a DEAE column scan, 1 of about 8 runs we have done on 6 different mouse genotypes; this is $H-2^d$ and here we have measured most of the specificities of the $H-2^d$ allele. It would be too complex to put them all on the picture. It shows that, for instance, H-2.4 is completely separated from H-2.28. Some of the antigens are incompletely resolved, but taking all of the different genotypes that we have examined so far, it is clear that most of the known 30-odd specificities are separable and that each

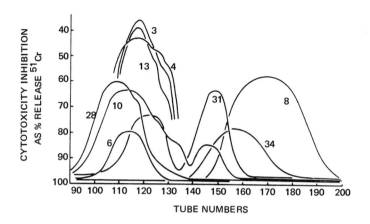

Fig. 49   Separation by DEAE chromatography of individual
specificities of murine H-2^d.

specificity is on a distinct molecule.

In the case where there is a double peak (e.g. H-2.31),
we take it to mean that there are two antibodies in the
serum but there is no mouse strain that does not either
have both or neither of the antigens.

We thus come to the point, that if one is to describe
any properties of transplantation antigens (and there are
so many descriptions) they are only valid if related to
one of these molecules and not to the unresolved mixture.

Table 39 shows some data for H-2.5. They are fairly
normal figures for a protein; there is some carbohydrate
present (about 15%) but we do not know whether it contributes to the specificity. In arriving at a molecular
weight of 47,000 we have made an assumption about the partial specific volume (which is not directly measurable).
The figures will differ for each different H-2 molecule.

What I have said about H-2 is equally applicable to HLA
in man. The HLA antigens can be extracted in the same way.
They can be solubilized by the same methods, separated out
by the same fractionation procedures, and at the end one
can show that here too each specificity is probably on a
different molecule. Fig. 50 illustrates an HLA separation

263

TABLE 39

Properties of isolated mouse H-2 antigen.

Stokes radius	32.2 Å
Diffusion coeff.	$6.2 \times 10^{-7}\,cm^2/sec$
Sed. coeff.	3.6 S
Buoyant density	1.33 gm/cc
Molecular wt.	47,000
f/f_0	1.28
Isoelectric pt.	4.8

on DEAE Sephadex. Whereas in the mouse one has a good
selection of monospecific antisera and gets normally single
peaks using each one, here one sees more complex patterns
because fewer of the sera are monospecific. The sera will be
more complex anyway, because the mouse experiments are
done with homozygous material whereas man is heterozygous
and would show up to twice as many specificities. We
have looked for most of the specificities of this particular

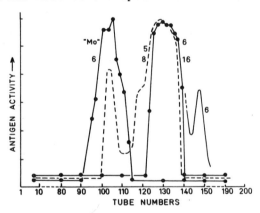

Fig. 50   Separation of HLA antigens on DEAE.

(Data reproduced with permission of Biochemical &
Biophysical Research Communications)

donor in collaborative work with Drs. Dausset, Colombani
and Viza. Only two sera give single peaks, 5 and 8 are
double peaks, and others are even more complex.

CHAIRMAN GOOD: Dr. Davies, it has now been observed in
many laboratories that there is a real difference with respect to tolerance induction with the HLA and the H-2 systems. Is this attributable to a chemical difference in
these antigens?

DR. DAVIES: Both H-2 and HLA antigens are by our analyses,
glycoproteins but we should be careful in any interpretation of this because we do not yet have evidence for homo-
geneity. The non-H-2 antigens are mostly simple proteins.

DR. SIMONSEN: Drs. Reisfeld and Kahan, speaking at the recent Transplantation Congress, described a purified transplantation antigen which did not contain sugar. Were they
referring to HLA, H-2, or what?

DR. DAVIES: They described guinea pig antigens that apparently contain no carbohydrate. One does not know, of
course, the genetic relationships of the guinea pig system.
We would judge, from our data, that HLA and H-2 are genetic
homologues, but one does not know if this is likely for the
guinea pig system. It should be noted that the Reisfeld
and Kahan method of hydrolysis of antigen was criticized.
They looked only for glucosamine, after some days of hydrolysis under very severe conditions, in the presence of a
great deal of amino acids. I do not wish to imply that carbohydrate really is present in their material, but we and
others find about 15% total carbohydrate in our preparations.

DR. SIMONSEN: You say that the complexity of the HLA locus
should make us pessimistic in regard to inducing tolerance
with the multitude of soluble components. Of course, it
would be nice if the locus were not so complex, but I think
the fact that the specificity is on different molecules may
be turned to our advantage. If we had 100 or more alleles,
so that almost any unrelated donor-recipient combination
would be incompatible, and if we had to produce soluble HLA
antigens as a single complex molecule from one particular
donor, then you would indeed be in trouble. But if you can
make up artificial cocktails of antigens, then almost any

donor material may be of some use, and this may prove to be of great advantage.

DR. DAVIES: Yes, it does have some advantage.

DR. BENACERRAF: I was going to ask the same question which was asked by Dr. Simonsen concerning the importance of comparing your data with those of Drs. Reisfeld and Kahan. Since they are now collaborating with Dr. Ceppellini on the HLA antigen. I wonder if Dr. Ceppellini could clarify this point as well.

The other question I wish to ask concerns the fact that you are using papain to extract your material from the cell membrane. The work of LaPrelle with HSA would suggest that the use of proteolytic enzymes is most likely to convert a single antigenic molecule into a variety of molecules with different determinants. The approach of Kahan and Reisfeld in contrast to your procedures, uses the mildest possible, purely physical, separation. It seems to me that this would be more likely to produce an undegraded molecule.

DR. DAVIES: The sonic method gives a very small yield. From discussions with Reisfeld I know he intends to compare the yield obtainable by our respective methods. Of course, the products are all artifacts when considered in the light of membrane structure, but I think the way we have split them, using papain, ficin or bromelin to give a single specificity on each molecule, they have some genuine reflection of genetic determination and each one does have a right to be called a molecule.

In reference to the other question, the material that Reisfeld and Kahan described has not been separated out into different specificities, as far as I know; indeed their data have not yet been published for our scrutiny. In our experiments we removed a great deal of impurity, mainly protein, before putting the material on DEAE columns for separation.

DR. CEPPELLINI: My collaboration with Drs. Kahan and Reisfeld has not involved either the preparative or physicochemical aspects of the work on HLA antigen, but rather the evaluation of its activity in vitro and in man. The product used in these biologic studies was derived from human

spleens and represents a single discrete band in acrylamide
gel (discontinuous electrophoresis). The preparations were
able to neutralize cytotoxic anti-HLA alloantisera. In general the neutralizing activity was expressed against all
determinants characterizing the HLA phenotype of the spleen
donors. These findings favor the view that HLA factors are
likely to be carried by a single molecule, or at most, by
very few molecules with similar physico-chemical characteristics. The association of the different HLA factors may
depend on (1) the genotype (coupling or repulsion phase)
and (2) their belonging to one or the other of the series
(so-called subloci) which make up the HLA system.

One thing is certain, the use of proteolytic enzymes for
isolating HLA antigens, considered by all to be proteic in
character, may very well result in the production of molecular fragments. These fragments could, therefore, carry
individual specificities which in nature characterize a
single molecule. An analogous situation is known in the
case of some of the Gm specificities, e.g. Gm-1 and Gm-3
that are carried respectively by the Fc and Fd fragment of
the same gamma-1 chain.

In Turin we found that the product obtained by Kahan
and Reisfeld, by a purely physical separation procedure,
was able to elicit a delayed type of reaction in subjects
who had been sensitized by skin grafts, as had previously
been demonstrated by Kahan for the analogous antigens in
the guinea pig system. It is also noteworthy that from
the physico-chemical point of view the products derived
from guinea pigs and man are similar. This is not likely
to be coincidental.

DR. MITCHISON: Dr. Davies, would you give some practical
advice to anyone who wants to do some more work on these
mouse antigens? If one wants an antigen that can be obtained in maximum yield and that at the same time will provoke a reasonably strong response, which one do you recommend? And which strains of mice should one use? Could
you give us an indication of roughly how many mice one
needs to obtain, say a microgram of antigen?

DR. DAVIES: I don't think it matters too much what mouse
strain one uses. We tend to choose those that breed well.
It is, of course, useful in tolerance work to choose a
simple barrier. For instance, $H-2^k$ to $H-2^a$ appears to be a

single specificity difference, and the reverse is a complex one.

For many purposes one does not have to use pure material. There are a variety of methods that permit the extraction of material from a spleen suspension; we normally use hypotonic salt extraction. The papain treatment is very simple, after that I would recommend that one does pass the material through G200 Sephadex and take away the higher and lower molecular weight impurities. To go beyond this and to recover material from DEAE columns is much more difficult and requires a rather large amount of starting material. In regard to yields, I think you get about 10 mg of relatively crude material from, say, 500 mice.

DR. SELA: I wonder, in view of the fact that the yields are not exactly splendid by column procedures, if once one has succeeded in getting some pure material, one might not be able to obtain monospecific antibodies to such fractions and use them to bind these to water-insoluble immunoadsorbents. This may be a great shortcut in isolation procedures.

DR. COHN: Why don't people, working in this field, use cell lines from the mouse and isolate (with cytotoxicity assays) mutants from them that lack each one of the surface antigens. Then one could start fractionating from the monospecific lines and get information at the same time about whether different molecules with different properties are involved.

DR. DAVIES: This has been done. We can extract tissue culture cells, but there are certain things that have to be established, for instance, their HLA status. HLA antigens are present, but it is not yet certain if all specificities are represented as on the parent cell. It also turns out that some cell lines have more HLA antigen and others have less.

CHAIRMAN GOOD: With Dr. Moore's cell lines you can prepare kiligrams of cells and there you have one source of HLA that is available in fantastic amounts.

DR. PLESCIA: I have a short practical question. If a chief objective for isolating a histocompatability antigen is to use it to induce tolerance to it, does it really make much difference whether the specificity of this antigen is part of the original molecule or part of the smaller molecule? In fact, it may be that you can induce tolerance much more effectively if the determinant is not part of a fragment. Also, does it make any difference whether the particular specificity is distinct and separate from all other specificities which might be shared by the recipient?

From the practical point of view, the problem may thus not be as hopeless as it seems now when we are concerned with the isolation and study of individual components.

CHAIRMAN GOOD: Before Dr. Davies answers, I will add one point to the question. It seems that in almost all systems where studies have been done, immunogenicity and tolerogenicity have gone hand in hand. One notable exception, with respect to transplantation antigens, are the antigens extracted from liver. We have found that these subcellular antigens are tolerogenic but not effectively immunogenic.

I wonder if you would react to this observation along with the previous question. Can we expect to have tolerance-inducing transplantation antigens that may not be immunogenic?

DR. DAVIES: The substances we have studied are immunogenic but not strongly so. We do not yet know how tolerogenic they are.

To answer Dr. Plescia, the original complex from which the soluble antigens are isolated is an insoluble material that is not suitable for induction of tolerance as far as one can see. After all, particulate matter gets mopped up by macrophages and this is one thing one must avoid. If one could get small soluble molecules that carry all the specificities, this would be easier for tolerance work.

DR. E. MÖLLER: First, I would like to say to Dr. Cohn that it is probably very difficult to select with the aid of cytotoxic antisera tissue culture lines that lack antigens. All the work that has been done so far shows that in this way you only reduce the concentration of antigens on the cells.

Secondly, I would like to ask Dr. Davies, whether he believes that transplantation antigens are integral parts of the cell membrane?

A third question: I have difficulties in seeing how the Old and Boyse experiments, demonstrating that a depression of TL antigens leads to an increase in various H-2 specificities in the same cells, can be interpreted in any other way than that all H-2 antigen specificities have to be present on the same molecule.

DR. DAVIES: In regard to the situation with TL: I think that one could hardly say that TL is not really some kind of H-2 antigen. It is very closely linked genetically and seems to be only separated from the H-2 locus by its own regulator gene. As you saw in one of my figures, TL antigen solubilized in the same way as H-2 and with the same kinetics; it is obviously a very similar kind of substance. It is possible that the TL gene just puts another determinant on an H-2 molecule. We are trying now to remove portions of the TL molecule to see if one can convert TL into H-2. Most of H-2 antigen is on the external membrane, I think the best estimate for internal H-2 is 20% (results of Dr. Boyle).

CHAIRMAN GOOD: I would like now to ask Dr. Silverstein to open the discussion on ontogenic development in relation to tolerogenesis.

DR. SILVERSTEIN: I would like to raise several questions with respect to ontogenic development and its relationship to immunologic competence and to the question of immunologic tolerance.

There are certainly more questions to be asked than answers to be given. To repeat Dr. Good's first question, is there a difference in kind between the so-called immunologically immature animal and the mature animal, and in the manner in which one induces tolerance at these stages of development? So we want to ask: Does immunologic immaturity really exist? And is it necessary to have an immunologically competent animal, competent in all of the respects that we have been discussing in the last few days, in order to achieve immunologic tolerance, or can one achieve it in the incompetent animal?

We know now that for most, if not all, of the species that have been studied (and the data here are very scattered) that there exists what appears to be a step-wise

maturation of an achievement of immunologic competence by
the developing animal.

We know more about the fetal lamb than about any other
species, but data from this species are corroborated in the
newborn mouse, the fetal rhesus, and in several other species, thus permitting a biological generalization.

Starting at conception and going on to birth at 150 days
gestation in the lamb, and then into the postnatal period,
we find that there is step-wise appearance of competence to
form antibodies or to reject grafts in the animal at different stages of gestation. Each antigen has its own critical
time in any given species, so that there is something like
a homeostatic control within each species, all animals developing competence to a given antigen at about the same
time. At the time competence is developed, e.g. to ϕX174
in the lamb, we see no ability to respond in any manner to
any of the other antigens that have been tested. As gestation proceeds, we then see a manifestation of the different
competencies upon appropriate stimulus. The differences
observed are not due to variations in the sensitivity of
the assay procedures employed, they appear to be real. For
a number of antigens immunologic competence does not appear
until after birth.

I'm not satisfied that we know as yet the basis for the
development of such competence; whether it represents the
appearance at that particular stage of gestation of antigen-
sensitive cells that have arisen for the first time from
stem cells, or whether as Braun and others have suggested,
it may be the appearance of a processing mechanism able to
provoke the participation of preexisting competent cells.

When competence first appears, does it appear in an all-
or-none manner? How does it relate quantitatively to the
competence that we are used to seeing in the adult? There
is some discrepancy in this respect in the literature.
Makinodan and Peterson (J. Immunol., 93, 886, 1964) have
suggested that the development of immunological competence
is a slow and progressive maturation, and they point out
that in the mouse, with respect to anti-sRBC, there appears
to be a slow increase in the number of stem cells during
postnatal life.

We do not see such events in any of the animals that we
have studied. We rather see an abrupt appearance of full
competence. If we perform an orthotopic skin homograft

before about 75 days of gestation, the fetal lamb is unre-
active to it. But if we apply the graft close to the day of
achievement of competence, the graft is dealt with by the
fetus in a manner precisely analogous, both quantitatively
and qualitatively, to the way that the adult handles the
graft.

As we have shown in studies with Dr. Uhr, injection of
ϕX174 phage into the fetal lamb, provokes a response entirely comparable to that obtained in an adult. We have
examined, with the aid of the Jerne technique, whether the
fetal Rhesus monkey, from mid-gestation, displays a paucity
of stem cells, i.e., of antigen-sensitive cells. Comparing
the adult and the fetal Rhesus, in respect to their first
response to sRBC, one cannot distinguish between the fetus
and the adult. The curves of their initial primary response
are almost superimposable, which suggests two things to us.
First, when the fetal Rhesus achieves competence, it has
the same proportion of antigen-sensitive cells (i.e., presumably of stem cells) that the adult has; and secondly,
there is no immaturity in the manner in which these cells
respond to antigenic stimuli with respect to their proliferative doubling time. The expansion of the population of
antibody-forming cells occurs at the same rate in both fetus
and adult.

It may be interesting to consider the mechanism for the
acquisition of tolerance in situations in which new antigens
appear during development. There are a number of situations
in which, for example, new enzymes appear during gestation
and immediately after birth, i.e., when the fetus is called
upon to perform functions that the mother heretofore has
taken care of. The developing animal must be called upon
frequently to develop tolerance to such new antigens.

We also have the interesting situation not only in the
fetus but also in the adult, of the animal being called
upon to respond very rapidly with immunological tolerance
(to take the most pertinent example) to a new immunoglobulin chain (or an antibody) with unique antigenic determinants, which it has never before had to produce in any significant amount. This may involve low-dose tolerance in
one situation and high-dose tolerance in another.

On the other hand, there are examples of an apparent
cessation of the formation of a protein with persistence of
a tolerance state to such protein. For example, the fetus

of most mammalian species makes a unique fetal protein,
called fetuin; in some species, its production ceases in
utero. Thereafter this protein can no longer be detected
and attempts to immunize adult sheep with such fetal lamb
fetuin have been uniformly unsuccessful.

DR. WAKSMAN: I would like to address myself to the last
point raised by Dr. Silverstein, which concerns the mechanism of tolerance induction during ontogeny as new components
appear in the circulating fluids and in the tissues. As you
know, we have published a number of papers showing that antigen which penetrates the thymus can quite readily induce a
high degree of tolerance in cells developing there. In fetal life, there is a point at which central lymphoid organs,
such as the thymus, are the only location in the body where
there are cells that can in fact be made tolerant.

Let us consider the question whether other central organs
besides the thymus can show a similar property. I would
like to describe to you a preliminary result obtained in
our laboratory by Dr. Hanaoka. It concerns the rabbit appendix and the production of mercaptoethanol-sensitive antibody which, on the basis of work done by others, is probably conventional IgM.

Dr. Hanaoka's procedure consisted of removing one popliteal lymph node, giving the rabbit lethal X-irradiation while
shielding the marrow in the extremity from which the node had
been removed, and either shielding or not shielding the appendix. Then alum-precipitated BGG was injected in a dose
of 200 µg, either intravenously or into an artery supplying
the appendix. The animal received a second intravenous
challenge 4 weeks later.

In animals that simply had the popliteal node removed,
there was a conventional antibody response following various
stimulations, the antibody formed being mercaptoethanol-sensitive (MES) and probably 19S. This was followed by a later
rise of mercaptoethanol-resistant (MER) antibody, presumably
7S. After secondary challenge there was again production of
MES antibody and a rapid rise in MER. In animals X-irradiated without shielding of any organs, there was at best a
minimal primary response. However, 4 weeks later, immunocompetence had recovered sufficiently so that these animals
gave a very substantial secondary response, and some of
them produced large amounts of MES antibody. When the

appendix was shielded during irradiation, there was a considerably exaggerated primary 19S response and, following secondary challenge, a good deal of both MES and MER antibody.

Finally, and this is the point of the experiment, two animals whose appendix was shielded during irradiation, were given soluble deaggregated BGG in a dose of 200 μg as the primary injection. There was practically no primary response. When secondary challenge with alum-precipitated antigen was carried out 4 weeks later, immunocompetence for the production of MER antibody had recovered, but there was only an insignificant amount of MES produced. In a second group of rabbits, the primary antigen was injected into the appendix artery. Almost all animals showed a considerable exaggeration of the MES response, compared with animals given BGG intravenously, and they showed a diminished MER response. In animals given deaggregated BGG into the artery, there was again virtually no response. After a secondary challenge with alum-precipitated BGG, there was little 7S memory and, again, almost no 19S response.

These preliminary data imply a definite inhibition of the production of MES antibody by soluble antigen that is delivered more or less directly to competent cells in the appendix. I suggest as a generalization that during ontogeny, as new blood and tissue antigens appear, most will probably induce tolerance in all available lymphoid cells and, in particular, in lymphoid cells in organs that are specialized in relation to certain types of immune responses.

DR. MÖLLER: I would like to pose a question to Dr. Silverstein. To determine the initiation of the immune response during ontogeny is complicated by the fact that variables not directly related to the presence of immunocompetent cells may influence the results, e.g., the maturation of antigen-capturing mechanisms. Tolerance induction, however, seems to be a more direct way of detecting immunocompetent cells. Do you have any data on the time of appearance of inducibility of tolerance with the various antigens that you have studied in the sheep?

DR. SILVERSTEIN: I have very little data on tolerance induction with only a few odds and ends of observations. The first is that, if one gives intravenous ovalbumin to

the fetal lamb, at about 60 days of gestation (and you will
recall that competence to ovalbumin appears at about 120
days of gestation) this ovalbumin disappears from the circulation and the animal subsequently does not react as if
it had ever experienced it. If we immunize this animal
with ovalbumin after 120 days, we get what appears to be a
primary response. If we put a skin graft on an animal prior
to let us say midgestation, when it is unable to manifest
competence, it does not subsequently behave as if it had
experienced the graft. Once the animal achieves competence,
we have a mixed result, about what one might predict. A
minority of the animals proceed to retain the graft for very
long periods of time, and seem to be fully tolerant. A majority of the animals have what appears to be a partial
tolerance, so that the graft is more or less slowly rejected. Sometimes the graft is able to keep up with the slow
rejection, so that the animal does not lose the graft.
Again, a minority of the animals will suddenly recognize
the existence of the graft on their skin at mid-gestation
and in very short order proceed to reject it. I am afraid
that all of this does not contribute very much to the question of whether there are antigen-sensitive cells prior to
this time.

DR. GELL: I want to talk about another sort of isoantigen
which is easier to cope with than histocompatibility antigens: that is the IgG allotype and the possibility of tolerance to allotypic determinants. Clearly the tolerance
situation for allotypes in certain genetic situations
ought to be an ideal one; that is to say, you have maternal
IgG transmitted prenatally which can contain up to 50% or
more of a foreign determinant. The IgG of the newborn
rabbit is of course practically entirely maternal; it
starts making its own IgG in about three to four weeks.

One, therefore, has a situation where there is prenatal
transmission of large amounts of a foreign determinant, an
isoantigen, which represents a relatively weak antigen. It
must be admitted that as far as immunogenicity is concerned,
this is a special situation, because allotypic antigens are
not immunogenic by ordinary intravenous injection, however
extensively you immunize, but need adjuvant.

As far as the tolerance to maternally transmitted foreign
allotype is concerned, Dr. Kelus and I could find no evidence

for such tolerance subsequent to routine immunizations to allotypes (Gell and Kelus, Nature 211, 766, 1966). After a couple of courses of the allotypic immunoglobulin, coated on Proteus vulgaris, which acts as an adjuvant, the recipient produces antibody against the allotype, whether or not there has been maternal transmission of the immunizing allotypic determinant. Obviously we could give additional injections and see if tolerance was produced by keeping up the level of antigen for a longer period of time (although one would expect that the level of about 2 mg/ml in the circulating blood at birth and continuing at any rate for some weeks would be enough to tolerize). We did a preliminary experiment along these lines and Table 40 illustrates the effect that I am referring to. To the first rabbit, which

TABLE 40

Effect of maternal allotype and injection of allotypic immunoglobulin
on the production of antibody to the allotype in rabbits

Animal No. & Allotype	Allotype of Mother	Injection.	Titre after immunization against As.6.	
			Course I.	Course II
81/63 3/4	3/4,6	14-56 days 20 inj. total 154 ml pool of As6 serum	Neg.	1/160
82/05 1/4	1/4	-do-	1/1250	1/5000
82/01 1/4	1/4	-do-	1/1250	1/5000
81/67 23/4	3/46	Nil	1/160	1/2500
82/03 1/4	1/4	Nil	1/5000	1/10,000
32/04 1/4	1/4	Nil	1/5000	1/5000

had an allotype of As 3/4 and maternal IgG As6, we gave injections of homozygous pooled As6 serum between 14 and 56
days after birth, 154 ml in all. The next two rabbits in
the table were of allotype 1/4 from a 1/4 mother; these,
therefore, did not receive any As6 maternally. They had
the same heavy tolerization course starting at 14 days.
The fourth rabbit is an animal with an As6 mother which had
no course of tolerization. The last two rabbits are controls.

After the tolerization courses, we gave all the animals
a routine immunization with As6 immunoglobulin coated on
Proteus. It can be noted that the first animal displayed
an appreciable degree of tolerance, whereas in the other
two animals, whose mothers were not As6, this heavy tolerization course was ineffective. In the fourth animal,
which did not have a tolerization course but did have the
neonatal transmission, there is slight evidence for some
resistance to immunization which disappeared after a second
course of immunization.

It is surprising that in a situation where you have the
exposure of "virgin" cells to a foreign substance (which is
immunogenic under appropriate conditions) you do not get
the tolerance you expect; even with very heavy tolerization, plus prenatal transmission, the sort of non-responsiveness obtained is not very impressive.

DR. CINADER: Dr. Roy, in collaboration with Dr. Dubiski
and myself, also attempted to render animals tolerant to
the allotypic specificity of the light chain. However, we
did not use an allotype that had been transferred through
the maternal circulation but rather one which was completely
new to the neonate. Our tolerance-inducing dose was small
compared to that employed by Dr. Gell and his colleagues;
it was 3 ml of serum. This serum was centrifuged at high
speed for several hours to avoid the presence of any aggregates of immunoglobulin. We immunized animals, in later
life, as shown by the syringe-symbols in the accompanying
figures, using Proteus vulgaris coated with antibody.

Animals injected at birth developed antibody later than
did animals that had not been injected at birth. The extent of the delay depended on the method by which the presence of antibody was determined. If we relied on double
diffusion, a delay of two weeks in the appearance of anti-

body could be observed (Fig. 51). If we relied on agglutination of tanned sensitized erythrocytes, we found an even

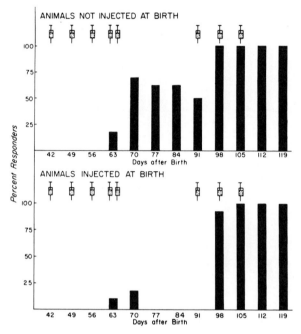

Fig. 51 Tolerance induction to the allotypic specificity
of the light chain as judged by double diffusion
in agar.

smaller difference in the responsiveness of animals injected at birth and of animals not so injected (Fig. 52). It
is clear that the maintenance of such tolerance, as may have
been induced, was unusually ephemeral. It is quite possible that this short-lived tolerance may not be due to a
unique fate of immunoglobulin but that it may result from
the fact that we are looking for antibody to a narrowly restricted number of determinants and not – as is usual in
this type of experiment – at the summation of responses to
many different determinants.

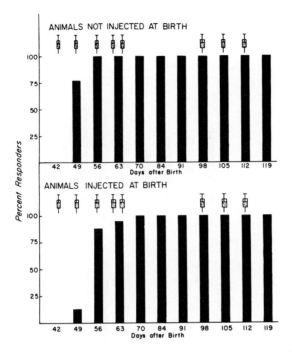

Fig. 52   Duration of tolerance to allotypic specificity of
the light chain as judged by agglutination of
tanned erythrocytes sensitized with immunoglobulin.

279

VI

SPECULATION ON CELLULAR AND MOLECULAR MECHANISMS INVOLVED IN IMMUNOLOGICAL RESPONSIVENESS AND TOLERANCE

A theory — Role of cellular recognition sites and of "carrier antibody" — Induction vs. paralysis of the antigen-sensitive cell — Monomers vs. polymers as tolerogens and immunogens — Common mechanisms for low-zone and high-zone tolerance — Antigenic competition — Sensing by the cell of conformational changes at the cell surface — Consequences of the continuous emergence of new antigen-sensitive cells — Origin of "carrier antibody;" significance of maternal transfer — Free or cell-bound carrier antibody?

VI. SPECULATIONS ON MECHANISMS

DR. COHN: I think it is clear to most of you that you can generate facts much faster that I can understand them, above all since I am an outsider to this subject. The only part of the discussion that I really grasped was the problem of naked antigen stimulating virgin lymphocytes.

The success of this meeting, as far as I am concerned, will depend on our ability to create a molecular model of the events that we are talking about, paralysis and induction. Supposedly this is what we are trying to get at. Actually, before coming to this meeting, a very bright young scientist, Dr. Peter Bretscher, and I were trying to develop such a model. At this meeting I found that many of the elements of our model had actually been thought of. The importance of such a model, and the reason I am going to present it in some detail, is to enable us to sense which results are suspect. That is what our present difficulty is. I am going to try to develop the model; I am going to point out what phenomena contradict it, and then you will have to decide whether the evidence or the model is stronger.

The assumptions with which I will start are those that I thought were accepted by everybody until I came here. Since they are not, I intend to begin as though I had not come to this meeting.

(1) The first assumption is that the only recognition element is antibody itself.

Most of us would agree on this. This means that a functionally poised recognition element must exist prior to the injection of the antigen whether it leads to tolerance or to induction (=antibody production). It also means that you cannot postulate mechanisms involving repressors, pathways of processing and so on, which do not involve the intervention of antibody itself as the only specific means of recognition. (I see that some heads are being shaken in disapproval; obviously, some of you are still not in agreement on this point, and we shall have to discuss this later.)

(2)   The second assumption is that there is a constant birth of new antigen-sensitive cells throughout life.

This idea is necessary in order to understand spontaneous recovery from paralysis and the breaking of tolerance.

These first two points are probably the least controversial, but I don't think that they are entirely accepted.

(3)   The third point is one which Dr. Mitchison has stated many times, and that is that the antigen-sensitive cell expresses only one kind of antibody receptor.   I would add: the one that the cell will produce as an antibody on induction.*

I am certain that a good number of you will disagree on this point and have already stated so.   But I don't think that there is any disagreement that the antibody-producing cell produces one antibody.   The disagreement is whether the antigen-sensitive cell is limited to one specificity.

(4)   The fourth assumption is one that a given antigen-sensitive cell can either go the pathway of paralysis or the pathway of induction upon contact with antigen.   In other words, as shown in Fig. 53, a cell, on interacting with properly prepared antigen, is either paralyzed or induced.

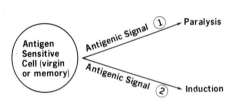

Fig. 53   Consequences of interaction between an antigen-
          sensitive cell and antigen

There are not two responding cell types in this hypothesis. I am pushing aside for the moment the whole problem of whether there is a two-cell interaction for signaling, either for paralysis or for induction.   I am simply saying that

*The term induction is being used by Dr. Cohn in the sense of "activation."   Eds.

the antigen-sensitive cell produces one antibody receptor that responds differently to a signal for paralysis or induction.

According to our first ground rule, each signal must derive its specificity uniquely from antigen-antibody interactions. The cell can go in two directions, paralysis or induction. Therefore, it must be presented with two different signals.

It must have a signal ① which says paralysis, and it must have another signal ② which says induction. Our ground rule says that these two signals, whatever they are, must in some way involve recognition by antibody itself.

Since the antigen-sensitive cell has only one antibody receptor, that is, of one specificity (it may have many identical receptors on the surface), and since the cell must sense two different signals, the simplest model would be that it senses these two signals by conformational changes in this receptor antibody itself.

So the object of the theory would be to identify the kind of signals that a cell can sense through its antibody receptor by conformational changes in this portein, leading either to paralysis or to induction.

Accordingly, when the cell receives signal ① , because there is a corresponding tolerogenic conformational change in the antibody receptor, the cell must have a read-out system for the tolerogenic conformational change ① , and when it receives signal ② , it must have another read-out system for a different inductive conformational change ② . Thus, there must be two separate conformational changes and two separate read-out systems.

There are two questions. How simple a model can deal with this situation? How precise a mechanism can be proposed at the molecular level? Fig. 54 depicts my first approximation model. We are considering only soluble antigens which behave as monomers and are taking BSA as an example.

The antigen that we are going to talk about will be pictured as follows:

I am putting on antigen A, a, which is the determinant against which we measure antibody formation, as well as two

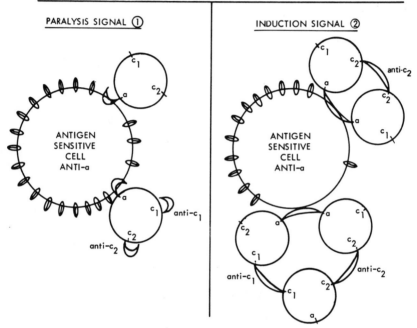

Fig. 54   The minimal model

VI. SPECULATIONS ON MECHANISMS

other determinants, c_1 and c_2, which are the carrier determinants on the protein. Thus, a would be equivalent to hapten and the other two, c_1 and c_2, would be equivalent to carrier determinants. In principle, a, c_1 and c_2 can behave identically until viewed by their respective antigen-sensitive cells.

Now, I am going to picture two situations, signal ① for paralysis; signal ② for induction.

The first thing that we need is an antigen-sensitive cell, which expresses, on its surface, receptor antibody molecules that are anti-a.

At this point I will not go into the question of the Generator of Diversity or the origin of specificity. We are talking about the question of regulation by antigen only. If we get into the problem of G.O.D., we will be sidetracked. Let us instead, consider only the facts that we have heard at this meeting. No facts have been presented concerning the origin of diversity, and in any case, for the question of regulation by antigen, it makes no difference whether germ-line or somatic mechanisms operate, simply because the antibody recognition elements must precede the antigenic stimulus. We are taking this for granted.

From what we have heard, one would postulate that one antibody receptor on the surface, combined with one molecule of antigen A through its determinant a, is responsible for paralysis signal ① . It does not make any difference whether the other two determinants c_1 and c_2 that I have referred to, are combined with antibody or not as long as the receptor antibody is combining with one site, a; one molecule of antigen combining with one receptor molecule which in turn responds to the interaction by a conformational change, sensed by the cell. This series of events leads to paralysis, and I have in Fig. 54 indicated two different configurations either of which can paralyze.

Now, let us look at signal ② , induction. For induction we start with an antigen-sensitive cell, anti-a. However, although our receptor antibody on the surface recognizes antigen A by its determinant a, it must also recognize something else which we propose is the reaction between carrier antibody, anti-c_1 or anti-c_2, and the other determinants on the carrier, which would be determinants c_1 and c_2. One polyvalent ($\geqslant 2$) receptor molecule, anti-a stretched between two determinants a, delivers the inductive signal ② .

Therefore, the antigen-sensitive cell, anti-a, would respond to another inductive conformational change which involves receptor and carrier antibodies complexing monomeric antigen between the two.

DR. BENACERRAF: The carrier antibody is external to the antigen-sensitive cell?

DR. COHN: Yes.

DR. CEPPELLINI: And where does the carrier antibody come from?

DR. COHN: We will come to the origin of the carrier antibody in a moment.

This simple model, elements of which we have been talking about these last few days, has gotten inundated somewhere. Let's come back to it. The model says that in order to paralyze, one needs only an antigen-sensitive cell, anti-a and determinant a. However, in order to induce, two elements are necessary; an antigen-sensitive cell, anti-a and a complex between antigen A and carrier antibody, anti-c_1.

The complex between antigen A and carrier antibody can be more complicated. One can build a large polymer of antigen A by having alternating connections made by carrier antibody between c_1 and c_2 and so on. The tolerogenic conformational change and the inductive conformational change must be fundamentally different, although the latter includes the former. The antigen-sensitive cell senses these differences as a result of which the cell receiving signal ② now goes on to make antibody and the cell receiving signal ① goes on to paralysis. Whether or not the carrier antibody is free in solution, as I have depicted it here, or bound onto a surface, we will leave for later.

I am trying to get together the minimum elements necessary for induction and paralysis. My argument stems from the fourth assumption that the antigen-sensitive cell can go in either direction and that, on the injection of antigen, there is competition between paralysis and induction.

VI. SPECULATIONS ON MECHANISMS

In other words, the cell going the pathway of paralysis, is responding because one of its polyvalent ($\geqslant 2$) receptors interacts with one determinant a on the antigen, whereas the cell going the pathway of induction has one of its poly-valent ($\geqslant 2$) receptors interacting with two identical deter-minants, a, because two molecules of antigen A have been cemented together by the carrier antibody, anti-c.

This first approximation model says that the antigen-sensitive cell on induction goes on to make antibody directly. No transfer of structural information between cells is in-volved (thymus to bone-marrow). Furthermore, no complicated intermediates in the pathway to an antibody-forming cell are envisaged although one of the intermediate steps might be a long-lived memory cell.

Secondly, under the simple model, the response to anti-gen is identical whether or not the antigen-sensitive cell is a virgin short-lived cell or a long-lived memory cell. The mechanism by which these two cell types will be induced or paralyzed will be identical. The differences in the kinetics of response to antigen will lie in the number of antigen-sensitive cells, the level of carrier antibody and possibly the level of other antibodies to antigen A.

This is the simplest hypothesis that I can envisage, but, since we have heard putatively contrary evidence, it is ob-vious to many of you that I am pushing it aside.

Why is the assumption crucial, that for induction you need both an antigen-sensitive cell, anti-a, and a carrier antibody anti-c? It is crucial because it implies that an animal could be unresponsive for two reasons, either because it lacks the antigen-sensitive cell, anti-a, or because it lacks the carrier antibody, anti-c. You can have a situa-tion in which the animal has all of the potentially respon-sive antigen-sensitive cells which cannot be induced because carrier antibody is lacking.

So as a consequence of this, I have to deal with Ceppel-lini's question. I now have to ask the question, where does the carrier antibody come from? I will assume that I am dealing with an adult animal and therefore I do not have to worry about the question of the very origin of carrier anti-body, that is, whether it is passed on from mother to off-spring via the placenta, the colostrum or the egg itself.

289

In order to make the theory clear, I will deal with carrier antibody from the moment that we see it in an adult animal. We can go on discussing later the fine points which I don't think are too important for the moment.

The reason we are concerned about the carrier antibody is that we want to understand, in the face of the second assumption that there is a constant birth of antigen-sensitive cells throughout life, how to maintain tolerance. It is the question of the maintenance and stability of tolerance that requires an understanding of the carrier antibodies.

There are two possibilities, and unfortunately we have no data on either. I will assume therefore the more difficult of these two possibilities and analyze it from that point of view.

The first possibility is that each virgin antigen-sensitive cell leaks a small amount of antibody. It spontaneously throws out a small amount of the antibody in the absence of antigenic stimulus.

The other possibility is that it leaks no antibody unless it is stimulated. This is more likely in the case of virgin antigen-sensitive cells as contrasted with memory antigen-sensitive cells which probably do leak. This is an esoteric point to be developed some other time.

DR. CEPPELLINI: What is the special nature of the specificity of the carrier antibody? Is it the same as that of the receptor antibody?

DR. COHN: Carrier antibody is simple antibody to antigen A produced by antigen-sensitive cells other than anti-a which we are assaying for. Nothing special has been assumed concerning either its class or structure for the moment. So far we are dealing with the simplest model.

Let us consider the situation in which a virgin antigen-sensitive cell leaks a little bit of antibody. Let us consider an animal tolerant to antigen A with the determinants $\underline{a}_{1-20}$. A new cell anti-a_3 is born. Since there is no carrier antibody present, the antigen A will interact with it, delivering signal ① and therefore the cell, anti-a_3, will be paralyzed. Thus, tolerance in this situation will be maintained.

290

VI.   SPECULATIONS ON MECHANISMS

Suppose now that two cells, anti-a_3 and simultaneously anti-a_7, are born.   Tolerance can still be stable.   There will be a race between the events that lead to the paralysis of these two cells by the tolerogenic interaction with antigen A, signal ① , and the rate at which these two cells build up a high enough level of carrier antibody so that either one of them can be induced.   If the interaction leadong to paralysis is much more rapid than the build-up of a critical level of carrier antibody produced by leakage, these two cells would be eliminated.

So you can maintain tolerance perfectly well even if two cells were produced of the same or different specificities when you are considering a situation in which virgin antigen-sensitive cells leak small amounts of antibody.   Of course if no carrier antibody is being produced, then there is no problem.

DR. SELA: One question.   Can the anti-a_7 serve as a carrier antibody for cell anti-a_3 and vice versa?

DR. COHN: I am assuming this for the moment, the qualification being that there is a special class of carrier antibody, in which case in order to have anti-a_7 serve as a source of carrier antibody for anti-a_3,   it must be in this special class.   The important point is, and I repeat it, that in the absence of carrier antibody, no antibody can be induced.

DR. SILVERSTEIN: Suppose you have a polyvalent antigen, that is, an antigen with a repeating determinant.   Can the cell release its own carrier antibody?

DR. COHN: I am only talking about monomeric proteins like BSA. Of course, we are going to have to face the problem of polymers, and when we face it, we will have to come to the problem of cell-cell interaction as well as the structural considerations for induction.   I am putting this aside for the moment.   I am talking only about monomeric BSA molecules on which there are no repeating determinants.

DR. EDELMAN: Is there anything that prevents a cell which makes anti-c_2 from reacting via antigen with the cell anti-a to make antibody?   Obviously, a cell which makes on its surface - -

DR. COHN: We shall come to that problem,too. In other
words, these two rare antigen-sensitive cells have to find
each other and the time to find each other, while each
carries around one antigen molecule (the paralytic signal
①) must be short compared to the time necessary to render
the cell tolerant.

DR. EDELMAN: Yes. And it may be disastrous.

DR. COHN: It may be. It is one way of explaining the thymus-
bone marrow interaction which will come up for consideration
later.

DR. NOSSAL: You have not yet considered the possibility that
the cell does not leak?

DR. COHN: If the virgin antigen-sensitive cell does not
leak, there is no problem but if you - -

DR. NOSSAL: But then you never make antibody of any sort to
anything?

DR. COHN: In the absence of carrier antibody you make no
antibodies of any sort to anything.

DR. NOSSAL: Never?

DR. COHN: Never. It is the critical point, exactly the
basis of the argument, and that is why the question of the
origin of the carrier antibody is crucial.

Now let us consider how we break tolerance under the present model. Let us suppose we have antigen A with determinants a_{1-20} and antigen B with determinants a_{1-10} and b_{1-10}.
The animal is tolerant to antigen A and we are breaking tolerance with antigen B. This is the situation that Dr.
Weigle and others have been studying. Suppose now that antigen-sensitive cell anti-a_3 arises. Since the determinants
b_{1-10} are now foreign to the animal, so that carrier antibody
to them is present, antigen B will now break tolerance because it will be able to induce an antigen-sensitive cell,
anti-a_3, by first interacting with carrier antibody-b_{1-10}.
The cell anti-a_3 will be induced because the signal ② is
provided to it, in which the interaction is between an antigen-sensitive cell, anti-a_3, and a polymer of antigen B and
carrier antibody, anti-b_{1-10}.

VI. SPECULATIONS ON MECHANISMS

This is the basic formulation under the minimum hypothesis for breaking tolerance with cross-reacting antigens.

DR. CEPPELLINI: I don't understand the point of introducing antigen B.

DR. COHN: It is an antigen that cross-reacts with antigen A, which is capable of breaking tolerance. It possesses in common with antigen A determinants $\underline{b}_{1-10}$ which are distinct from those of antigen A and foreign to the animal tolerant to antigen A.

DR. BENACERRAF: One point of fact. The antibodies produced under this situation are only directed against $\underline{b}_{1-10}$.

DR. COHN: Do you mean that you cannot break tolerance by injection of cross-reacting antigens? Tolerance to $\underline{a}_{1-10}$ is broken in the experiment I described.

DR. BENACERRAF: When the experiment is performed the antibodies are only directed against $\underline{b}_{1-10}$.

DR. COHN: You will have to decide later if the experiments which contradict this simple theory are more convincing than the theory. Let us go back to my point. I am dealing here with two cross-reacting antigens. The animal is tolerant to one of them. I am breaking tolerance with the cross-reacting antigen. This is the situation I am trying to analyze. The various experiments are those which I heard reported here. We will have to clarify this point if I have misunderstood the evidence.*

---

*On re-reading this discussion, I went back to the original papers of Weigle on breaking tolerance and realize that the actual findings do not correspond precisely to the situation I described. However, the principle remains the same. I am, therefore, restating the explanation for the breaking of tolerance so that it corresponds to known findings. The difficulty is due to the fact that, in practice, two cross-reacting proteins, A and B, do not possess determinants $\underline{a}_{1-20}$ for antigen A and $\underline{a}_{1-10}$, $\underline{b}_{1-10}$ determinants for antigen B. Antigen B, in reality, has determinants $\tilde{\underline{a}}_{1-10}$ which cross-react with the $\underline{a}_{1-10}$ determinants of antigen A. Therefore, I will restate the interpretation of the phenomenon.

Now let us consider what happens when cross-reacting anti-gens-A and B are injected simultaneously. Experimental data, reported here earlier, show that the tolerant state of the animal to antigen A is much less easily broken under these conditions.

Since antigen A is a tolerogen in the tolerant animal, it will compete with inducing antigen B. Since antigen A cannot act as an immunogen, but only as a tolerogen, the competition between paralysis by antigen A and induction of antibody by antigen B in the presence of antigen A will favor paralysis. When you inject something to which the animal is tolerant in competition with something to which it will respond, it is quite obvious that the antigen to which it is tolerant will tend to drive the system towards tolerance. The two antigens will compete.

Consider an animal whose tolerance to antigen A, with determinants $\underline{a}_{1-20}$, can be broken by administration of an antigen B, with determinants $\underline{\tilde{a}}_{1-10}$ which cross-react with $\underline{a}_{1-10}$ and foreign determinants $\underline{b}_{1-10}$. If a new antigen-sensitive cell with specificity anti-$\tilde{a}_7$ appears, it may be induced to make anti-$\tilde{a}_7$ antibody by antigen B, as this anti-gen has determinants $\underline{b}_{1-10}$ to act as carrier sites; in this way tolerance to A can be broken. Moreover, it is observed that if A and B are injected simultaneosuly, the tolerant state of the animal towards A is much less easily broken; this is to be expected since A cannot act as an immunogen but can act as a tolerogen and the additional $\underline{a}$ determinants will favor paralysis in the competition between paralysis and antibody induction. This last observation cannot be recon-ciled with the view that the specificities of the antibodies produced against A by the injection of B were not originally paralyzed by A on account of the weakness of their inter-action with A; if this were the case the injection of A to-gether with B would be expected to have no effect on the in-duction of antibody to determinants $\underline{a}_{1-10}$, whereas A inhibits the response as I will discuss later.

The missing step in the experiment is to take the animal now making anti-$\underline{\tilde{a}}_{1-10}$ and immunize it with antigen A with determinants $\underline{a}_{1-20}$ to which it was originally tolerant. The presence of anti-$\underline{\tilde{a}}_{1-10}$ should now act as carrier for antigen A and tolerance should be completely broken with the produc-tion of anti-a_{1-20}.

VI. SPECULATIONS ON MECHANISMS

This is the point to the fourth assumption that antigen-sensitive cells can go via either path, paralysis or induction. Also, I should say, within the framework of this theory it is clear that any antigen which has but few foreign determinants will tend to act as a tolerogen as against one which has many foreign determinants which tends to act as an immunogen. This may apply to the kind of fragment that Dr. Nossal isolated as the tolerogenic fragment A in the flagellin system.

Now I would like to consider the relationship between low-zone and high-zone tolerance, using my minimum model. The model says that low-zone tolerance is mediated by single antigen molecules interacting with receptor antibody on a 1:1 basis whereas induction is mediated by a polymer or complex of antigen with carrier antibody which in turn induces the antigen-sensitive cell because the complex reacts with one receptor through identical determinants, a. Therefore, in order to discuss the effect of dose of antigen, we must assume a level of carrier antibody that will have a profound effect on the response. Let us assume we are dealing with naive animals with a low level of carrier antibody, and we inject antigen in increasing doses.

In low zone we will form in general the complex $Ag\ Ab_n$, but we will also have free antigen present depending on the equilibrium constants of the reaction. Since we are dealing with a monomeric antigen only, it will induce low-zone tolerance by presenting signal ① to the antigen-sensitive cell.

As the concentration of antigen is increased, you begin to produce $Ag_m\ Ab_n$, in which case you present signal ② to the cell, i.e. the inducing stimulus for antibody synthesis.

What is interesting about this very simple formulation is that you predict high-zone tolerance because the inducing complex $Ag_2\ Ab$ and the paralyzing free antigen will compete, with paralysis being favored as the free antigen concentration increases. As the free antigen concentration increases, it begins to compete with the inducing complex and you set up a state of high-zone tolerance.

The interesting feature of the simple model is that it leads to a prediction of the existence of high-zone tolerance. Furthermore, it shows that at the level of the antigen-sensitive cell the mechanism of low zone and high-zone paralysis is identical.

295

What about the question of antigenic competition? Here again I am going to oversimplify the situation. Let us consider two determinants, hapten 1 (H_1) and hapten 2 (H_2), which are unrelated to each other, e.g., arsanilic acid and dinitrophenol. These two haptens are present on identical carriers, for example on BSA. When the two are injected together the unrelated haptens will compete with each other and mutually reduce the anti-hapten response. Since the cell anti-H_1 and the cell anti-H_2 have receptors with nothing in common as regards their specificity, the competition cannot be at the level of the antigen-sensitive cell by our model. Consequently, it has to be at the level of competition for the carrier antibody in a condition where the amount of carrier antibody is limiting. Otherwise you could not see this competition.

In this way one can explain the competition data in the naive animal, the competition being seen only when the carriers are similar or identical. Hapten competition is not seen when you put H_1 on BSA and H_2 on ribonuclease, because now you are no longer competing for carrier antibody. This I believe is the take-home-lesson, from our earlier discussions, of the role of carrier antibody.

At this point the model is clearly oversimplified because the picture would change somewhat for cell-bound carrier antibody.

Thus far I have dealt only with a first approximation model and a lot of phenomena have been put aside. I shall now try to come to grips with some of them.

First of all, I have not told you anything about the postulated conformational changes in the receptor that you can expect and how they would be sensed by the cell. I have a very precise model for it, but I don't feel that we should deal with it for the moment. I would rather first come back to the cell kinetics, to see what kind of difficulties may develop and then, if possible, I shall come to a more precise model.

The important point here is that we are dealing with a carrier antibody whose only function is to create a polymer of antigen. As far as the receptor on the antigen-sensitive cell is concerned, it does not care how the antigen is glued together, provided that required structural considerations

are met. The only function of the carrier antibody at this
point is to create two identical antigenic determinants so
spatially and rigidly related that the receptor antibody, on
interacting with them, undergoes a conformational change
corresponding to signal ② . This means that we could
imagine situations in which a cell confronted with a huge
repeating determinant on an antigen, like sRBC, a flagellum
or a bacterial virus, would be induced in the absence of
carrier antibody. We could imagine this situation, but
everything depends upon structural considerations. The inductive conformational change depends upon the distances between identical determinants and how rigidly they are kept
apart in their reaction with receptor antibody. Conceivably,
however, an inductive signal ② could be delivered in the
case of large polymers without carrier antibody.

In general, large polymeric substances, like sRBC, are
ingested and broken down by macrophages. Dr. Sela made the
point that any extensive degradation may lead to loss of the
antigenic determinant. You can, however, break large polymeric antigens down to smaller fragments in the following
manner: ABABABABABABAB → AB, ABA, BAB, BABA, ABAB, etc.
Thus, a phagocyte could break down the polymer randomly into
pieces that would then follow the same pathway, involving
carrier antibody, as would any monomeric or simple antigen
that we have been dealing with.

DR. SELA: When you say polymeric and monomeric, they are
not building blocks?

DR. COHN: The word monomeric has been used loosely since I
am considering even bovine immunoglobulin to be a monomer.
In this context, I am considering lysozyme and BSA as soluble
monomers as contrasted with a large insoluble particle with
repeating determinants like flagella, sRBC or bacteriophages.

DR. NOSSAL: Can I whisper two words? Passive antibody.

DR. COHN: I will return to that question. That is something
we have to worry about.

DR. NOSSAL: Very much so.

DR. CEPPELLINI: When you discussed two determinants a and c,
you were not dealing with a monomer.

DR. COHN: On a single polypeptide chain you would not expect
to have any repeating determinants. Antigenic determinants
a and c are unrelated, as those found on BSA. As I was point-
ing out to you, there are many more "facts," and I am putting
the facts in quotation marks, than could every be put together
by a simple model. But as I understood the available data
there does not seem to be anything to contradict my model.
My model allows you to understand why you need macromolecules
in order to induce. You require a sufficient number of determinants to build an inducing polymeric structure with
carrier antibody. But what this model does not predict is
that you should need macromolecules in order to paralyze.
As a matter of fact it predicts just the opposite. According
to this model, you should be able to paralyze with hapten itself or with antigens possessing a single foreign determinant.
I think that this is a crucial prediction. Therefore, one
of the tests of the model would come out of a discussion of
how good the data are concerning carrier effects in low-zone
paralysis.

How good are the data that you do not induce tolerance
with single haptenic determinants? We have alluded to this
several times during the meeting, but I have not seen anybody
get up to present data on this issue. To quote Dr. Benacerraf
he said, "in order for a substance to be a tolerogen it must
be an immunogen." He has thus made the problem absolutely
clear. If that statement is a fact it is in contradiction
with my simple theory.

There are still other points in the model that need amplification. For example, does the carrier antibody have to be
soluble and freely diffusable or could it be on the surface
of a cell? As far as the model is concerned, the carrier
antibody could be either on the surface of a cell or freely
diffusable.

But there is a limitation that I would like to bring up
and that is, if the carrier antibody is on cells, it is im-
probable that the interaction would be between a unispecific
antigen-sensitive cell, anti-a, and another unispecific antigen-sensitive cell, anti-c. In other words, intuition dic-
tates that you do not want to create a situation in which a
very rare cell interacting with antigen to give a paralytic
signal ① races to interact via this antigen with another
very rare cell before it is paralyzed. In a simple model
you would want to have one of the cellular components in

298

enormous excess. Therefore, putting this carrier antibody non-specifically on the surface of a macrophage or reticulum cell, offers less difficulty to the theory than would be the case if one would put the carrier antibody on another rare unispecific antigen-sensitive cell, such as has been visualized in the thymus-bone marrow interactions.

The easiest interpretation of the thymus-bone marrow interaction would be that the cell suspension from the thymus has in it cells which I will call macrophage-like, meaning that they are non-specifically adsorbing large amounts of carrier antibody, and it is essentially this thymic-carrier antibody which interacts with antigen to induce the antigen-sensitive cells of the bone-marrow. At this moment I am not even certain that the thymus "hormone" is not simply carrier antibody.

Would such interactions behave specifically? Of course, the thymus cell suspension would show specificity because the thymus from an animal rendered tolerant to a given antigen would have no carrier antibody and as such, would not stimulate a bone-marrow population transplanted into an irradiated host.

What is the evidence that in the thymus-bone marrow interaction both populations could provide unispecific cells of the antigen-sensitive type, to be induced via an antigen bridge between them?

DR. CEPPELLINI: You said "macrophage-like." Do you mean a cell adsorbing cytophilic antibody?

DR. COHN: Yes.

DR. EDELMAN: The cell that makes the carrier antibody, does it have to be induced too? Because in that case you are going to have an infinite mess.

DR. COHN: I have discussed two situations, one in which the virgin antigen-sensitive cell leaks antibody, and the other and more likely one in which it does not. In the case of memory antigen-sensitive cells, I would guess that they do leak. In any case, I would like to point out that in order to make liver glycogen, you need glycogen. Where does that come from. The second problem we have to face is the one that links regulation to the origin of the specificity or to

the Generator of Diversity (G.O.D.). This is a point that
really bothers me. Until now, I just decided to close my
mind to is complications, but I will now state it.

We spent an entire session discussing what was termed a
crucial problem, namely, whether paralysis was to be equated
with death or silence? (Nobody told us why this is an important problem, except that for some of us death and silence
are synonymous.) It is a crucial problem because in order to
break tolerance by the rebirth of antigen-sensitive cells we
must postulate an enormous rate of generating new cells
throughout life. In order to break tolerance during the
short period of time involved in experimental situations
that have been described, a high rate of rebirth is mandatory.
Therefore, if paralysis is equal to death, how would you re-
generate all of these new cells? If these cells are, instead, tucked away and silenced, the problem would be less
difficult. From the kinetics that have been discussed here
it would appear that the problem is nowhere near solution.

There are two ways to generate an unresponsive state and
I want to repeat it so it is clear. You either get rid of
the antigen-sensitive cells or you get rid of the carrier
antibody. Aging may do this. I am not certain. In the newborn, in the presence of maternal carrier antibody, it may be
the size of the antigen-sensitive cell population that is
limiting.

Certainly, X-rays, cyclophosphamide, and all of the various immunosuppressive drugs, and also aging may reduce by
non-specific killing the antigen-sensitive cell population
to a level close to the threshold level that we call tolerance. It is the very last nudge of a specific tolerogenic
antigen that brings the animal over the threshold level and
renders it specifically tolerant. This is why immunosuppre-
sive treatment makes it easier to render an animal tolerant
to strong immunogens and polymers, particularly in the low
zone. The half life of carrier antibody determines the
kinetics of the response after X-irradiation and I would
guess that it is short.

Two last questions which I will raise are in regard to
the relationship between the number of receptors on a cell
and the number necessary to trigger. Under the simple model
you would only have to trigger one receptor in order for the
cell, possessing on the order of thousands of receptors, to

300

go down the pathway of either paralysis or induction. Suppose that only one site has to be triggered in order to induce or to paralyze. If you carry out a competition experiment, using the technique of adoptive immunity, between a free hapten and a hapten on a carrier, you should find that you need enormous levels of hapten to blank out everything else compared to the concentration of hapten carrier that you would need to induce. You would find that it would be difficult to turn a cell off by free hapten in this situation. Whether or not you need one hit or two hits or three hits by antigen to trigger paralysis or induction should be considered in the discussion.

CHAIRMAN UHR: Can't the signal ① , due to hapten, take precedence over signal ② , due to a polymer?

DR. COHN: Although I did not specify, it is simpler if signal ② takes precedence. This is a point concerning the postulated conformational changes in the receptor which I have not discussed. Signal ② actually includes signal ① as you will see.

The other question I wanted to stress involves the uniqueness of the carrier antibody class. We can look to three lines of evidence. We can look to the class-specific agammaglobulinemics and ask in each case if they are blocked in responding to antigen. If there were a unique carrier class missing, that class should make the individual non-inducible.

We can go back to evolution and ask the question, if the lamprey only has IgM and is inducible, isn't IgM itself the carrier antibody?

We can also ask questions based on structural considerations. For example: can we build inducing polymers with carrier antibody that are dimers, trimers or pentamers such as found in the IgA or IgM class but not in the IgG class?

We do have various handles for making good guesses, but I won't make those guesses for you right now although a unique class of carrier antibody, probably cytophilic, appears favored and, in fact, I assume it in the model.

There is one closing remark. The more inducing antigenic contacts you have in life, in other words, the more experiences you have, the easier it is to learn. The reason is that you build up your library of carrier antibody as rapidly and effectively as you build up your library of antigen-sensitive cells. These two factors interact so that the more antigen you see, the greater the diversity of antigens you can respond to.

CHAIRMAN UHR: Let us begin the discussion with questions concerning clarification of the model. When that phase has been completed we can begin the more difficult task of relating Dr. Cohn's model to various facts that have been presented during the meeting.

It is, indeed a pity that Dr. Niels Jerne was unable to be with us, because it was Dr. Jerne who more than a decade ago first suggested a central role of serum antibody in the induction of antibody formation.

Now, let us begin with questions concerning clarification of Dr. Cohn's model.

DR. HUMPHREY: I want to know whether your theory predicts that it would be impossible to induce antibody against a single foreign determinant on an antigen.

DR. COHN: Yes.

DR. CINADER: May that perhaps be the reason why it is so difficult to make antibody to allotypic specificity? Though it is not a single determinant, there are probably only two foreign determinants, one on each of the two light or two heavy chains.

DR. BUSSARD: Do you think it is impossible, in fact, to induce antibody with one foreign determinant? Cinader mentioned that it is difficult to get antibody against the allotypes, but the fact is that one can get them. Also I remember an experiment of Dr. Humphrey in animals tolerant against either HSA or BSA, where he was unable to find precipitating antibody. He postulated that you may have antibody attaching only to one determinant on HSA and this was demonstrable by the Farr technic. In this case, then, you may have had an antibody against one determinant.

DR. SMITH: What is the postulated origin of the carrier antibody? I am not clear on that.

VI. SPECULATIONS ON MECHANISMS

DR. COHN: "In the beginning was carrier antibody" which was passed on to the newborn via either the egg, the placenta or by means of colostrum. Once primed, when antigen-sensitive cells appear during ontogeny, induction can occur with maternal carrier antibody-antigen complexes. From then on, there is a continuous building up by experience of this library of antigen-sensitive cells and carrier antibody.

DR. SMITH: Then you are proposing that carrier antibody is a virus that is transmitted vertically or something like that, and not a genetically determined - -

DR. COHN: Why? In embryology there are many examples of primers which are necessary for development and which are passed on in the egg. There is either leakage, for which I gave you an example, or the carrier antibody priming the system is derived essentially from the mother. The model does not depend upon a precise hypothesis as to the origin of the carrier antibody. I would like to make that clear. It is analogous to saying that our understanding of the interactions of matter in the solar system depends upon a knowledge of its origin.

DR. SELA: The mother certainly seems to be a logical source of carrier antibody, when one looks at it from the artist's point of view. However, I could immunize, for example, with homopolymers of amino acids that are not natural.

I am very gratified to hear a discussion of the carrier, because until recently, to talk about the carrier was to attack central dogma. The carrier certainly has a role. But do you really have to assume that you work through antibodies to recognize the carrier? Could it not be a reaction of the carrier with the cell involving merely the formation of non-specific complexes. You would not have to assume the formation of a separate antibody, which, although an easy way out, in many ways makes the situation more complicated.

DR. COHN: May I answer why I have postulated that the carrier is recognized by antibody? You have to agree that the carrier has specificity in order to explain why animals rendered tolerant to the carrier are non-responsive to the hapten. Since I am assuming that the only specific recognition of carrier is by carrier antibody, it is easy to explain why tolerance to the carrier is incompatible with the induction of antibody to any given hapten determinant linked to it. That is the beauty of the model.

DR. LESKOWITZ: Would you predict on your model that several simple haptens covalently bound together could function as an antigen?

DR. COHN: In principle, yes. The reason it is difficult to predict is that if you make this stereochemical unit so small that it is smothered by the structure of the carrier antibody itself, you wouldn't see induction because of steric hindrance to a reaction with the receptor. The better way to put this question would be to ask if three different determinants linked in a compatible way, that is in a large enough molecule, would be sufficient to induce. The answer is yes, two are enough.

DR. CINADER: Would you consider that signal ① is all that you need to explain suppression by antibody against allotype?

DR. COHN: Yes, in the rabbit. However, this phenomenon could be irrelevant. Suppression could be due to complement-mediated lysis of the cells unrelated to signal ①.

DR. SIMONSEN: You seemed to suggest that the thymus-derived lymphocyte is provided with receptors formed by marrow-derived cells. If this is so, the thymus lymphocyte is presumably covered with receptors in a random fashion, which then implies multipotentiality at the receptor level.

DR. COHN: That is correct. But I want to make certain that you and I are using the word multipotential identically. A multipotential cell implies to me that it is multipotential in its synthetic capacity for these antibodies. On the model described here, the thymus "macrophage" is not multipotential in its synthetic capacity, but is multipotential in what it may have picked up by adsorption from other cells. Thus, if you are willing to use the word multipotential to indicate that it carries specificities independent of where it arose, the answer is "yes."

DR. SIMONSEN: I expected you to say that. I am just curious to know whether you think that the response which is given by certain artificially multipotential cells can proceed without the participation of the unipotential marrow cell, because the evidence is that you can get a good reaction with thymocytes alone.

DR. COHN: I would assume that a washed thymocyte or thoracic duct population, capable of responding to an antigen, is heterogeneous, containing a unispecific antigen-sensitive cell and other cells that are multispecific. If two cell populations act synergistically, e.g., thymus-bone-marrow, then the antigen-sensitive cell population is either interacting with free carrier antibody-antigen complexes or with multi-specifically cell-bound carrier-antibody antigen complexes supplied by other members of the population.

You would have to prove that a responding thymocyte population is indeed homogeneous and free of carrier antibody. (I am assuming in this discussion that the X-irradiated host in which the assays are performed contributes no cell interactions. This assumption is weakest for the contribution of macrophages.)*

---

*As an afterthought to the discussion on thymus-bone marrow interactions, I would like to add the following: the thymus may be the source of carrier antibody of a special immunoglobulin class; the bone-marrow may be the source of antigen-sensitive cells in all immunoglobulin classes. Inductive antigenic stimulation of thymus cells results in a synthesis of carrier antibody. The cells making this antibody of a special class would not be detected by the Jerne plaque assay. The induction of carrier antibody-producing cells takes place via the same mechanism that acts for any antigen-sensitive cell. The antigen complexed with carrier antibody is an inductive stimulus for carrier antibody producing cells which proliferate and secrete carrier antibody.

Since washed cell suspensions of antigen-stimulated thymocytes which have been incubated with antigen in an irradiated animal's spleen can, in the presence of antigen, stimulate the antigen-sensitive cells of bone-marrow to make antibody in a second irradiated host, three possibilities come to mind:

1. The thymocytes secrete carrier antibody that interacts with antigen to provide inductive signal ② to bone-marrow antigen-sensitive cells.

I hope it is clear to you that in general the normal level of carrier antibody would be below that detectable by present assay methods ($\leq 10^{10}$ molecules of antibody/ml).

CHAIRMAN UHR: In the model, the carrier antibody need not be on the cell surface. You probably prefer not to have it on the cell surface?

2. The thymocytes secrete carrier antibody that is adsorbed to macrophages or reticular cells of the donor or host and this surface-bound carrier antibody reacts with antigen to deliver signal ② to bone-marrow antigen-sensitive cells.

3. The unispecific carrier antibody-producing cell in the thymus could interact via antigen with a unispecific antigen-sensitive cell in the bone-marrow to induce the latter. Since a special class of carrier antibody is assumed, only the bone-marrow cell would be induced as a result of the interaction. In principle, possibility 2 and 3 differ in that a multispecific carrier antibody cell is assumed in possibility 2, and a unispecific antibody cell carrier antibody cell is assumed in possibility 3.

I consider possibility 3 to be unlikely in the intact animal responding to antigen. Since both unispecific cell types would normally be rare, this interaction does not appear to be the way in which inductive triggering would normally occur. However, under certain experimental conditions, such as those described by Miller for the thymus-bone-marrow interaction, this case is not ruled out. The antigen stimulated thymus might result in a proliferation of cells sensitive to the complex of carrier antibody and antigen. This proliferation of specific carrier cells must depend on the same mechanism, i.e. antigen-carrier antibody complexes with antigen-sensitive cells. Under these conditions, the thymus with its greatly amplified population of a specific carrier class of cells, can in the presence of antigen, trigger bone marrow-derived antigen-sensitive cells, the interaction occurring with reasonable frequency because the carrier cells are in large numbers. If true, this would probably be a special case. Normally, the thymus would be expected to provide carrier antibody either circulating or on the surfaces of macrophages and reticular cells. This component of the inductive signal ② being in large excess over the unispecific antigen-sensitive cell would insure rapid responses to antigen stimuli.

VI. SPECULATIONS ON MECHANISMS

DR. COHN: Yes, that is true, but I do not feel sentimental about it. If you prove that another cell type is essential in order to trigger antigen-sensitive cells then this cell could either break particulate antigens into small pieces that are activated by free carrier antibody or it could transport, nonspecifically, an array of carrier antibodies on its surface that can serve to activate antigen. This distinction is not a test of the theory.

DR. SILVERSTEIN: I think you are asking for a lot of trouble to demand different origins for the genesis of the carrier antibody and the recognition antibodies that you postulate. There are many species in which there is no evidence at all of passive transfer of any sort of antibody-like substances from the mother to the fetus via the placenta or any other route.

You appear to suggest that prior immunologic experience helps to prepare the animal for a better response, or for any response to a subsequent antigenic challenge. There is, however, no indication that prior experience has any positive effect. We tested this possibility with our fetal lambs, and were unable to demonstrate that active responses to other antigens and the accompanying induction of a precociously mature lymphoid system had any effect on the subsequent response to a new antigenic stimulus.

DR. COHN: That is what theories are for.

DR. WEIGLE: A point of clarification. Did you imply that in order to have antigenic competition, the competing haptens or determinant groups must be associated with the same carrier?

DR. COHN: The same or related carriers.

DR. MITCHISON: What are you prepared to do without?

DR. COHN: I am not prepared to do without 1) an antigen-sensitive cell of limited specificity that can either be paralyzed or induced and 2) a carrier antibody-antigen interaction to signal induction in the case of monomeric antigens.

In the case of rare polymeric antigens, such as sRBC or flagella, induction may be triggered directly. Normally, however, polymeric particulate antigens are chewed up,

307

following which the fragments would have to go through the same pathway as BSA.

If sRBC can induce antibody directly, then a special mechanism must be envisaged to prevent induction of antibody formation by autologous red blood cells. Both of us can imagine such a mechanism, but a discussion of it will make for an unnecessary digression.

DR. RAJEWSKY: I find that I have chemical difficulties with your model. Wouldn't you think that carrier antibody acting as you picture it would function very rarely. Wouldn't it put very stringent requirements on the position of the two determinants on the molecule? Would it work with a larger molecule? I find it would be much easier to imagine the molecule as Dr. Mitchison has suggested, where you have the antigen between two cells with antibodies on both sides of it (Fig. 55).

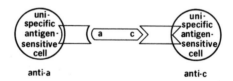

Fig. 55 Possible reaction of antigen with two antibody-
forming cells

DR. COHN: You have not changed the problem. You still have a conformational change in the receptor in order for the antigen-sensitive cell to recognize a paralytic or inductive stimulus. (1) You do not wish triggering by a non-specific touching of antigen-sensitive cells, 2) You do not expect only one tiny antigen molecule of lysozyme to cement the two huge antigen-sensitive cells together, and 3) You do not want two rare cells to hunt for each other while carrying around the paralytic signal ① due to their reaction with the anti-gen a-c. You need the carrier cell, anti-c, in excess so that interaction with the antibody-producing cell, anti-a, will occur with reasonable frequency, and as a signal ② for the induction of the antigen-sensitive cell.

VI. SPECULATIONS ON MECHANISMS

There is a lot of evidence that antibody-antigen interactions can result in conformational changes of the type
that could be read by the cell. After all, you do fix complement to the Fc portion in an antigen-antibody complex
whereas antibody alone does not fix it. I can give you other
examples of that kind. There are also known conformational
changes provoked by the hapten-antibody interaction. Why
should not the antigen-sensitive cell sense the same types
of interaction?

DR. PLESCIA: My question relates to your definition of the
carrier antibody. By this I suppose you mean that you have
a carrier determinant on an antigenic molecule. However,
such a determinant may function either as a carrier determinant or it may serve as a determinant to which the antibody is made and measured. There is nothing very unique
about a determinant itself. In a given molecule, one determinant may function either as a carrier or as a recognition
determinant, and vice versa.

DR. COHN: Yes, of course. I am trying to explain the kind
of data that Dr. Benacerraf has presented, namely, that when
you inject DNP-PLL-BSA into a non-responder guinea pig, you
get a response to DNP. If you make the animal tolerant to
BSA, you do not get a response. The tolerance implies 1)
that the carrier effect of BSA is specific and 2) that antibody recognition of the carrier is involved.

DR. NOSSAL: It seems to me that this whole area that Dr.
Cohn is directing himself to now was first thrown into focus
at Cold Spring Harbor, when Drs. Benacerraf and Mitchison
described their carrier effects. At that time I asked, and
I ask again, what about passive antibodies? If this model
is correct, then in either of the two situations passive
antibodies ought to be able to do the job. And it doesn't.
Specifically, passive antibody cannot mimic the Mitchison
or the Benacerraf effect. Why?

DR. COHN: The problem of the ineffectiveness of passive
antibody is two-fold. If there is a special class of carrier
antibody, then the passively injected antibody would affect
the system as a function of the ratio of carrier to non-
carrier antibody. The passively injected antiserum could
have no carrier antibody in it. If all classes can act as
carrier antibody, the level of carrier antibody relative to

that of antigen would be crucial to the outcome of an experiment. You have to show me an experiment in which this phenomenon has been studied with monomeric antigens at a wide range of concentrations, using early and late antisera. Only then can we say something definite about the effects of passively administered antibody.

DR. SMITH: Would it make any difference to your model if the receptor on the cell and the carrier antibody were the same molecule, one which had been secreted and the other which was fixed?

DR. COHN: This is one of the alternatives. I considered the case in which the virgin carrier antibody cell leaked a little bit.

CHAIRMAN UHR: I wonder if anyone else is disturbed about the low-zone, high-zone antigen-antibody aggregates you predicted. That wasn't clear to me. It seems to me that as you go into higher concentrations of antigen, where you generate more of the Ag_2 Ab complexes, the low zone-high zone relationship is not explained.

DR. COHN: In effect the question being asked is, "Do you believe that high-zone and low-zone paralysis take place by the same mechanism?" Of course the answer is yes.

I wish to stress that if I present a model in which a single monomeric antigen interacting with a single receptor site turns off that antigen-sensitive cell, that is paralyzes it, then the identical mechanism should operate in the low and high zone. What I am saying is that in low zone you have free antigen and the complex Ag Ab_n, and in high zone you have free antigen Ag_2 Ab. In low zone, you paralyze because only monomers of antigen are present, whereas in high zone, as you increase the concentration of antigen, free antigen competes with the Ag_2 Ab complex to paralyze the cell and eventually this will lead to complete tolerance when the free antigen concentration is high enough.

CHAIRMAN UHR: You said more. You said that on the basis of your model the explanation of the conditions for low-zone paralysis and induction enables one to predict high-zone paralysis. I really didn't understand how you brought that about. In other words, if your mechanism of high-zone

310

paralysis is correct, then the conditions of low-zone paralysis should lead to induction.

DR. COHN: In low-zone paralysis, I picture the complex Ag $Ab_n \geqslant_1$, that is at the very low antigen dose level. Possibly the antigen is coated with carrier antibody but this point is not relevant as long as one determinant is available to the antibody receptor and the antigen remains monomeric. Any antigen-sensitive cell that interacts will receive signal ① and be paralyzed. As the antigen concentration is increased the complex $Ag_m Ab_n$ is made. This is an inducing complex because signal ② is delivered. However, as the antigen concentration is further increased, free antigen begins to appear and at the limit we have $Ag_2 Ab$. We revert essentially to the low-dose zone conditions as these two begin to compete with each other. This competition must eventually lead to paralysis because the free antigen concentration is always increased but not that of the complex, until high-zone paralysis is attained. This formulation applies only to carrier antibody in solution, not on the surface of macrophages or reticular cells. If antibody is surface-bound, then a modification of the formulation is necessary.

DR. SILVERSTEIN: In low zone, isn't it a question of whatever is left to react - -

DR. COHN: You know you have low-zone paralysis. Therefore, you must have monomeric antigen left to react with antigen-sensitive cells.

DR. LESKOWITZ: I am confused about your answer to Dr. Uhr's question. Your high-zone tolerance complex, $Ag_2 Ab$, looks to me just like the complex you have in induction. You have one antibody with two antigen molecules on it.

DR. COHN: Yes, but you are ignoring the free antigen. In high zone, I have a ratio of free antigen to complexed antigen in which the denominator is constant and the free antigen is being increased. Therefore, I am increasing the ratio of free antigen to complexed antigen. The complex induces and the free antigen paralyzes. Since the cell has a choice of going one way or the other, as I increase the paralytic free antigen concentration, I tend to go towards paralysis, and away from induction. That seems to me to be straightforward

311

competition. I am assuming these two forms of the antigen, free and complexed, compete with each other.

DR. BENACERRAF: Are you ready to accept that antigen A can be made into a multivalent antigen simply by putting 10, 20 or 50 groups of hapten on it, and then it should behave like a polymer? Or, as an alternative, just put 10 to 20 DNP groups on BSA.

DR. COHN: Is the role of the polymer in question?

DR. BENACERRAF: No. Suppose I rid the preparation of contaminating polymer by filtering it through an animal or by centrifugation so that you don't have any aggregate.

DR. COHN: Is the point whether the inducing conformational change can take place only via antigen-carrier antibody complexes or can it occur under certain conditions with antigens like sRBC or flagella without carrier antibody?

DR. BENACERRAF: That is it.

DR. COHN: Normally in the animal, I would say that carrier antibody is always necessary, but it would not be a test of the theory if certain polymers induced in cell transfer experiments even in the absence of carrier antibody.

DR. BENACERRAF: You have carrier antibody to determinant $\underline{a}$ that can do the same job as that of $\underline{c}_1$ and $\underline{c}_2$.

DR. COHN: You mean, can all of these determinants be the same?

DR. BENACERRAF: Yes, in which case you could have an antigen which would not be tolerogenic at low zone.

DR. COHN: Let me think about that. It may be a good point. Yet, why shouldn't an antigen with repeating identical determinants be a low-zone tolerogen on this model?

DR. CEPPELLINI: Why should it not react to give signal ① ?

DR. COHN: Yes, of course it would be tolerogenic on this model. I thought you were worrying about the subtle point of induction of tolerance. The fewer the number of different

determinants, the better it would be as a tolerogen. What
then is the problem?

DR. CINADER: I think the question has been raised before,
but I didn't understand your answer. Consider signal ②.
Your two antigens are linked in such a way that the carrier
antibody happens to link the two c determinants which are on
opposite sides and are equidistant from one another? You
have a special configuration with relation to one or another
determinant. How do you achieve that?

DR. COHN: A conformational change occurring in a macromolecular antigen-antibody complex is, for example, revealed in
complement fixation. When I make an antigen-antibody complex,
I fix complement. There is, therefore, a conformational
change in the antibody molecule. Free antibody does not
complex complement, nor does antibody binding a hapten.

All I am doing here is illustrating what is a well-known
conformational change in antibody on reacting with antigen.
We visualize this change as a stretching in the molecule.
There are many people who have proposed conformational
stretching of this kind, and there are electron microscope
pictures, from the laboratories of Valentine, Feinstein and
Rowe, which show such events. The existence of a conformational change in antibody interaction in a complex with antigen has been known for a long time. Such changes have been
revealed by the existence of anti-antibodies to antibodies
in complex with antigen; I am referring to the work of Najjar,
Gell and others.

CHAIRMAN UHR: I don't think that is what Dr. Cinader has in
mind.

DR. CINADER: You have an antigen and an antibody which is
bivalent. The specificities of the two combining sites are
identical. Let us assume you have your determinant c on the
first antigen on the near side and your determinant c on the
other antigen on the far side, so that the stretching by a
single carrier antibody molecule over this system becomes
almost certainly an impossibility.

DR. COHN: In order to produce an inducing complex, the two
antigen molecules presented to one receptor molecule must be
identical and linked together by carrier antibody. Your

assumption applies to a complex with non-identical antigen molecules.

Consider antigen A with determinants $\underline{a}$, c_1 and c_2. In Fig. 56 I have put carrier antibody, anti-c_1, between them to make a complex. The presence of the two determinants $\underline{a}$ enables the reaction with the polyvalent ($\geqslant 2$) receptor anti-a such that inducing signal ② is delivered.

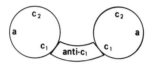

Fig. 56   Possible reaction between carrier antibody and antigenic determinants

I am trying to give you a simple direct model. If you want me to build a bigger inducing complex of antigen and carrier antibody, I can build it by allowing reactions of carrier antibody with determiants c_2, c_3 and so on. I can also put the complex on the surface of the macrophage, but this is not what is critical in the argument. What is critical in the argument is that in order to induce with monomeric antigen, you need a specific signal ② with two elements, a carrier antibody and a cell receptor antibody such that one receptor has two of its combining sites reacted on a stretched conformation.

DR. CINADER: One more clarification. In one case you have drawn a reaction of the cell with one antigen molecule and you get one signal delivered. In the other case you have two antigen molecules reacting and you get two signals delivered. Why is it not sufficient to have one or two doses of signals?

DR. COHN: The inducing and paralyzing conformation must be different and the cell has to sense these two different signals.

DR. CINADER: Why is it not sufficient to have two doses of the same signal?

VI. SPECULATIONS ON MECHANISMS

DR. COHN: You propose, then, a counting mechanism which detects one hit as low-zone paralysis, two hits of the same kind as induction, and more hits as high-zone paralysis. This proposal to count hits makes high- and low-zone paralysis fundamentally different since it accounts for low-zone paralysis and induction but does not predict high-zone.

DR. CINADER: The antibody-forming situation would result when one antigen-sensitive cell reacts with two antigen molecules combined with different surface receptors.

DR. COHN: You wish to have a cell distinguish between a reaction of one of its receptors with one antigen molecule and two of its receptors each with one molecule of antigen bound?

DR. CINADER: Yes.

DR. COHN: I do not see how this situation gives you any predictable or understandable change at the molecular level. How is the interaction with receptor sensed and made additive?

It is not a test of the model whether or not I can at this moment provide a convincing argument that conformational changes in the receptor determine the destiny of the antigen-sensitive cell after reaction with antigen. I want to make a distinction between the validity of postulating a conformational change in receptor and whether or not enough is known, or I am intelligent enough to present you with a plausible conformational change to explain the paralysis or inductive signal. I consider it rational to postulate a conformational change in receptor as a signal for the antigen-sensitive cell unless you are prepared to say that such changes are out of the question. I repeat, I may or may not have a convincing case for the sensing of signals ① or ② by conformational changes but that still does not have anything to do with the validity of the model.

I am now going to give you one possible series of conformational changes in the receptor which delivers paralytic signal ① or inductive signal ② . If you are going to have one signal for paralysis and another signal for induction, you must also have a conformation that is a signal for neither.

Let me start then with the postulated structure of the unbound receptor molecule, anti-a, in a configuration U

315

which is a signal for neither. In this unbound conformation
(U) of the receptor molecule it is possible that the two
light chains interact, with a minimum interaction between
the light and heavy chain forming the combining site which
therefore is inactive. I will label this the Unbound state
(Fig. 57).

ANTIGEN SENSITIVE CELL

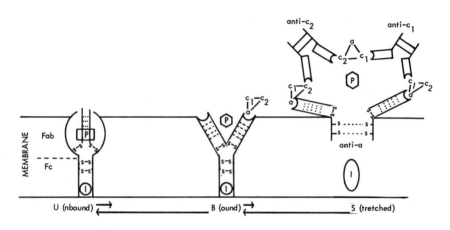

P = Paralytic signal ① in the off state.

Ⓟ = Paralytic signal ① in the on state. The cell is paralyzed.

① = Induction signal ② in the off state.

Ⓘ = Induction signal ② in the on state. The cell goes on to make antibody.

= Antigen with haptene a and carrier determinants c_1 and c_2'

The induction signal ② takes precedence over paralytic signal ① .

Fig. 57 A model for conformational changes in Ig light
chains at the cell surface and consequent induction
or paralysis

This interaction between light chains has been suggested
by a recent paper of Stevenson and Straus in which they show
that when you take a random mixture of serum light chains and
let them dimerize, identical light chains find each other
in the dimers. What is remarkable is that the probability

316

of identical light chains finding each other is much higher than that found when light and heavy interactions leading to restoration of a combining site are studied. This L-L interaction is probably selected for during the production of antigen-sensitive cells.

So one proposal is that the conformation in which there is L-L binding, and weak or no combining site activity, is the unbound configuration, U.

This is the state of the receptor on the antigen-sensitive cell before antigen is presented to it.

The unbound form (U) is in equilibrium with the bound form (B) which delivers signal ① . The B configuration can be pictured as I drew it in Fig. 57, and it differs in the following way:

The binding site is formed as the result of a postulated appearance of a new L-H interaction. This new interaction is part of a conformational change, probably largely in the Fab portion of the molecule, signal ① , which is sensed by the cell.

The L-L interaction can increase or decrease, as pictured here, there being no a priori arguments, but it should change in passing into the B configuration.

The hapten or antigenic determinant selects for the bound configuration as follows: U ⇌ B + H ⇌ BH.

It is the recognition of this change, provisionally pictured to be in the Fab fragment, which determines that the cell will follow the pathway of paralysis. This is what is read as signal ① . This conformational change, my mentor, Dr. Jacques Monod, would call orthodoxy.

The conformational change, a signal ② , postulated by Dr. Bretscher, is truly a new idea of great interest. It is the receptor molecule stretched by the complex of antigen with carrier antibody, possibly possessing its signal ② residing in the Fc portion.

I have drawn it as the stretched molecule and I will illustrate it as antigen A with determinants a and c complexed with carrier antibody, anti-c, and receptor antibody, anti-a, in which the latter is stretched; the L-L interaction drops to zero, the L-H interaction is now high.

317

In other words, what I am doing is dimerizing antigen A with carrier antibody anti-c in a reaction of this complex with receptor antibody anti-a, stretching the latter. This is a picture, of course, elements of which you see in the electron microscope when you analyze antigen-antibody complexes. This is the kind of image that Valentine, Feinstein and Rowe have published. There is additional evidence that there is a change in the Fc region, namely, that antigen-complexed molecules fix complement via determinants in Fc.*

DR. SMITH: Does your model predict the following type of experiment: if we had antigen-sensitive cells in vitro, and if we added a single determinant to it, you would predict that the cells, if they went into some environment in which their reactions could be tested, would be tolerant cells; but if you put an antigen carrier-antibody complex into this population of cells, introduced under the same conditions, you would have cells producing antibody. Is is that simple?

DR. COHN: Yes.

DR. STERZL: I have a similar question. If you have a deficiency of carrier antibody, you would have tolerance and not induction. If you isolate lymphocytes and put them in vitro with antigen, you would predict the easy induction of tolerance and not induction of antibody formation.

DR. GOTTLIEB: It seems to me you require additional postulates in the case of low-zone tolerance; that is, you cannot insist on the production of the carrier antibody at the same time. Is it reasonable to say that because you made sufficient

---

*The way in which antigen-antibody interactions are pictured here to signal paralysis and induction are rather primitive. I regret that I had to present premature thinking rather than a polished story on conformational changes in antibodies on interaction with antigen. Dr. Bretscher who is more knowledgeable than I will certainly develop a more comprehensive theory. However, I do not regret that the discussion pointed out the reluctance of some of the best known investigators of structure to consider as possible, conformational changes in immunoglobulins when they interact with antigen. The model may stimulate an interest in this subject which is being pioneered by Feinstein, Gell, Henney, Najjar, Pressman, Rowe, Stanworth, and Valentine.

carrier antibody you would have induction rather than low-zone tolerance at a proper antigen concentration?

DR. COHN: Yes.

DR. GOTTLIEB: Can you go down to a single molecule of carrier antibody?

DR. COHN: Why not? Given an infinite length of time, two antigen molecules and one antigen-sensitive cell, you might be able to induce it.

DR. SILVERSTEIN: I think it is an amusing game we are playing with Dr. Cohn's minimal theory but I would suggest that it is not a minimal theory, that the time has come to pass onto things that will be more fruitful for an understanding of tolerance, even though something is bound to come out of this because it is amusing. If we don't pass on, then at least let us admit some facts, shoot it down right away and move on.

CHAIRMAN UHR: Now we move from the area of modeling and theory to that of facts. For example, Dr. Cohn, you felt that one of the critical points in your theory was whether or not haptens can induce immunologic tolerance and you quoted Dr. Benacerrf on that point. Does someone want to comment on that? I frankly was rather puzzled. I thought that Chase and Battisto had induced tolerance to haptens, or am I wrong?

DR. BENACERRAF: Maybe the data are not all in on this problem but from what is known, you can produce tolerance specific for a hapten; that is correct, but it can only be induced by substances that are immunogenic and carry the hapten. In one experiment we tried to induce tolerance to hapten alone. Injection of DNP-lysine alone, before immunization with the DNP-protein or even concomitant with it, in tremendous amounts, did not render the animal tolerant.

I am aware that Dr. Leskowitz has induced tolerance to benzo-arsanyl tyrosine, but that is by his own admission not a hapten, it is an immunogen. The question that can be asked is whether the binding of the carrier anti-lysine is sufficient by itself to be capable of fixing this substance to the cell that was postulated by Dr. Cohn. The binding is

supposed to be about 70% of the total of the binding of the
specificity involved. Is such binding large enough? One
has no further data that I know of, because larger molecules
of this type have not, to my knowledge, been tried.

DR. MITCHISON: What was the injection schedule of the DNP-
lysine?

DR. BENACERRAF: It was injected two or three times a day in
large amounts, but the animal was constantly excreting the
excess hapten in his urine.

DR. MITCHISON: I would like to add that J. M. Dubert kept
rabbits chronically infused with sulphanilic acid without
immunizing them, or as far as I remember, influencing their
subsequent response to sulphanyl-azo-protein.

Mr. Gosling and I gave mice 2×10^{-6} molar of NIP-aminocaproic acid for 3 days without impairing their subsequent
ability to respond to NIP-protein conjugate. Since the hapten is cleared from the circulation within $T_{\frac{1}{2}}=45$ minutes,
infusion is probably better than repeated injections. I
should add that I don't believe it is possible to keep an
animal above the concentration of 2×10^{-6} molar with DNP-
lysine or NIP-aminocaproic acid without killing it.

CHAIRMAN UHR: In essence it is a negative experiment and
in this regard would not be meaningful you would say?

DR. MITCHISON: I think it is probably meaningful if infusion
is performed. The hapten concentration corresponds roughly
to 200 µg of protein/ml circulating in the mouse, and that
is a reasonable dose from which to detect tolerance.

Is it not sufficient to let the cell simply have a binding
site, and then let the cell read in some other way whether it
has a macromolecule or a micromolecule binding to it?

DR. COHN: In principle, you are correct. One receptor molecule on the antigen-sensitive cell only has to distinguish
a monomer from a polymer. However, there was an enormous
amount of data presented during this meeting by all of you
that the carrier effect was specific. If you are prepared
to say that the carrier effect is not specific, then I would
not think of a specific mechanism to account for it. Since

the specific carrier is comprised of a random collection of foreign determinants, as are the haptens you happen to be looking at, I naturally would postulate that the recognition of the carrier is via an antibody. But if you are prepared to state that the carrier effect is non-specific, then your comment is perfectly justified.

To answer the second point: in all of the negative attempts to induce tolerance with haptens, it is not how one injects the haptens that is critical. It is how one challenges the animal to test tolerance. It must be established that you are not under conditions that break tolerance thereby masking the initial state. This is certainly what is happening in the experiments described by Drs. Benacerraf and Mitchison.

DR. MITCHISON: I think there was a misunderstanding. I was not questioning your carrier antibody at all. The question I am talking about is this: I felt it was a quite unnecessary part of your theory to assume that a conformational change is being read by the cell. Isn't it equally plausible to say that the cell does not read the conformational change but that the cell has a specific binding site, and all that the cell reads is that it has a macromolecule there. It may be able to tell whether it has one macromolecule or another macromolecule bound to another binding site by your antibody. This would enable the cell to distinguish between hapten and antigen, and also it could account for such nonspecific inducers as phytohemagglutinin.

DR. COHN: I can't think of any other way to explain all of the data. How does a cell sense the size of a substance ranging from a hapten to an average protein and respond specifically to both the hapten and the carrier? I do not know how the cell could weight the molecule and, to satisfy Dr. Cinader, count them also with no intervention of a conformational change in the receptor.

DR. GELL: I would like to cite another kind of experiment which depends on two assumptions. One, the assumption that the anti-allotype binding to the cell is a model of antigen binding to the cell, and the other that proliferation is the first stage, or relevant to the induction stage we are talking about. With these two assumptions, there are some experiments which Dr. Sell and I have just run and which may be relevant to what is happening on the surface of antigen-sensitive cells.

We found that with certain antisera, anti-A3, for instance, you can expose the cell and they hardly respond at all by proliferation to any dose of antiserum. With certain other antisera, anti-A3, they respond by transformation; these particular antisera are relatively weak and will not cause transformation of blood lymphocytes. If on top of this you add an antiserum to the anti-allotype, that is to the anti-A3 antibody, so that you pile up antibody on the surface of the cell, then you get a very marked proliferation effect up to 30 or 40 percent. Would this constitute a model for the effects of macromolecules on the surface of the cell?

CHAIRMAN UHR: Can the first interaction with antibody anti-A3 induce tolerance in that population, which would in Dr. Cohn's system be analogous to the antigen whereas the anti-antibody would be analogous to carrier?

DR. GELL: It is a reverse model, really.

DR. WEIGLE: I would like to address two questions to Dr. Cohn. The first one: I think there is good evidence with all the serum protein antigens that the monomer itself will induce tolerance and will not induce an antibody response. If you biologically filter BSA and/or gamma globulin and then induce an antibody response, would you consider the dimers and the trimers as possible substitutes for your antibody, your carrier antibody?

The second question: If you give mice deaggregated rabbit gamma globulin, isolated from normal rabbit serum, you can induce tolerance. But if you take gamma globulin isolated from anti-mouse lymphocytic sera, which goes to mouse lymphocytes, and inject this you don't get tolerance but an antibody response. Do you think this could replace the carrier antibody?

DR. COHN: The carrier antibody is not necessary in this model for the trigger, although normally it is used. What is necessary in this model is that the cell sense specifically a paralytic signal which could be a single foreign determinant and an inductive signal which requires multiple determinants in a special configuration. If the carrier effect were not specific, then you would look for a non-specific way for the cells to sense these signals.

VI. SPECULATIONS ON MECHANISMS

DR. CINADER: You said at the beginning that if you made animals tolerant to antigen A and then immunize with a cross reacting antigen B, you will get antibodies to the first tolerance-inducing antigen A. This is not a fact. You get antibody which cross-reacts with A and you get antibody to B. This has been shown very clearly. I thought this was used by you as part of your initial argument.

DR. COHN: If the experiments on breaking tolerance are not good enough then of course I should not cite them. However, how do you explain the appearance of cross-reacting antibody to antigen A? The principle is the same.

May I cite an experiment of Dr. Sher in my laboratory. The experiment was inspired by Gell, elements of it were first carried out by Lieberman and Potter. I didn't present this study earlier because I thought that we had enough data to establish the point.

The experiment is extremely simple. One can provoke in BALB/c mice a large number of different myelomas, each producing a unique protein. The proteins I am going to deal with are of the IgA class. They differ in their allotypic markers. The IgA of the BALB/c mouse is A12, 13, 14 whereas the A/J strain mouse is A-, 13, -. These markers are in the Fc region of the IgA molecule.

If we inject these unique myelomas into the BALB/c mice by various routes we never get a response as determined by precipitating antibody. Over 20 myeloma proteins have been studied in two hundred mice. You might say that the BALB/c mouse is tolerant to its own immunoglobulin and that I am only looking at a unique example of this. However, if the same proteins are injected into C3H mice of identical IgA allotype, no response is found either. In contrast, if these myeloma proteins are put into the A/J mouse, the prediction would be that I would make anti-allotype, because they differ by an allotypic marker. As a matter of fact, the major antibody that is made, is directed against the idiotypic marker. It is made against the Fab fragment. Antibody is often, but not always found to the allotypic marker, also sometimes to both.

The surprise is that in the A/J mouse the antibody produced is directed against a determinant in the Fab portion. This antibody to the idiotype can distinguish the myeloma from almost all the other myelomas of the 250 that I have in my collection.

You need a foreign determinant in the Fc portion in order to induce antibody to the Fab portion. In other words, we have rediscovered the carrier effect in a rather special case that allows you to explain why the system is not choked to death by the constant production of anti-antibody. If you take these two determinants apart, by making Fab and Fc, you get no antibody to Fab.

CHAIRMAN UHR: Can you get tolerance?

DR. COHN: I never thought of looking for that until I came to this meeting.

DR. BENACERRAF: You are quite right in stressing that the greatest problem involved is the fact that in the induction of the system there is specificity for the carrier. There is no way of getting around it, neither in the experiment on tolerance nor in the experiments on boosters that have been done by Drs. Mitchison and Rajewsky. But that is not all there is. There is also the fact that the molecule is an immunogen by other characteristics; it is a proteinaceous substance that normally is able to start an immune response of a certain class or type.

This created the question whether we should assume that the determinant on a carrier and the determinant on the hapten are entirely analogous, that is simply capable of binding an antibody, or binding to a cell that has an antibody. The whole thing could be mimicked at will by making synthetic products which by themselves would have no antigenicity, but would bear the two types of haptens that one would expect, either in the province of initiating the response or in situations where one attempts to boost (the experiments carried out by Dr. Rajewsky). I think this is one of the relevant questions to which I would address myself if I were you.

DR. SILVERSTEIN: This relates to the question of carrier also. Dr. Cohn was apparently exercised over the question of carrier and felt the need to incorporate it in his theory. I think, however, that he may be trying to incorporate it in a form which may not be appropriate, under the impression that Dr. Benacerraf has fully settled the problem.

VI. SPECULATIONS ON MECHANISMS

Historically, the original notion of the role of carrier protein was its contribution to the antigenic determinant site by that small area of the carrier in the immediate vicinity of the haptenic focus. Then Dr. Benacerraf came along and seemed to suggest that this was not so; that the carrier protein was working as a whole molecule in the transport and perhaps the penetration of the hapten into the appropriate cell.

But there is one bit of datum that I think brings this latter concept into question. That is the demonstration that the same hapten (aminobenzoic acid) put onto the same carrier (guinea pig albumin) on two different loci (tyrosine or lysine) appears to the guinea pig as two completely unrelated antigens.

DR. BENACERRAF: That doesn't matter.

DR. BRAUN: I am sure that you will agree that any new model should have the merit of answering as many of the available facts as possible, and at the same time be the most efficient model. What I fail to see is how Dr. Cohn's very ingenious model answers problems that cannot be answered in a very simple fashion by the model that I discussed briefly in a prior session. Also, I am afraid that Dr. Cohn's model cannot answer some of the facts that can be explained by the model that I have discussed.

There is one aspect lacking in the material that I discussed earlier and if I now add that aspect it may turn out that Dr. Cohn and I are not really very much in disagreement.

I talked about an initiation via a two-cell system in which the first cell system does something to the antigen, such as possibly hooking on an activator (Fig. 37). Now, I have always made the assumption that the first cell system can recognize foreign material presumably via the carrier.

If we assume that the macrophage, the first cell type with which antigen has an encounter, has recognition sites with broad specificities this may be equivalent to Dr. Cohn's carrier antibody. The antibody-like recognition sites on the second cell type, namely, on the stem cells of the lymphocyte population, may have a narrower spectrum of specificity, recognizing either hapten or the entire antigenic molecule.

I discussed previously how tolerance may be achieved by a simple recognition event, leading to a blocking of the second recognition site. Tolerance is conferable, by this model, in at least two ways, at the level of the first recognition or at the level of the second. It seems to me that all of the available data can be fitted into such a scheme. In addition, I also referred to the participation of antigen in later events, i.e. for the stimulation of the proliferation of activated clones, and modifications at this level also may lead under certain conditions, to non-responsiveness.

Dr. Cohn reiterated the fact that non-responsiveness to a carrier will confer on the animal a subsequent non-responsiveness to haptens put on the same carrier. This would obviously involve a non-participation of the first events at the macrophage level in my model, making unnecessary any of the more complex assumptions that Dr. Cohn used in his model.

Finally, what I fail to see in Dr. Cohn's model is an explanation for our observation that it is possible to convert a specific response into a non-specific response by agents which are known, or claimed to have, an effect on the permeability of lymphocytes.

I thus would very much like to have Dr. Cohn comment on a comparison between the two models. I feel that my simple model can explain as much as his, and possibly more.

DR. COHN: I don't think the role of non-specific agents is relevant to the present dicussion. Certainly one could bypass signal ① and signal ② and turn the cell on by interactions which interfere with, or simulate, one of the subsequent steps. The agents which do turn on cells will tell us a great deal about the mechanism of the derepression after specific recognition.

I am sure if you are clever enough, you can turn on all the antigen-sensitive cells, bypassing the specific triggering reaction due to antigen that we are both supposedly talking about, and derepress each antigen-sensitive cell along the pathway to paralysis or induction.

What I think we are interested in now is the specificity. We want to explain how one cell distinguishes two antigenic signals, paralysis or induction. If you don't believe that one cell can go along both these paths, then we have no problem. We simply have two different cell populations and we are talking about another phenomenon.

If one cell can go two ways, then you must set up two different signals. You can have the paralysis signal (1) as a direct 1:1 interaction of antigen with receptor and the inductive signal (2) as a carrier antibody-antigen complex with receptor. I insist only that you assume that this cell recognizes the antigen in a specific way, and according to our ground rule, this recognition is by antibody itself both as receptor and carrier.

Whether or not carrier antibody is on a cell surface or free in solution is a question for experimental testing and further discussion. If carrier antibody is on the cell surface it is probably adsorbed from the circulation on a multi-specific cell (macrophage or reticular).

What is critical to the model is that there are two signals, depending on whether one determinant or two determinants interact simultaneously with a given receptor. If you have no specific carrier effect, then you can have non-specific recognition along these lines. If you tell me that there is a specific carrier effect, then you must say by this simple model that it is antibody itself which recognizes the carrier.

This is all that is being said here. If I am asked what is the detailed mechanism, I am interested in the conformational changes which occur when antigen interacts with antibody because I am betting that this is how a cell senses the interaction.

Furthermore, this hypothesis tells us what experiments should be done. We should be looking at the interaction between soluble antibodies and antigens to see whether they actually do undergo conformational changes, and we can go back to the literature and see whether conformational changes have been observed but ignored because no theoretical framework then existed for their application.

DR. NOSSAL: Could Dr. Cohn entertain us for a minute on his thoughts of how polymeric antigen can provoke excellent tolerance in many immunological situations and in others antibody formation. Why is that a critical question? I think it is a critical question, because Dr. Cohn's model needs, I think, more than one way of making a polymer for signal number ② . He needs more than one way for the very simple reason that he hasn't fully explained to us how the first carrier antibody molecules got there. I don't think any of us were deeply impressed with his thoughts on maternal trans- fer as a source of priming carrier antibody. So you have to have more than one way of making a polymer and you've got to put that into your model, as he in fact did do, the idea being that structurally compatible polymers of a monomeric antigen determinant would be obligatorily immuncgenic. In point of fact a long history of tolerance research, going back to Dr. Mitchison's studies of 1953 with sRBC, and being continued by many others, e.g. by Dr. Friedman and ourselves, say that under circumstances where one eliminates the complication of antibody formation, particulate and polymeric antigens are excellent tolerogens, every bit as good as soluble antigens.

DR. COHN: I do not believe that I said that polymeric anti- gens are obligatorily immunogenic. They are, in general, processed via phagocytic cells and broken down. Their sub- sequent fate depends upon the state of the immune system. Clearly, aggregation favors antibody induction in the normal animal. If, however, the animal is X-rayed or immunosuppressed there are conditions where strong immunogens behave like weak ones and induce tolerance. Dr. Mitchison made this point re- peatedly and it is easily explained as a diminution in the size of both the populations of antigen-sensitive and carrier antibody-producing cells.

Clearly, if being a polymer were sufficient, the animal would constantly make antibody to its own RBC. Some mechan- ism, e.g. the thymic barrier, exists to separate the contact between the antigen-sensitive cells and polymers that are effective immunogens without the carrier antibody.

DR. SELA: I have a comment and a question. First, for clarification, the experiment on induction of antibody to the idiotype is a very nice one. From the model you assume that there is an absolutely minimal amount of antibodies in A/J mice to the specificity controlled by A12 and A14. The comment I want to make is that this is a new model and it is the first time that a different kind of nomenclature is in- troduced. I think it would be horrible if we talk about a "determinant" determinant and the "carrier" determinant.

VI. SPECULATIONS ON MECHANISMS

If I understand it correctly, I think this would confuse most people.

What you are saying is that there are many determinants on a macromolecular antigen, and when you need to find a given determinant among all the other determinants it is up to you what you call a carrier determinant. Accordingly, to answer the question that Dr. Nossal asked, I think that one has simply to answer that the origin of the carrier antibody is exactly the same as that of the antibody that is unique to the specific haptenic determinant.

My question is the following: As we mentioned today, there are many reasons for a role of the carrier in tolerance and in antigenic competition; but I want to come back to the one in which I have been most involved, namely, the correlation between a net charge in the antigen and the type of antibody formed. We can get anti-polyalanine antibodies which will be of one gamma globulin type or another, and you can separate them. The decision depends exclusively on the fact that I attach the dinitrophenol determinant to a more negative or a more positively charged carrier.

I do not see that in this case I need a carrier antibody. The simplest explanation would be that if you have, let us say, 10,000 antibody-producing cells which make antibodies, some of them will be more acidic, some more basic, and some will be more hydrophobic or less hydrophobic; so, if you throw in the hapten attached to a certain macromolecule, this macromolecule will bind much quicker to one type of cell that will make a given antibody, since I assume that the cell is more acidic or more basic on its surface by virtue of the nature of the antibody that it makes.

DR. COHN: Let me restate the observations that Dr. Sela has identified because they are extremely interesting. If you put dinitrophenol on a negatively charged carrier, then you will produce antibody with positively charged Fab fragments that have their specificity directed against dinitrophenol. If you put dinitrophenol on a positively charged carrier, then you will induce anti-dinitrophenol which has negatively charged Fab fragments.

This observation could say there are amino acid replacements distributed over a large surface contributing to the combining site. Since the only long range forces that are

known to biological interactions are electrostatic ones, it
is necessary that in addition to the combining site interaction, there not be a negative contribution to the inductive
signal ② by repelling charge interactions between antigen
and receptor. But these findings don't tell us anything
about the requirements for the reaction with the carrier
antibody, because in this case you are looking only at the
receptor antibody to the dinitrophenol.

DR. MÖLLER: Is there a difference between a nonreactive cell
and a cell which has reacted in low-zone tolerance?

DR. COHN: Yes.

DR. SILVERSTEIN: As Dr. Cohn suggests, a good theory serves
the function of suggesting good experiments, and his theory
suggests an experiment that we did three or four years ago.
Our question was whether or not this hypothetical carrier
antibody is out free in the system or was on the cell surface.
You were explicit in saying that the carrier antibody as
well as the receptors on the cell could be classical immunoglobulins. Is this correct or do they not have to be different? I would say no. How about the carrier antibody?
Should this be a classical immunoglobulin with the normal
light and heavy chain?

DR. COHN: Yes. Let's make the simple hypothesis and see
what it leads to.

DR. SILVERSTEIN: What it leads to is the following perplex-
ing situation. In the fetal lamb which has minimal amounts
of IgM and no other immunoglobulins, one can pump in tremendous amounts of rabbit anti-sheep globulin chains of the
normal type. We have done this and in the presence of those
anti-immunoglobulin chains, the animal can give what looks
like normal immune response. It rejects grafts and it makes
antibodies. This would seem to argue against the presence
in this serum of an anti-carrier antibody with the usual
immunoglobulin chains.

What disturbs me somewhat is that these data may argue a
little bit against the receptor molecule itself being exposed
to any appreciable extent, since it was composed of normal
immunoglobulin chains; it would be neutralized by the rabbit
anti-sheep immunoglobulins employed in this experiment.

330

VI. SPECULATIONS ON MECHANISMS

DR. LESKOWITZ: I want to return for a moment to the question of the carrier and wonder whether the carrier is really necessary to function as Dr. Cohn has suggested. We know that haptens do not function as immunogens. They are presumably not complete in some way. There are, however, some examples in the literature where if you inject DNP_1 $lysine_6$, the hapten becomes a complete immunogen, and there is also the same situation with arsanilic acid, where, if you inject Ars_1 $tyrosine_6$, it becomes an immunogen.

Why can we not consider a carrier as merely being the mode for holding in the proper configuration, six or so amino acids adjacent to the hapten? Isn't this all that a carrier has to do.

DR. COHN: When you inject a small molecule into an animal, it can undergo a series of interactions making it an immunogen. You can have a complex formed with serum albumin, for example, in which you bring out new determinants that render the complex an immunogen. Unless we know what happened we can't interpret the findings in terms of molecules and the triggering of receptors. Since molecular biology is telling us a lot about molecular interactions that trigger responses we must try to see if we can't interpret our findings in molecular terms. We know the components, antigen and antibody. It is easiest to start with them.

If you find that DNP_1 $lysine_6$ and DNP_1 $tyrosine_6$ induce, the model says that two sites, one involving carrier antibody, are involved. The carrier site could be on the small molecule if structural considerations permit it, or on a larger self protein which is distorted by an interaction with the hapten so that it becomes a carrier.

DR. CEPPELLINI: It is quite possible that an excellent theory arises from a bad experiment. You say that you are stimulated to work out this theory on the basis of your ability to induce antibody to idiotype only when the allotype difference was present. But as far as I know, there are two allotypic differences and besides the molecule should be bivalent. Why isn't the antibody formed largely or only to the allotype?

DR. COHN: I do not wish to leave the impression that this theory was derived only from Dr. Sher's experiment. Dr. Ceppellini's point is very well taken and Dr. Sher was

331

conscious of it, which automatically makes his experiment a good one.

The point is, when you have only two foreign determinants that are close together, and rare, the probability of getting antibody against them is low. Further, there are probably structural limitations on how close two determinants can be for one of them to act as carrier for the other. The general case is that BALB/c IgA myelomas are non-immunogenic in any strain of mouse with the same allotype and are immunogenic (to produce anti-idiotype) in any strain of mouse with differing allotypes.

The sequence of events upon injection of BALB/c IgA myeloma protein into an A/J mouse would be as follows: 1) a reaction with carrier antibody directed against the allotype in the Fc portion; 2) the induction of anti-idiotype by the first reaction as well as carrier anti-idiotype; 3) induction of anti-allotype. This is how tolerance to the idiotype is broken. Remember that, normally, tolerance of a mouse to the idiotype is essential for the functioning of the anti-body system.

Maybe if you pushed the sensitivity of the analysis of the system down several orders of magnitude, you may see in rare cases a response in BALB/c to its own myeloma protein because the idiotype presents two foreign determinants. The point is you don't get antibody against the idiotype easily. You don't get antibody against the idiotype unless you have two differences between the molecules, one of which acts as a carrier. That is all I wanted to illustrate.

DR. GOOD: I have a real fear of riding a hobby horse. I think it is extremely important that you can get tolerance involving one class of antibody and immunity involving another. In the experiments with suppression by 6-mercapto-purine, Borel and Schwartz got data indicating that some cell classes can be made tolerant while others remain immune-responsive. Is it perfectly acceptable to your theory to have multiple types of receptors, separable types of receptors and separate lines of differentiation of cells?

DR. COHN: Without being able to account for the phenomenon you cite, the receptor is not the problem. The receptor by definition in this system is identical to the antibody that the antigen-sensitive cell is going to make.

332

VI. SPECULATIONS ON MECHANISMS

DR. GOOD: The carrier antibody, then, has to be different.

DR. COHN: The carrier antibody is probably distinct, a new
class, or a cytophilic antibody.   In a more unprejudiced way,
I would say that either all classes could behave as carrier
antibody or there is a special one.   However, if you could
remove the carrier class, as in certain agammaglobulinemics,
you should see an effect.   In humans the only solid case I
could find involved specifically an IgA-negative individual
that responded to every antigen given to him.

   Therefore, you can have two situations.   Either all classes
act as carrier or you have one unique unrevealed class that
is not IgA.

DR. GOOD: Critical experiments might be done, then, in
attempting to induce immunological tolerance of the cell-
mediated type in animals that cannot make demonstrable
amounts of circulating antibody.   Theoretically, the human
situation would be ideal, but I think the only situation
in man that we accept as representing the absence of one of
the immunoglobulin types is IgA deficiency, and this is not
very likely to involve carrier antibody.   We have to wait
until somebody finds a really reproducible system for complete IgM deficiency or isolated IgG deficiency in man.   You
can, of course, produce these separate states in the chicken.

DR. COHN: It is predictable that if you have no carrier
antibody, the animal will be agammaglobulinemic.

DR. GOOD: Unless that carrier antibody is of the thymus-
dependent IgX type.

DR. PLESCIA: I would agree with Dr. Cohn that the evidence
is overwhelming that the effect of the carrier is specific.
So in essence, what one has to think of is a means whereby
this specificity can be translated.

   I think Dr. Cohn has made a model which can, perhaps,
fulfill this possibility.   But to put it simply, I would
say that the role of the carrier would be to facilitate the
interaction between a determinant and that antigen-sensitive
cell for which it is specific.   Whether this interaction
leads to tolerance or leads to antibody is not the point I
want to make at the moment.   The point is that this encounter

must be made with such frequency that it becomes meaningful. I would envision that the role of the carrier through its own specific determinants would facilitate this interaction.

Dr. Cohn has given us one way in which this facilitation can occur. I think we can take the carrier-specific antibody as Dr. Cohn has postulated it and put it onto a cell which serves to localize and concentrate the antigen in regions where antigen-sensitive cells are found, thus facilitating the interaction between antigen-sensitive cells and other determinants present on the antigenic molecule. The determinant on the antigenic molecule which reacts with the localizing cell type functions as a carrier determinant and does not react with an antigen-sensitive cell, permitting, however, other determinants on this molecule to react with antigen-sensitive cells.

DR. COHN: This raises the question of my third assumption, whether one antigen-sensitive cell can make only one type of antibody receptor. It is because of this assumption that an inductive interaction between two receptors, anti-a and anti-c, on the antigen-sensitive cell was not considered. Actually such a model is inelegant on many grounds.

Isn't that the point you are making? Or, are you saying the different unispecific cells can interact?

DR. PLESCIA: If you have a molecule with determinants a and c, this molecule could react with an antigen-sensitive cell because of determinant a. Now you can have a cell which is specific for c. These two would interact with this molecule because the c determinant is free in one case and the a determinant in the other case. Such an interaction would then lead to stimulation.

DR. COHN: That is what you presented, two cells interacting - -

DR. PLESCIA: We transfer your specific antibody to a cell so that one need not look for ways in which the specific - -

DR. COHN: I did not want two rare unispecific cells interacting. I wanted the carrier component, however it is pictured, to be in excess over the antigen-sensitive cells.*

---

*An afterthought by Dr. Cohn: On rereading the foregoing,

VI. SPECULATIONS ON MECHANISMS

CHAIRMAN UHR: Dr. Cohn touched very briefly on the problem whether tolerance represented silence or death. I wonder if there is anyone else who would like to comment on this problem of deletion versus paralysis of the cell and perhaps also on breakage of tolerance. Would you like to speak to this, Dr. Weigle?

DR. WEIGLE: I can say something about the termination of tolerance induced by heterologous serum proteins. We previously felt that the termination of tolerance involved the production of antibodies to two different determinants by the same cell. Obviously, this assumption was wrong, since it has been shown that a cell makes antibody to only one determinant. One explanation is that tolerance is not induced to all of the determinants on the antigen. The "avidity" of the interaction between certain determinants and corresponding cell receptors may be too low to result in tolerance or antibody production. However, related determinants located on cross-reacting or altered antigens may form a more "avid" interaction with these receptors,

---

I feel somewhat embarrassed. First of all, the model I presented is largely the result of ideas originated by Dr. Peter Bretscher with whom I am currently preparing a formal presentation of the model. The overstatements and errors in the preceding text are mine.

Secondly, the informality of the proceedings and the recording of the heated discussions may give the impression that I am unaware of the many ideas due to other workers whom I admire and whose work I quoted without citation. This, of course, is what a formal paper would have avoided. However, most of those workers were at the meeting and I was addressing my remarks to them. I need not apologize to Drs. Mitchison, Benacerraf, and others present for having profited by their ideas. However, Dr. Jerne, whose place I haltingly filled, was unfortunately not present. The meeting attests to his experimental contributions.

Most important, however, are his two great insights, first that antibody is the recognition element for antigen and second that an immunogen must have two specific foreign determinants. These two ideas are for me the clues to the role of antigen in its regulatory function. I can only hope that Dr. Jerne gets as much pleasure out of his ideas as I do.

335

resulting in an antibody response in the tolerant animal.

CHAIRMAN UHR: Do you have an idea about the mechanism by which this responsiveness to cross-reacting antigen disappears with time? If I am not mistaken, you said that in the animals in which you break tolerance (in which you get a response to cross-reacting antigen) this responsiveness disappears with time.

DR. WEIGLE: The antibody response (to the tolerated antigen) resulting from the termination of tolerance is weak and not like the response in a normal animal. Moreover, the avidity of the antibody to the previously tolerated antigen is considerably lower than that produced in normal rabbits. There is no significant increase in avidity after subsequent injections of the previously tolerated antigen. The return to the unresponsive state is probably the result of diluting out antibody-sensitive cells by cell death, to a point that a detectable response can no longer be made to the tolerated antigen.

CHAIRMAN UHR: Do you think this finding can be interpreted at the cellular level in terms of the alternatives of death or silence of tolerant cells?

DR. WEIGLE: Tolerance may be the result of death of the majority of competent cells, but there may also be "competent" cells that are silent in that they have the potential of responding to determinants on the tolerated antigen provided that these determinants are presented in a different form (i.e., on either cross-reacting or altered antigens). The reaction between the cells and the determinants may be of sufficient avidity that the cells are stimulated to differentiate and proliferate.

CHAIRMAN UHR: Dr. Sercarz has done experiments along the line of tolerance, does he have any comments to make?

DR. SERCARZ: I don't think that we have discussed the overshoot phenomenon, described by Mitchison and by Coons, in which animals that originally were tolerant to an antigen, later become hyperresponsive to that same antigen. If one looks at Mitchison's classical low-dose paralysis paper carefully, one also sees that low-dose paralysis is followed by a hyperreactivity to that same antigen. One can look upon overshoot as a kind of recruitment of reversibly inhi-bited cells for tolerance. You accumulate tolerant cells that later are able to respond to challenge. I think that our experiments on delay indicate a return to responsiveness in vitro in a system where you cannot get recruitment from a stem cell compartment; in such a case it is very hard to postulate cell death.

I would like to add one experiment performed by Dr. Scibienski, which might support some aspects of Dr. Cohn's theory. If you paralyze mice to hen lysozyme, and one week later inject them with turkey lysozyme (which differs by several amino acids), you get specific antibodies to the turkey determinants shortly thereafter and you get none that react with hen lysozyme. If you wait longer before challeng-ing with turkey lysozyme, e.g. three weeks, you now get anti-body that is reactive not only with the specific turkey de-terminants but also with cross-reactive hen determinants, as Dr. Cohn predicted. We have not determined whether the animal ever makes antibody to specific hen determinants.

CHAIRMAN UHR: Let me ask you this: You mentioned a delay in antibody responsiveness. Do you consider that a form of tolerance? Should this be considered under the definition of tolerance?

DR. SERCARZ: I think it fits all the criteria for a valid experimental test model of tolerance.

DR. HUMPHREY: I would like to go back to the question of a possible return of responsive cells after paralysis. To take up what Dr. Weigle was saying, the time required for a return (by a cross-reacting antigen for this antibody) after termination of tolerance was rather long. It seemed to me to be of the same order as the return of spontaneous responsiveness in rabbits that were paralyzed by the tolero-gen in the first place. I would have thought that the rates of recruitment of new cells which were able to respond to determinants of the original tolerogen had not been acceler-ated in Dr. Weigle's experiment on the termination with the aid of cross-reacting antigens.

CHAIRMAN UHR: I thought, Dr. Weigle, they were all cross-reacting, i.e. they were all absorbed out by the cross-reacting antigen.

337

DR. WEIGLE: That is true. Following the termination of tolerance with cross-reacting antigens, the animals will respond to injection of the tolerated antigen; however, all of the antibody made can be absorbed with the antigen used for terminating tolerance.

I believe that the experiments Dr. Humphrey referred to are those published by Dr. Linscott from our laboratory, where following the termination of tolerance he injected the tolerated antigen periodically over a long period of time. After monthly injections for 9 or 10 months, two of five animals produced antibody that had a quality different than that of the antibody produced immediately following termination of tolerance. However, all of the antibody could be absorbed from the serum with the antigen used to terminate the tolerant state.

CHAIRMAN UHR: In any event, regardless of that, as I understand the message, Dr. Humphrey, it would be that the tolerant cells probably die and that when tolerance is broken you have to wait for new stem cells to be recruited into the pool of immunocompetent cells.

POSTSCRIPT

Everyone who participated in the conference, or has read the preceding material, will form his own opinion regarding the major points that emerged. We are appending here a list of six generalizations that appear to us particularly noteworthy. These statements should not be taken as being necessarily the *most* important points, *all* of the important points, nor the *consensus* of conference participants.

1. The same cell appears to be involved in antibody formation and in tolerance.

2. Antibody formation is the result of interactions among several cells that probably originate in different sites.

3. Antibody formation involves several distinct antigen-dependent steps.

4. The steps leading to antibody formation must include recognition for carrier as well as for hapten; such recognition events may involve two interacting cells or two separate events on the same cell.

5. Activation of lymphocytes can lead to the formation of performing (antibody-producing) cells as well as to non-performing (memory) cells.

6. The induction of specific non-responsiveness in adults does not appear to involve a deletion of a clone but rather silent cells; natural tolerance, on the other hand, may involve clonal deletion.

ML
WB

ABBREVIATIONS

ALS	antilymphocyte serum
BGG	bovine gamma globulin
BSA	bovine serum albumin
DNCB	2,4-dinitrochlorobenzene
DNP	2,4-dinitrophenol
FUDR	5,-fluoro,2-deoxyuridine
GMP	guanosine monophosphate
GVH	graft vs host
HLA	the major system of human leucocyte antigens
hRBC	horse red blood cells
IgA IgG IgM	standard nomenclature for human γ-globulin classes; also used here to name analogous proteins in other species.
KLH	keyhole limpet hemocyanin
LPS	lipopolysaccharide
MER	mercaptoethanol resistant
MES	mercaptoethanol susceptible
NIP	4-hydroxy-3-iodo-5-nitrophenylacetic acid
OA	ovalbumin
PFC	plaque-forming cell(s)
PLL	polylysine
RES	reticuloendothelial system
RFC	rosette-forming cell(s)
RSA	rabbit serum albumin
sRBC	sheep red blood cells
SSS	specific soluble substance (pneumococcal capsular polysaccharides)

AUTHOR INDEX

343

SUBJECT INDEX

A

Adjuvant
  activities of, 208, 209
  beryllium as, 180, 208
  B. pertussis as, 180, 201-204
  effect on macrophages of, 180, 181, 208,
    209
  Eperythrozoon as, 212
  lipopolysaccharide as, 190, 212
  lysosome activation by, 116, 181
  oligonucleotides as, 151, 209
  particulate antigens as, 3
  Proteus vulgaris as, 276, 277
  vitamin A as, 180
AKR mice, leukemic development in, 48
Albumin, *see also* individual albumins
  tolerance to, 87
Allergic reaction, proliferative response
  and, 47
Allotype antigens, tolerance to, 275-279
Allotype specificity, transfer of, 127,129,
  141
Anti-allotype antibody
  blast transformation and, 155, 156, 322
  production of, 275-279
Anti-β-galactosidase, assay of, 237
Antibodies, *see also* individual antibodies
  antigen charge and, 206
  cellular fate of, 52
  effect on antibody affinity of, 223-225
  heterogeneity of, 8, 12, 13, 22, 208
  interaction with lymphocytes of, 154,155
  regulation of antibody production by,
    193, 197-200, 205, 217-233,239,
    242, 243, 247-249, 252, 253
Antibody affinity
  antigen dose and, 15, 46, 47, 109, 225-
    227, 241
  effect of antibody on, 223-225
  heterogeneity in, 12

role of carrier in, 15
specificity and, 13, 14, 22-24
tolerance and, 8, 10-12, 14, 16, 17, 229,
  241, 242
Antibody producing cells
  anatomical distribution of, 142-148
  antibody and, 227, 228
  anti-lymphocyte serum and, 227, 228
  heterogeneity of, 8
  origin of, 127-133, 136-138, 165-169
  recruitment of, 38, 251, 252
  separation of, 228, 229, 243, 247
Antibody production
  allergic insult and, 47
  antigen dose and, 46, 238, 239
  antigen retention and, 223-233
  cetophenicol and, 193, 194
  cytokinetics of 104-108
  delayed hypersensitivity and, 152-154
  differentiation and, 4-6, 8, 25, 27, 35-39
    41, 43-45, 47, 48, 64, 65, 252
  effect of antibody on 193, 197-200, 205
  endoplasmic reticulum in, 46
  genetic control of, 18, 20
  Golgi apparatus in, 46
  histology of, 174-176, 252, 253
  immunosuppressants and, 4, 32, 98, 109,
    110, 129-132, 245, 300, 328, 332
  intercellular reactions in, 21, 22, 121-125,
    127-132, 142-148, 163-169, 187-
    191, 299, 304-306
  intracellular regulation of, 231-236
  in vitro, 16, 43, 48, 59-63, 200-204
  kinetics of, 44, 46, 104-108
  6-mercaptopurine and, 245, 332
  in neonate, 11, 24, 31-35, 39, 55-70
  ontogeny of, 270-273
  by peritoneal cells, 195, 196, 201-204
  poly-A + poly-U and, 245
  proliferation and, 5, 6, 8, 27, 29, 33, 37-
    40, 43-45, 47, 48, 76, 252